W9-CVW-681

# PRODUCTIVE SHEEP HUSBANDRY

By WALTER C. COFFEY

DEAN, COLLEGE OF AGRICULTURE, UNIVERSITY OF MINNESOTA
FORMERLY PROFESSOR OF SHEEP HUSBANDRY, UNIVERSITY OF ILLINOIS

---

EDITED BY
KARY C. DAVIS, Ph.D. (Cornell)

LATE PROFESSOR OF AGRICULTURE, KNAPP SCHOOL OF COUNTRY LIFE, GEORGE PEABODY COLLEGE FOR TEACHERS, NASHVILLE, TENNESSEE; AUTHOR OF PRODUCTIVE FARMING, ETC.

BRED AND FED TO PRODUCE HIGH CLASS MUTTON AND WOOL

# PRODUCTIVE SHEEP HUSBANDRY

BY

WALTER C. COFFEY, PH.D.

DEAN, COLLEGE OF AGRICULTURE, UNIVERSITY OF MINNESOTA
FORMERLY PROFESSOR OF SHEEP HUSBANDRY, UNIVERSITY OF ILLINOIS

THIRD EDITION REVISED BY

WILLIAM G. KAMMLADE, PH.D.

CHIEF IN SHEEP HUSBANDRY, UNIVERSITY OF ILLINOIS

J. B. LIPPINCOTT COMPANY
CHICAGO PHILADELPHIA NEW YORK

PRINTED IN THE UNITED STATES OF AMERICA

DEDICATED TO

THE MEMORY OF MY FATHER
WHO LOVED SHEEP

# PREFACE TO THE THIRD EDITION

During the past fifteen years the sheep industry of the United States has continued an almost uninterrupted expansion. This means that returns have been generally satisfactory to the sheep raisers. Today, due to a renewed appreciation of the unique qualities of wool, refinements in the technical processes of manufacture, and judicious and energetic promotion of the use of wool by the unified efforts of growers and processors, this fiber seems assured of an important role in the future.

Efficient use of land and the conservation of soil fertility now command a nation-wide interest. Certain readjustments in agriculture may result in still greater advantage to sheep production. If more land is to be turned to pasture and forage production, sheep, if given a fair chance, will undoubtedly continue to prove their unsurpassed abilities in converting these products of the soil into highly useful and eminently desirable products for food and clothing.

Advances in the breeding and improvement of sheep are in evidence. Self-reliant breeders are realizing more than formerly that utility is the chief object of sheep breeding and the dictum of the show yard is not to be blindly followed.

Given proper guidance the young people in 4-H clubs, high schools, and agricultural colleges will develop an industry superior to that now existing or that which existed in the past.

The revisions of this book have been undertaken with the hope that they will aid in this development.

# PREFACE TO THE SECOND EDITION

Many of the changes in progress at the time of the first edition of this book have contributed to put sheep raising on a sound basis. There are reasons to believe that the sheep industry is on a fundamentally sounder basis today than ever before. Basic changes in methods of husbandry and in the territorial distribution of sheep have characterized the past thirty years. As these readjustments approach completion, new ways are opened for the sheep industry to find its place in a system of permanent agriculture. This place will be based on efficient and intelligent use of land rather than on the exploitation of natural pasture resources.

The demand for the products of sheep compared with the demand for the products of more or less competitive enterprises will be of great importance in establishing the position of the sheep industry in the agricultural scheme of this country. That we shall continue to witness changes is beyond question.

Careful study of all phases of the industry will equip the farmer, rangeman, teacher, and student to more completely understand the nature and consequences of these changes.

The full revisions in this edition have been made to conform to present-day conditions. A full job analysis of the farm operations has been included.

The author is deeply appreciative of the reception accorded the first edition of this book and hopes that the new edition will be even more useful.

Grateful acknowledgment is extended to my former colleague, W. G. Kammlade, Professor of Sheep Husbandry, University of Illinois, for his work in completely revising the text for this second edition. His intimate contact with the sheep industry has contributed largely in making this edition conform to present conditions.

# PREFACE

ALL indications at the present time point to the beginning of a new period in the sheep industry of the United States. For the first time in our history we are attempting to give attention to the whole problem of mutton and wool production. We are awakening as never before to the fact that successful flock husbandry is based upon a careful consideration and attention to breeding, feeding, shepherding, and marketing. As a result, farm flocks are emerging from the depraved stage of scavengers, and bands of sheep on western ranges no longer have "to take pot luck" on the natural feed of the range.

The sheepman now realizes that "the march towards the setting sun" in search of new and cheap range is over, and that various phases of agriculture are demanding and receiving recognition in regions which he once regarded as solely his own. He also realizes that land values have advanced and the cost of operation increased to the point where the haphazard and wasteful methods once practiced in handling sheep can no longer be depended upon to yield profits.

All of these changes presage a better and more successful sheep husbandry, and this book is offered with the hope that it will be of use both to the student and to the sheep raiser in comprehending the place which sheep justly deserve in our agriculture and the methods of handling which will result in permanent occupancy of this place.

The author fully realizes that this volume is not a complete treatise on sheep husbandry. He also realizes how unfortunate it would be for sheepmen generally to attempt to apply without any modification whatever all of the suggestions this book contains; for no absolute rule can be laid down for each and every practice in flock husbandry.

To my various friends engaged in sheep raising, most grateful acknowledgment is due for the encouragement and help they have given me in preparing this volume, and especially do I feel indebted to my colleague, Prof. J. A. Detlefsen, for his helpful suggestions on the discussion pertaining to sheep breeding, and to my assistants, Mr. Claude Harper and Mr. E. K. Augustus, who have rendered me most valuable assistance in various ways. I also wish to express my very great appreciation of suggestions given by Miss Anna Cushman Glover, Secretary of the Illinois Agricultural Experiment Station, and by my brother, Professor J. S. Coffey, on the arrangement of the material for this book.

WALTER C. COFFEY.

# CONTENTS

## PART I—HISTORY OF SHEEP RAISING AND OF SHEEP BREEDING



## PART II—STRUCTURE AND JUDGING



## PART III—BREEDS

## PART IV—THE MANAGEMENT OF THE FLOCK



## PART V—SHEEP FEEDING



## PART VI—SHEEP MANAGEMENT ON THE RANGES IN THE WESTERN STATES



## PART VII—MISCELLANEOUS

# JOB ANALYSIS OUTLINE

**Jobs and References.**—The following twenty-six jobs include the operations in the sheep enterprise. References are to the chapter numbers in this revised text, to available U. S. Farmers' Bulletins, and to U. S. Yearbooks. See also *Sheep Production* by Horlacher.

1. **Tracing the Development of Sheep Raising,** Chapter 1; U. S. Yearbook, 1923.
2. **Determining the Present Status of the Sheep Industry,** Chapter 2; U. S. Yearbook, 1923.
3. **Improving Sheep,** Chapters 3 and 4; Bulletin 1167.
4. **Comparing the Relation of Structure to Judging and Care,** Chapter 5.
5. **Determining the Relation of the Nature and Habits of the Sheep to Management,** Chapter 6.
6. **Comparing Mutton and Wool Types of Sheep,** Chapter 7; Bulletin 576.
7. **Judging Sheep,** Chapter 8; Bulletin 1199.
8. **Comparing and Choosing Sheep of Mutton Breeds,** Chapters 9 to 24; Bulletin 576.
9. **Comparing and Choosing Wool Breeds,** Chapters 25 to 28; Bulletin 576.
10. **Establishing the Commercial Flock,** Chapter 29; Bulletin 840, 929, 1051, 1199.
11. **Managing the Flock at Mating Time,** Chapter 30; Bulletin 1167.
12. **Caring for Ewes During Pregnancy,** Chapter 31; Bulletin 929, 1051.
13. **Caring for Ewes and Lambs at Lambing Time,** Chapter 32; Bulletin 840.
14. **Caring for the Growing Lamb,** Chapter 33; Bulletin 1134.
15. **Managing the Flock in the Summer,** Chapter 34; Bulletin 712, 798, 857, 1181, 1268, 1330, 1155.
16. **Handling the Wool Crop,** Chapter 35; Bulletin 1144.
17. **Tracing Developments in American Sheep Feeding,** Chapter 36; U. S. Yearbook, 1923.
18. **Studying Market Classes of Sheep,** Chapter 37; Bulletin 1360, 1502.
19. **Considering Essentials in Sheep and Lamb Feeding,** Chapter 38.
20. **Determining Factors Affecting the Rate and Economy of Gain,** Chapter 39.
21. **Meeting the Requirements of Field Feeding,** Chapter 40; U. S. Yearbook, 1923.

22. **Utilizing Range Lands by Sheep,** Chapter 41; U. S. Yearbook 1923.
23. **Managing Sheep on the Western Range,** Chapter 42; Bulletin 1245, 1428.
24. **Tracing Changes in Range Conditions During Recent Years,** Chapter 43; U. S. Yearbook, 1923.
25. **Providing Buildings and Equipment for Farm Flocks,** Chapter 44; Bulletin 810.
26. **Preparing Lamb and Mutton on the Farm,** Chapter 45; Bulletin 183, 1172, 1324.

## Job 1. Tracing the Development of Sheep Raising

**Conditions Usually Found.**—(1) Little is generally known regarding the main events that have influenced sheep raising in a community. (2) The importance of a state or county as a sheep-raising center changes from time to time. (3) Sheep raising has long been a pioneer enterprise but its character is changing in many countries.

**Aims.**—The student should try to determine what events have been of importance in influencing sheep raising in his country and community and should study the effect of competitive industries upon the present condition and future prospects of sheep production.

**Problems for Study and Discussion.**—

1. What kind of sheep were formerly kept in your community?
2. What events have effected changes in sheep raising?
3. What local events or conditions have been important in the past?
4. What flock has been in existence for the longest period in your locality?
5. Who in your region may be considered the leading improver of sheep?
6. How has the type of sheep changed in the last twenty-five years?
7. How does the present value of a sheep compare with the value of a few years ago?
8. How important have foreign countries been in influencing sheep raising in the United States?
9. How has sheep raising in different sections of the United States had any effect upon sheep raising in your region?
10. What factors indicate that sheep and their products will be in greater or less demand in the future?
11. Compare the development of sheep raising with the development of beef cattle raising.
12. To what influence is the keeping of sheep of a particular breed in your section due?

**Activities.**—(1) Prepare a chart on which to list the significant events affecting sheep production. (2) Prepare lists of reasons for and against increasing sheep production in your county.

### Job 2. Determining the Present Status of the Sheep Industry

**Conditions Usually Found.**—(1) The sheep industry in many sections of the United States is carried on as a side line to general farming. (2) In general farming areas flocks are either grade or pure-bred. (3) Flocks of more than 100 breeding ewes are not often found. (4) In the range areas the flocks may include many thousand sheep. (5) Lamb feeding is usually conducted with at least a car lot of lambs. (6) Some regions are noted for their extensive feeding operations.

**Aims.**—Farmers should be able to decide which type of sheep raising is best suited to their communities and to understand the general requirements for conducting each type.

**Problems for Study and Discussion.**—

1. List the number and size of sheep flocks in your community.
2. Get the opinions of farmers about the advisability of handling sheep under the different systems.
3. Get opinions of sheep raisers regarding the possibilities of profits from sheep compared with profits from other farm enterprises.
4. What prices are received for lambs and for wool?
5. Inquire of farmers raising pure-bred sheep about the advantages of pure-breds compared to grades.
6. What special qualifications should the producer of pure-bred sheep possess?
7. What crops are grown partly or wholly for sheep?
8. What factors make lamb feeding a prominent or minor enterprise in your community?
9. Why are larger flocks kept in the western rather than in the central states?
10. Compare the sheep industry of the United States with that of the British Isles, Australia, and New Zealand.

**Activities.**—Make a comparison of sheep raising as a side line and as a major enterprise.

### Job 3. Improving Sheep

**Conditions Usually Found.**—(1) The average sheep has not been developed to the highest possible degree in meat and in wool production. (2) While all sheep are more or less adaptable to all localities there is much variation in this respect. (3) Many of the sheep within a locality are of a similar type. (4) Some well-bred sheep are not fed and handled so as to permit their full development while others are not bred so as to respond well when given good feed and care. (5) The most successful breeders of pure-bred sheep make a careful study of the systems of breeding, and the production of pure-bred sheep is a specialized business.

**Aims.**—(1) Students need to become acquainted with the problems in the improvement of sheep and with the characteristics of various types of sheep that make some especially adapted to certain localities. (2) They need to know the various systems of breeding and to understand that good breeding without good shepherding will not give the best results.

**Problems for Study and Discussion.—**

1. What are the chief features in which the sheep in your locality may be further improved?
2. To what extent are farmers making an attempt to improve the sheep in your community?
3. How are the sheep raisers bringing about improvement?
4. Why do sheepmen generally study the display of their particular breed at the shows?
5. How does the fact that sheep are kept to produce both meat and wool increase the difficulty of improvement?
6. Learn, by asking the various owners, which flock in the community is the most prolific. Try to find out why this is so.
7. Would you expect to get improvement quicker through breeding all the ewes in your flock to one ram or by mating them to different rams?
8. Try to determine if certain ewes in a flock consistently produce better lambs than other ewes. How does this afford a basis of selection?
9. Find out the percentage of sheep raisers in your locality who use pure-bred sires. To what extent are the lambs and wool produced in their flocks better than the average?
10. Give facts to show whether the best lambs and wool are produced by the use of rams of a certain breed year after year or by changing breeds from time to time.
11. Describe the improvement of sheep in the best pure-bred flock you have seen. In what respects was it incomplete?
12. List the things which you consider utility points in sheep improvement.

**Activities.—**Prepare an outline to show how you would bring about improvement in the lamb and wool producing qualities of a flock.

### Job 4. Comparing the Relation of Structure to Judging and Care

**Conditions Usually Found.—**Sheep are a clearly defined group in the animal kingdom and afford a good opportunity for the study of the relation of various parts of the body to the kind of feed and care they require.

**Aims.—**The sheepman who has a fair understanding of the structure and physiology of the sheep learns to distinguish quickly between the normal and abnormal and between suitable and unsuitable feed and care.

**Problems for Study and Discussion.—**

1. Compare the skeleton of the sheep with that of the cow and indicate the ways in which they are similar.
2. Study the skeleton of the sheep noting the effect which it has on the body conformation of the animal.

3. Determine what differences there are in the forms of several sheep and learn if possible how much skeletal variation influences this.
4. What parts of the body may be most closely associated with constitution or vigor?
5. In which parts of the body is lean flesh most important in determining form?
6. In which parts would fat show a decided effect upon the conformation?
7. Compare the skin of a sheep on various parts of the body and point out the peculiarities.
8. How many functions can you assign to the glandular secretions found beneath the eyes and at the feet?
9. Study the mouth parts of a sheep and learn the relation these have to the way sheep graze.
10. List all the variations you can between the wool fibres on various parts of the body.
11. Learn what relation exists between the structure of wool fibres and their use as clothing materials.
12. What is the chief difference between the wool of a lamb and of a mature sheep?
13. What relation might exist between the wool covering of a sheep and the kind of shelter or housing provided?
14. What do the shape and size of the digestive organs indicate regarding the character of feed for sheep?

**Activities.**—(1) Look for outstanding differences in sheep in your community. (2) Obtain a sheep to slaughter. Study its internal organs and then remove the flesh from the bones by boiling. A small amount of lye in the water will aid and will whiten the bones. Mount the skeleton. (3) Examine a number of different wool fibres with a microscope. (4) Take a handful of wool and dip it in gasoline to remove the grease and dirt. If possible weigh it before and after dipping. (5) Examine the feet of several sheep and practice trimming them.

## Job 5. Determining the Relation of the Nature and Habits of Sheep to Management

**Conditions Usually Found.**—(1) Most flocks contain sheep of different ages. (2) The age of sheep is generally estimated by the appearance of the front teeth. (3) There are variations in the natural tendencies of sheep in regard to breeding and feeding habits.

**Aims.**—By understanding the nature and habits of sheep the student can learn the wisdom of certain details of management.

**Problems for Study and Discussion.**—

1. What are the ages of the breeding ewes and rams kept on farms in your locality?

2. If any ewes are found that are ten or twelve years of age learn why they have been retained.
3. What other things besides the teeth may be taken into consideration in determining age?
4. Observe a flock of sheep and note at what times of the day they graze.
5. How often during the day do the sheep drink?
6. How much do sheep move about as they graze?
7. How close do the sheep stay together in pastures? Indicate differences among breeds in this respect.
8. Considering the grazing abilities of sheep and cattle give objections for pasturing them together.
9. To what extent do the flocks in your region seem to have a decided preference for high places, and for short grass?
10. Locate breeders having Dorset sheep.
11. Find out how Dorsets and some other breeds differ from the average sheep in breeding habits.
12. How does this fit them for a special purpose?
13. How much variation may there be in the breeding dates of the average flock?
14. Find out from various farmers which ewes in their flocks have the earliest lambs.
15. How do you think the breeding season in sheep could be changed through selection? By feeding?
16. Ask farmers if it is easy to recognize sickness in sheep.
17. To what extent do the same ewes generally produce twins? Why would this be important in selection?

**Activities.**—(1) Observe or weigh a group of lambs from time to time and determine when the rate of growth is most rapid. (2) Make a list of the weeds and grasses in a pasture and note which ones the sheep eat.

## Job 6. Comparing Mutton and Wool Types of Sheep

**Conditions Usually Found.**—(1) Sheep are often described as mutton type or as wool type. (2) A number of breeds have been developed with the idea of combining the two types. (3) Type divisions generally are based on the conformation of body and character of the fleece. (4) In some cases there is more than one type within a breed.

**Aims.**—It is important to know the different types of sheep and how they are adapted to localities and in what respect each type is superior.

**Problems for Study and Discussion.**—

1. Look at a flock of sheep and decide to which type it belongs.
2. Further classify the flock on the basis of its wool.
3. Why does a certain type predominate in your locality?
4. To what extent is size an important factor in determining type?
5. In just what respects do the sheep you have seen differ?

6. List the essential features of the mutton and the wool types.
7. Which type do you prefer? Why?
8. Show that type has a relation to hardiness. To amount of feed required. To rate of growth.
9. From a utility standpoint which is more important, breed type or general type?
10. How do the features of breed type indicate constitution?
11. Compare the conformation of a ram and of a ewe.
12. In selecting a ram for a grade flock, which should be emphasized most —breed type or masculinity?
13. Find out if there is any difference in profits in accordance with the type of sheep kept.

**Activity.**—Inspect the rams and their lambs in your neighborhood and note if the more masculine rams have the best lambs.

## Job 7. Judging Sheep

**Conditions Usually Found.**—(1) Too many sheep raisers are likely to be satisfied with inferior animals because they are unable to determine just what constitutes superiority of conformation or fleece. (2) The best judges usually have the best sheep. (3) Through long experience many men have become adept at selecting, breeding, and feeding sheep.

**Aims.**—(1) The student must endeavor to train himself so that he can distinguish between sheep with respect to great and small differences. (2) The superior flocks usually excel in a number of points, and the grower should learn what these are.

**Problems for Study and Discussion.**—

1. Contrast the handling and visual inspection of sheep. Why does visual inspection alone not suffice?
2. Name the external parts of a sheep. The shape of what parts is determined by the bony framework?
3. Discuss which view—front, side, or rear—is most important in selecting breeding animals.
4. Explain why the various parts of a sheep are handled.
5. What parts of a sheep are generally examined for quality?
6. Which parts are of most importance in determining condition?
7. What are the most important features of a market sheep?
8. In what kind of sheep is a careful study of the head necessary?
9. In what respects does the judging of sheep differ from the judging of beef cattle?
10. Explain why each character observed in the examination of the fleece is important.
11. Make a list of the most important defects in sheep.
12. Why is it desirable to be able to give reasons for preference of one sheep compared to another?

**Activities.**—(1) Practice judging sheep available in your region. (2) Assist a lamb feeder or sheep raiser in sorting out fat lambs or culling ewes.

### Job 8. Comparing and Choosing Sheep of Mutton Breeds

**Conditions Usually Found.**—(1) Only a small percentage of the sheep in the United States are pure-bred. (2) Rams of the various breeds differ greatly in the kind of lambs they sire. (3) The different breeds are adapted to different conditions and purposes. (4) It is generally a good plan to get sheep of the same breed produced in a community.

**Aims.**—Students and growers need to know the characteristics and properties of the breeds in order to choose wisely.

**Problems for Study and Discussion.**—

1. Enumerate the number of sheep of each breed kept in your section.
2. Which breeds of mutton type sheep are especially adapted to meat production?
3. Which breeds do not rank so high in meat production but rank higher as wool producers? Why is this true?
4. Which may be considered as small breeds? As medium breeds? As large mutton breeds?
5. In what way does your community afford special advantages for the production of a particular breed?
6. List all considerations that may be involved in the choice of a breed.
7. What has the native home of each breed to do with the breed characteristics?
8. What American breeds of mutton sheep do we have?
9. Determine to what extent your community has tried various breeds in the last twenty years.
10. What do you think as to the advisability of a grower's keeping more than one breed?
11. Why should a community have only one breed?

**Activities.**—(1) Collect pictures of good animals of each of the mutton breeds. (2) Make a chart of the characteristics and properties of the different breeds. (3) Make a list of prices received for pure-bred animals of various breeds.

### Job 9. Comparing and Choosing Wool Breeds

**Conditions Usually Found.**—(1) In some communities in the eastern, central, and southern sections of the United States, few sheep of the wool breeds are found. (2) In other areas and in the range regions, sheep, especially ewes, of the wool breeds predominate.

**Aims.**—(1) The student and grower must decide whether to raise sheep of the mutton or wool breeds or to cross the two. (2) It is important to consider this because under certain conditions greater profits are made from lambs and wool by crossing than by using one breed.

**Problems for Study and Discussion.—**

1. What breeds of fine-wool sheep are found in your community?
2. How do they compare with the breeds of mutton sheep in date of breeding, number of lambs, and amount of wool produced?
3. In crosssing mutton and wool sheep, would it be better to use mutton rams on fine-wool ewes or fine-wool rams on mutton ewes? Why?
4. Do you think the American Merino, Delaine, or Rambouillet would be most suitable? Why?
5. Describe the main differences between a cross-bred lamb and a fine-wool lamb.
6. Give arguments for and against crossing.
7. Which fine-wool breeds are gaining most in popularity? Give reasons.

**Activities.**—Make a table of the fine-wool breeds of sheep. In suitable columns give comparisons covering such points as age of breed, introduction to America, distribution, weights of sheep, weights of fleeces, sizes of flocks and prolificacy.

### Job 10. Establishing the Commercial Flock

**Conditions Usually Found.**—(1) The grower who has been most careful in establishing his flock is likely to be most successful. (2) Well established flocks have been fitted into the general scheme of farming.

**Aims.**—(1) The farmer should benefit from the experience of others. (2) It is necessary to realize that the ram is the most important individual to select.

**Problems for Study and Discussion.—**

1. Tell how growers procured their first flocks of sheep when they started.
2. Which methods have been most successful?
3. What prices would have to be paid for good stock for breeding?
4. Compare the prices asked for grades and pure-breds.
5. Decide on what stock and what numbers you would procure in starting the sheep enterprise yourself.
6. Make a list of the main points to consider in selecting ewes.
7. Make a list of the advantages and disadvantages of securing ewes locally and on the central markets or from producers in other sections.
8. Upon what will the returns of the ewes purchased depend?
9. What parts of breeding ewes should be given special attention?
10. Give reasons for selecting ewe lambs from your own flock for replacements, or for purchasing them.
11. Which is most costly per lamb—the ewe or the ram? Why?
12. Does this have any bearing on the price which may be paid for a good ram compared to the price paid for the ewes?

13. If you were securing a large number of ewes what points would you emphasize most?
14. How can you finance a sheep enterprise?

**Activities.**—(1) Observe the new flocks established in the community and tabulate the costs in all cases. (2) Find out from growers how often they purchase rams and what prices are paid. Calculate the annual cost per farm for rams. (3) Make out record sheets for the sheep enterprise including feed record, labor record, miscellaneous expenses, income record, and summary.

## Job 11. Managing the Flock at Mating Time

**Conditions Usually Found.**—Under farm conditions ewes sometimes do not receive the attention they should at the breeding season. The best shepherds prepare ewes for mating.

**Aims.**—An effort should be made to learn when ewes and rams are in proper condition so as to insure a good lamb crop.

**Problems for Study and Discussion.**—

1. What is "flushing"?
2. How many sheepmen in your section follow the practice?
3. What feeds do they use?
4. If they do not do so now, find out if they have tried it and discontinued it and the reasons for so doing.
5. How many farmers keep records of breeding dates?
6. Find out from farmers how many ewes failed to lamb the past season and the explanation of these failures.
7. Study the effect of exercise on vigor.
8. How much grain would a ram require during the breeding season?
9. How many rams are kept per one hundred ewes?
10. What records are required during breeding season in pure-bred flocks not needed in grade flocks?

**Activities.**—(1) Tag ewes. (2) Trim the feet of rams and ewes. (3) Prepare a marking paint for a ram. (4) Make a list of reasons why rams and ewes may fail to breed, with reasons for each.

## Job 12. Caring for Ewes During Pregnancy

**Conditions Usually Found.**—(1) The importance of the right feeding and care of pregnant ewes is realized by the best sheepmen in many communities. (2) Skilful management in this period is the best assurance of strong, vigorous lambs.

**Aims.**—(1) Successful students and growers need to know when the nutritional needs of the ewes are being supplied. (2) Economical features of feeding to get best results should be understood.

**Problems for Study and Discussion.—**

1. Observe feeding practices in your community and find out what use is made of the unmarketable roughages.
2. To what extent are legume roughages relied upon to furnish needed nutrients?
3. What feeds are grown especially for the use of breeding ewes?
4. To what extent are purchased feeds used?
5. How do the feeding practices of the more successful farmers differ from those of the less successful?
6. What results have been secured when silage is used as part of the ration?
7. How many sheep raisers in your section grow root crops for sheep?
8. What provision is made in order to exercise the ewes?
9. Study the types of shelter provided for pregnant ewes. Compare the differences in economy with which shelter is provided.
10. How are the rams handled during the winter months?

**Activities.—**(1) Make a list of the crops grown on farms in order of their suitability as sheep feeds. (2) Prepare rations for pregnant ewes and calculate the cost of each ration. (3) Find out how much land would be required to produce the feed for a flock of fifty ewes during the winter; then draw a plan of a farm showing the acreage for each crop, for pastures, and indicate the rotations.

### Job 13. Caring for Ewes and Lambs at Lambing Time

**Conditions Usually Found.—**(1) Many preventable losses occur at lambing time. (2) The best shepherds are able to control losses at lambing time by proper care.

**Aims.—**(1) Students and farmers should know what losses are likely to occur at lambing time. (2) They should learn how to prevent these losses.

**Problems for Study and Discussion.—**

1. What care does a good sheep raiser give his flock at lambing time?
2. How many shepherds make special preparation for the lambing season?
3. What supplies and equipment do they have on hand?
4. Give the numbers of lambs dropped and the numbers raised on each farm in your community.
5. Calculate the percentage of loss in each case.
6. Calculate the percentage lamb crop on the basis of the number of ewes bred.
7. Why are sanitation and hygiene so important at lambing time?
8. Explain the best methods of feeding ewes just before and after lambing.
9. What do sheepmen do to make ewes own their lambs, or own strange lambs?
10. What precautions need to be taken to prevent lambs from chilling? How are they treated if they become chilled?

11. How do farmers raise orphan lambs?
12. What are the most common causes of deaths of lambs in your community?
13. What could be done to prevent these losses?

**Activities.**—(1) Make some lambing pens and prepare lambing quarters. (2) Try raising an orphan lamb. (3) Look over a group of lambs to detect young lamb troubles and treat those lambs that are ailing. (4) Practice managing a flock at lambing time.

## Job 14. Caring for the Growing Lamb

**Conditions Usually Found.**—(1) The best shepherds know many points in management which contribute to their success. (2) Neglect, poor feeding, and management often cause serious losses.

**Aims.**—Farmers should learn the essential details of good management and devise means of putting them into use.

**Problems for Study and Discussion.**—

1. Upon what does the growth of lambs depend?
2. Does the pregnancy or suckling period cause the greater demand on the ewes? Give reasons for your answer.
3. What factors may influence the manner in which suckling ewes are fed?
4. Discuss the advantages and disadvantages of early and late lambing in your locality.
5. What grain mixtures do farmers use for young lambs?
6. Describe a lamb creep.
7. Calculate the amount of grain a lamb will eat before it is four months old if it is kept in a dry lot. Do the same thing for a lamb on pasture.
8. Discuss pastures of various kinds for ewes and for lambs.
9. What pastures are used in your community?
10. What percentage of farmers who raise sheep in your locality dock and castrate their market lambs?
11. What methods do they use?
12. Find out why others who fail to trim their lambs do not do so.
13. Make a list of the reasons why lambs should be docked and castrated.
14. What percentage of local farmers market their lambs at weaning time?

**Activities.**—(1) Construct a lamb creep. (2) Prepare a grain mixture for use in a lamb creep. (3) Practice selecting some of the fastest growing ewe lambs to add to the flock. (4) Dock and castrate lambs with the help of an experienced person.

## Job 15. Managing the Flock in the Summer

**Conditions Usually Found.**—(1) Practically all sheep are kept on pastures during the summer. (2) Parasites and predatory animals are the main enemies of the flock at this season.

**Aims.**—How best to maintain the health and to protect the flock from enemies in an economical way should be understood.

**Problems for Study and Discussion.**—

1. Give experience of farmers as to ages when their lambs are weaned.
2. How are the ewes treated after the lambs are removed?
3. Under your conditions how would you provide shade for the flock?
4. Report how long certain pastures have been used for sheep.
5. In what way do sheep raisers in your community try to rotate pastures from year to year?
6. How do local sheepmen treat lambs and sheep for internal parasites?
7. What remedies have they used?
8. What is the best season for dipping sheep for external parasites?
9. Why is dipping at other times occasionally necessary?
10. How can external parasites be controlled in other ways than by dipping?
11. How can foot-rot be prevented?
12. Of what is goitre an indication?
13. What sheep are most likely to be over-heated?
14. What is the extent of losses by dogs in your locality?

**Activities.**—(1) Examine sheep for external parasites. (2) Outline a sheep-raising system and a pasture system to control internal parasites. (3) Assist in treating sheep for internal and external parasites. (4) Make a post mortem examination for internal parasites and disease symptoms. (5) List the provisions which should be included in a law to control dogs.

## Job 16. Handling the Wool Crop

**Conditions Usually Found.**—(1) Wool accounts for a good percentage of total flock receipts. (2) The best sheepmen shear and care for the fleeces in a satisfactory way. (3) The income of many growers is reduced because of the careless way they handle their sheep and wool.

**Aims.**—(1) Students should understand what constitutes good wool and the things which determine its value. (2) They should know the best methods of shearing and of handling fleeces to secure the best market prices.

**Problems for Study and Discussion.**—

1. What factors influence the value of wool?
2. Explain the difference between the class and the grade of a fleece.
3. Explain the differences between the old and the new systems of grading wool in the United States.
4. What are the best times for shearing?
5. What are the best methods of handling sheep to prevent burs, dirt, and other foreign material in the wool?
6. What instruments are used for shearing?
7. Explain why special twine should be used to tie wool.
8. What agencies may be involved in the marketing of wool?

**Activities.**—(1) Shear some sheep. (2) Roll and tie the fleeces. (3) Collect samples of wool from various breeds of sheep and of the various grades of wool. Mount on black cardboard and study them carefully. (4) Assist an experienced person in grading wool.

## Job 17. Tracing Developments in American Sheep Feeding

**Conditions Usually Found.**—Sheep feeding is conducted in many sections.

**Aims.**—Farmers should understand what conditions favor sheep feeding.

**Problems for Study and Discussion.**—

1. To what extent is the feeding of lambs practiced in your territory?
2. What are the benefits that feeders derive from sheep feeding?
3. How long have farmers in your section fed sheep?
4. What methods of feeding do they use now compared to those of twenty-five years ago?
5. Give the local conditions for and against sheep feeding.
6. Debate increasing vs. decreasing sheep feeding locally.
7. Define what is meant by "feeder" sheep in American markets.
8. Explain how farmer feeders manage their business if they buy "feeders" in the stockyards.

## Job 18. Studying Market Classes of Sheep

**Conditions Usually Found.**—(1) There are many factors which enter into a determination of market values. (2) The sheep raiser has the most control over the factors which are associated with the character of his product.

**Aims.**—Students need to have a good idea of market requirements in order to understand why prices and values vary.

**Problems for Study and Discussion.**—

1. Why are sheep classed and graded on the markets?
2. Explain the basis for the various classes.
3. What is the relation between sheep judging and market grades?
4. Discuss the importance of form, of quality, and of condition in market sheep.
5. How does the weight of market lambs affect the kind of sheep to keep?
6. How is it possible to eliminate the lower grades of lambs on the markets?
7. Ask feeders what things they consider of most importance in selecting feeder lambs.
8. Under what conditions may the lower grades of feeder lambs make top-grade slaughter lambs? Why is this seldom?
9. Find the grade of the lambs, prices they brought, and the time of sale for lambs in your community.

10. To what markets were the lambs sent, by whom shipped, and by what agency were they sold?
11. What agencies in your community are endeavoring to improve market quality of lambs and marketing procedure?
12. To what extent can market classes of sheep be further developed in the United States?

**Activities.**—(1) Look over groups of sheep and lambs to be shipped, estimate their weight, market grade, and probable selling price on the basis of the prevailing market. (2) Handle as many lambs as possible to find out their condition on back and ribs. (3) Tabulate prices for lambs and determine in which months of the year prices are usually high and in which low. Make a graph of these figures. (5) Visit shipping agencies and markets to study marketing. Count number of lambs or sheep per car. Which cars are graded before and which after shipment? What grades are made in yards? Calculate percentage of standard lambs. (6) Secure shipping blanks and fill them for actual or supposed shipments.

## Job 19. Considering Essentials in Sheep and Lamb Feeding

**Conditions Usually Found.**—(1) Most successful feeders follow a definite type of feeding. (2) They try to evaluate all factors that influence their business. (3) These men know the importance of a good feed supply and have the necessary equipment.

**Aims.**—Students of sheep feeding should learn what are the requirements of success in this work and know how to reduce the risks.

**Problems for Study and Discussion.**—

1. What type of lamb feeding is most profitably followed in your region?
2. Give reasons why some other type would not be as successful.
3. Find out from feeders what they consider the main risks to be.
4. Why is it that roughages alone are not satisfactory feeds for this type of sheep husbandry?
5. What items enter into the cost of feeding lambs?
6. What factors influence the length of the feeding period?
7. Why is the beginning of the feeding period important?
8. Explain the dangers of increasing feeds too rapidly.
9. How do feeders in your neighborhood feed lambs?
10. Why is it not advisable to exercise or excite fattening animals?
11. What diseases have feeders reported as causing losses of their lambs during the past few years?
12. How is it possible to feed lambs and not have some of them go "off feed"?
13. Explain why lambs should be "topped out" if a large number is fed and sold at different times.
14. Discuss the various methods of buying feeder lambs.

**Activities.**—(1) Draw up a plan for a lamb-feeding plant large enough to feed a double deck car lot of lambs. (2) Keep a record of the cost of feeding lambs.

### Job 20. Determining Factors Affecting the Rate and Economy of Gain

**Conditions Usually Found.**— (1) Lambs constitute by far the greater percentage of sheep fed at present. (2) Feeders make no effort to separate ewe and wether lambs. (3) Special methods of preparing feeds seldom prove profitable. (4) A great variety of feeds are used in various sections.

**Aims.**—Farmers should develop skill and judgment in selecting efficient and economical rations for fattening lambs.

**Problems for Study and Discussion.**—

1. Under what conditions would you try to purchase sheep older than lambs for feeding?
2. How many feeders in your vicinity use self-feeders?
3. What feeders in your neighborhood shear lambs at the beginning of the feeding period? A short time before they are shipped to market?
4. Study the reasons they give for so doing.
5. List the roughages available, in the order of their usefulness, for fattening lambs.
6. If feeding a large proportion of roughage of grain to lambs, what roughages would be best?
7. Compare corn silage and corn fodder as feeds for fattening sheep.
8. To secure good gains and finish, if oat straw is used alone as roughage, what protein concentrates should be added? Why would such a ration not be desirable?
9. On the basis of digestible nutrients calculate the relative value of some common legume and carbonaceous roughages.
10. Under what conditions can you afford to build a silo to feed several hundred lambs?

**Activities.**—(1) Prepare a feeding schedule for a car lot of lambs using feeds available on your farm. (2) Calculate the cost of buying supplementary feeds, and decide what effects these would have on the gains of lambs. (3) Prepare a table showing the amounts of various feeds it would take to fatten a double deck load of 300 lambs and the acreage required to produce the feeds.

### Job 21. Meeting the Requirements of Field Feeding

**Conditions Usually Found.**—(1) Sheepmen who practice field feeding prepare in advance. (2) Those who try to fatten lambs in cornfields without additional feed are usually disappointed.

**Aims.**—The feeder needs to know how to handle lambs in fields to get results comparable to those in dry-lot feeding.

**Problems for Study and Discussion.**—

1. What characters should be given special emphasis in selecting lambs for field feeding?

2. Compare pasture and cornfield feeding with cornfield and an intercrop.
3. What crops are generally planted with corn for fattening lambs?
4. What are the chief causes of losses in field feeding?
5. Discuss ways of reducing such losses.
6. How can the wasting of corn in field feeding be overcome?
7. Calculate how many lambs would be necessary to lamb down a forty-acre field of corn and an intercrop on your farm.
8. Is it better to have the lambs harvest all the corn or just field feed until the roughage has been consumed and then shift to dry-lot? Give reasons.
9. How can the watering problem be solved in field feeding of crops?

**Activities.**—Make a comparison of field and dry-lot feeding in your section; list the quantities of feed required in each plan for fattening the lambs.

### Job 22. Utilizing Range Lands by Sheep

**Conditions Usually Found.**—(1) There are great differences in range areas. (2) Different types of range seem to demand different kinds of sheep. (3) Range-sheep raising is largely dependent on natural vegetation.

**Aims.**—The student needs to understand how range lands are secured and controlled and what kind of sheep will probably do best under various range conditions.

**Problems for Study and Discussion.**—

1. Find out how much of the land area in each of the western states is unsuited to general farming purposes.
2. What are the prevailing types of vegetation on the various range areas?
3. What are the costs of range lands?
4. Contrast with the costs of farm lands.
5. What breeds predominate in your area?
6. Which are adapted to large ranges and which to small?
7. Of the many breeds of sheep not now found in your area which do you think would prove more adaptable than those now used? Why?

**Activities.**—(1) Prepare a map of the country showing the various kinds of range and their locations. (2) Consult census reports to learn the relative importance of sheep raising compared to other industries in the large range areas.

### Job 23. Managing Sheep on the Western Range

**Conditions Usually Found.**—(1) Western sheep ranching is a specialized business. (2) The equipment required is not the same in all sections. (3) Western rangemen have many difficulties to overcome.

**Aims.**—(1) It is necessary to know the basis of managing sheep on the range. (2) Understanding ways to reduce losses is imperative.

**Problems for Study and Discussion.**—

1. How important is the character of the range in determining how many sheep a herder can handle?
2. What methods are followed in moving sheep from winter to summer range?
3. How much could a sheepman afford to spend for extra labor at lambing time if he were able to increase his lamb crop by ten per cent?
4. How much winter feed, in addition to range, is required per thousand ewes?
5. What are the chief criticisms of the way wool is handled?
6. Of the methods of marketing wool which do you think will bring the greatest benefit to the wool growers over a period of years? Why?
7. Outline a method for overcoming some of the losses of sheep and lambs which the western rangeman experiences.
8. Does the rangeman need to practice sanitation to the same extent as the farmer?

**Activities.**—(1) Make a calendar of operations for handling a range outfit of 10,000 ewes. (2) Outline a plan for the improvement of range flocks, giving probable annual costs for pure-bred rams for immense flocks. (3) Calculate the costs of loading a wool crop from 2,000 Merinos 100 miles from a railroad. (4) Make a dipping vat suitable for dipping a large flock rapidly.

## Job 24. Tracing Changes in Range Conditions During Recent Years

**Conditions Usually Found.**—(1) Significant changes have taken place in range-sheep production. (2) Some sheepmen have been backward in adopting new methods of management and marketing.

**Aims.**—The student should realize the necessity of efficiency and progress in range-sheep raising.

**Problems for Study and Discussion.**—

1. Name or describe the most progressive rangeman in your locality or elsewhere.
2. What are the most significant changes in sheep raising and range management since such men have been producing sheep?
3. How can the carrying capacity of a range be increased?
4. What changes should be brought about in regard to the kind of sheep kept?
5. What changes do you foresee in the next few years?
6. What provision should be made now to meet these new demands?
7. What are the most important influences, both favorable and unfavorable, now affecting the range-sheep industry?

**Activities.**—(1) On a map of the western regions indicate areas now abandoned by sheepmen for grazing. Show what railroads have influenced the range areas. Locate the federal and state reserves not open for grazing. (2) Secure a good road map of one or more western states, marking on this the leading range areas, to show the effects of roads on marketing of lambs and wool.

## Job 25. Providing Buildings and Equipment for Farm Flocks

**Conditions Usually Found.**—(1) Experienced sheepmen seldom provide unsuitable shelter and equipment. (2) Sometimes the buildings are too expensive or are located poorly.

**Aims.**—(1) It is necessary to understand the essential requirements of shelters and equipment for sheep raising. (2) Farmers should understand planning with regard to economy, suitability to the kind of sheep raising, and efficiency in use.

**Problems for Study and Discussion.**—

1. Describe shelters and equipment for sheep in use in your region.
2. What are the essentials of a good shelter for sheep?
3. Under what conditions is it advisable to provide storage space for both grain and roughage in a sheep barn?
4. How many different types of feed racks for sheep are there? Which would you choose? Why?
5. How would you construct a dog-proof corral?
6. In planning a barn what provision would you make for shearing sheep and caring for wool?
7. Discuss the exposure and warmth of barns for sheep.
8. Discuss also the means of securing dryness, light, and ventilation.
9. What type of floor would you prefer for a sheep barn?
10. How can you plan a hay rack to avoid litter in the wool?

**Activities.**—(1) Draw plans for the interior arrangement of a shelter for fifty breeding ewes. For fifty ewes and their lambs. (2) Draw plans for a western lamb-feeding plant. (3) Make a loading chute. (4) Construct a watering trough. (5) Build a good rack for hay and a grain trough. (6) Obtain samples and prices of wire fencing suited for use in field feeding. Include samples and costs of iron posts. (7) Calculate the entire cost of a suitable farm layout for sheep, including shelters, fences, and small equipment.

## Job 26. Preparing Lamb and Mutton on the Farm

**Conditions Usually Found.**—(1) Some farmers butcher lambs and sheep for home use. (2) In many sections little or no farm butchering is done.

**Aims.**—(1) Those who live on sheep farms should know good methods of butchering. (2) Special markets can be developed in some communities.

**Problems for Study and Discussion.—**

1. Explain the advantages of home-dressed lamb.
2. What are the chief reasons why farmers do not consume more lamb?
3. Compare the equipments necessary to butcher a lamb and a hog.
4. Explain the care of the carcass. How can fresh meat be saved until used?
5. Learn the names of the cuts of lamb.
6. Compare local prices of these cuts.
7. How would you dispose of the pelts of home-butchered lambs?
8. Under what conditions would shearing before slaughter be advisable?
9. Describe the procedure in dressing lambs for home use.
10. Give the advantages of a community meat ring.
11. Contrast the care in butchering lambs with that required for swine.

**Activities.**—(1) Assist in slaughtering some lambs. (2) Examine the carcasses carefully and weigh the various cuts. Calculate the dressing percentages. Calculate the percentage of carcass weight for each wholesale cut.

# PART I

## HISTORY OF SHEEP RAISING AND SHEEP BREEDING

# CHAPTER I

## THE DEVELOPMENT OF SHEEP RAISING IN VARIOUS COUNTRIES

**Early Domestication and Importance.**—It is thought that sheep were first domesticated in Asia, probably in Turkestan. There is evidence that they may have been under domestication in Europe in prehistoric times, for the bones of sheep have been found in caves and lake dwellings, where the primitive people of that continent lived. We can only surmise that primitive man used the skins for raiment and shelter, and the meat and milk for food.

As man advanced in civilization and became more settled in his habits, his principal wealth often consisted of flocks and herds. The Old Testament contains many passages which refer to the pastoral occupation of sheep herding. Rome developed skill in handling her flocks, and sheep abounded in Spain prior to the Christian era.

The development of sheep raising as it concerns those now interested in the production of mutton and wool centered in England and in Spain. Before the year 1000 both of these countries attached great importance to their flocks, and by the year 1500 they were recognized as the greatest sheep countries of the world. Although their wools were considerably unlike, they were regarded as competitors for several hundred years on the great wool markets of Flanders.

**Sheep Raising in Spain.**—Spain, at a very early period, developed the Merino, a type of sheep which produced wool of unusually fine fiber, suitable for making such fine, soft fabrics as broadcloth (Fig. 1). This wool met with so large a demand and was so fertile a source of revenue, that the most powerful classes, the nobility and the clergy, engaged in sheep husbandry. They collected great flocks for which they secured almost unlimited privileges. Carefully tended by shepherds of long experience, these flocks were travelled from the southern to the northern part of the kingdom and back again each year in order to secure the best grazing and the most favorable climatic conditions for the sheep (Fig. 2). Certain laws of the kingdom stipulated that the owners of large flocks should be allowed a path 90 paces in width for their sheep through enclosed lands. The use of this privilege often brought hardships upon the peasants, who often complained of having their crops and vineyards devastated.

The production of sheep and of wool of a type unlike that of

**Fig. 1.—Old type of Spanish Merino. These old sheep had long necks, high shoulders and were comparatively free from wrinkles.**

any other country became so important in Spain that the owners of flocks, being very few in number, easily established a monopoly which they maintained for many years. To allow a sheep to leave Spain alive was a crime punishable by death. The king was the only one exempted under this law. Sheep owners reinforced statute with argument, contending that in any other country their sheep would deteriorate in quality of fleece because of different soil, climate, and vegetation, and also because of inefficient shepherding. But later events proved them wrong in their contention.

**Spain's Monopoly Broken.**—There came a time when

Spain's wool monopoly was broken and her sheep industry went into a period of decadence. Early in the nineteenth century Napoleon invaded Spain and overthrew the government. In connection with this conquest he seized large numbers of Merino sheep and shipped them to other countries where they added new chapters to the history of sheep raising. A few years later Spain tried hard to regain her former place as a great sheep country,

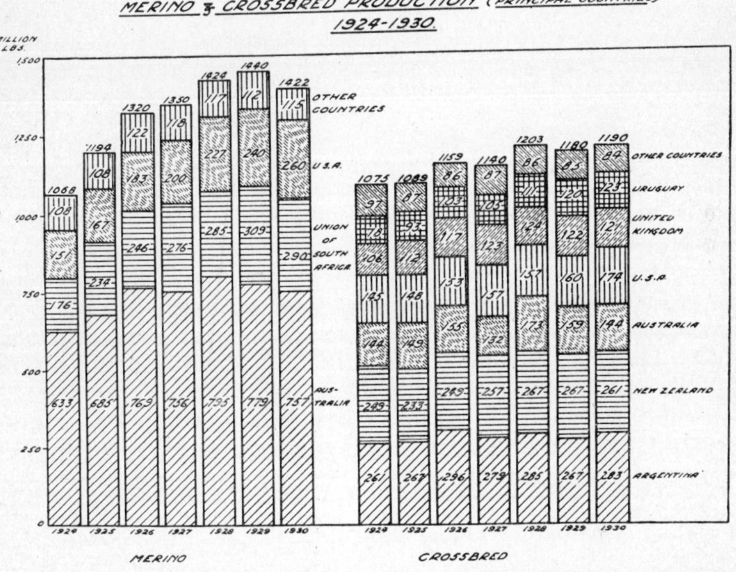


FIG. 2.—The various types of Merino sheep are a very important factor in the world's wool production at the present time. They account for practically all the fine wool and, of course, contribute much to the crossbred production. (From Empire Marketing Board.)

but Napoleon's act really marked the beginning of her steady decline as a producer of Merinos. Spain is now the third largest wool-producing country in Europe, and sheep are the most numerous livestock, exceeding cattle, horses, goats and pigs in the aggregate. Coarse-wooled sheep now constitute about three-fourths of the total number; Merinos comprise the remainder.

**Characteristics of Merinos in Spain.**—Mention should be made of three characteristics of Merino sheep in Spain that have had an important influence upon their subsequent history: first, the production of very fine wool; second, the hardiness of the mature sheep and their ability to travel; third, the disposition to stay close together when feeding, resting, or traveling.

**Stationary Flocks.**—Spain also had stationary flocks, some of which had coarse wool and others wool resembling that of the travelling flocks. These stationary flocks were of importance numerically in Spain, but they contributed little or nothing to sheep raising in outside countries.

**Sheep Raising in England.**—England, instead of developing one or two general types of sheep, saw fit to encourage several types that were markedly different in the length and fineness of their wool. None of the wools from these breeds was as fine as that of the Merino, but they sold readily in the markets nevertheless, for they were more suitable for a variety of uses than wool from Spain.

Aside from the difference in the nature of the wool, the sheep industries of England and Spain were dissimilar in other ways. The flocks of England were not in the hands of a very few powerful owners as they were in Spain. Travelling flocks were not established. The great problem of the English sheep farmer of earlier times was to procure sheep that were adapted to his particular locality. This largely accounts for the fact that there were many types. Another factor may have been the poor conditions for travelling, which kept the English farmer close to his home. With cold winters, scarcity of winter feed, and diseases to contend with, conditions were hard, and the owner was content with a type of sheep that would best withstand these hardships whether or not it would produce the kind of wool he most desired.

**Events Affecting Sheep Raising.**—The great plague, or Black Death, of 1348, served as a great impetus to sheep growing in England. Laborers were so reduced in number by this plague that land owners were obliged to turn their lands into pastures. As sheep paid better than other classes of livestock, owing to the high price of wool, sheep raising became the "sheet anchor of English farming." Flock husbandry, however, was still only a partial success because of inability to cope with the severe winters. The fact that it was profitable at all shows what a great demand there was for wool.

During the reign of Edward III (1327–1377) a grant of special protection made in favor of all Flemish weavers, dyers, and fullers, who would settle in England for the purpose of following their trade, resulted in securing artisans skilled in the then most improved methods of cloth making. Soon afterwards, English wools came more and more to be made up at home so as to more nearly suit home demands. Later, in the reign of Elizabeth (1557–1603), still more of these artisans, as well as others of their countrymen, came to England as refugees. Thus was laid the foundation of England's great expansion in manufacturing.

Settlers from Flanders also brought the root and clover crops, the cultivation of which soon became of far-reaching benefit to the sheep industry, for they made possible an adequate supply of good winter feed. As a result the death rate of sheep was greatly reduced, and the production of wool per sheep was increased.

**Robert Bakewell.**—Aside from improvement resulting from

Fig. 3.—Mutton sheep of the present-day type on a pasture in Great Britain. They are wide, deep and compact in form. They mature early and fatten easily.

better feeding, there was no great progress until the time of Robert Bakewell, 1725–1794. Wool had declined in price until, with the rapidly advancing values of English lands, it alone would no longer justify the keeping of sheep. With the enormous expansion of manufacturing and of other industries in England, there were developing great urban populations demanding meat. Bakewell was able to see that these changed conditions demanded a new type of sheep, and accordingly he set to work to make of the long, ungainly, coarse-wooled, late-maturing sheep of his community a compact, early-maturing, easily fattened animal. He succeeded so well and his work impressed breeders so profoundly that he is generally acknowledged as the first great improver of livestock. He demonstrated that certain fundamental laws of breeding aided in attaining what he sought. He thus inaugurated a period of improvement in the sheep industry of his country such as the world had never seen. It was essentially an improvement securing better mutton and early maturity, but many other points received careful attention. The work Bakewell started attained such importance that England became the native home of nearly all of the modern mutton breeds, and sheepmen from all parts of the world still go there for breeding stock (Fig. 3).

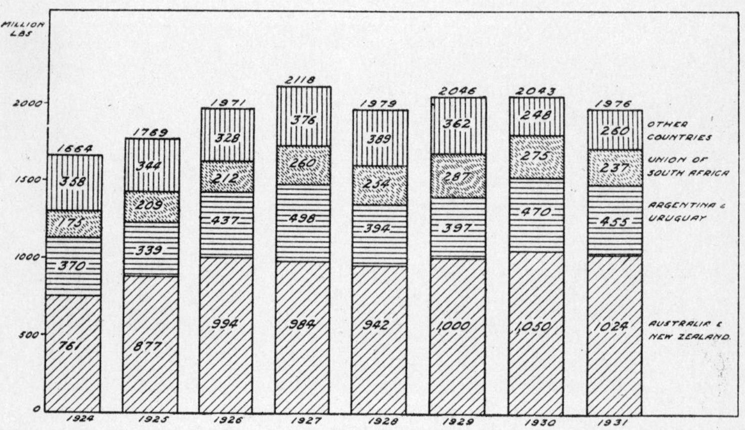


Fig. 4.—The newer countries of the southern hemisphere are the leading exporters of wool and European countries the chief importers. (From Empire Marketing Board.)

**Importance of Wool in New Countries.**—Sheep first advanced to great importance in Spain and in England because of their wool. They were also of value as meat-producing animals, but it was the demand for wool that first made them profitable in these countries and caused them to gain prominence in the lands which now rank as the great sheep-growing countries of the world. Value considered, wool is light in weight, and imperishable with respect to time involved in getting it to market. It was only natural, therefore, that the colonizers of Australia, of New Zealand, and of Argentina should turn to the production of wool.

**Sheep Raising in North America.—Colonial Times.—** Domestic sheep were brought to North America by early colonists. It is thought that the Spaniards who founded old Santa Fe, New Mexico, brought with them the sheep from which the multi-colored flocks of the Navajo Indians have descended. If, as is generally supposed, sheep of this original stock were taken out of Spain, special permission to do so surely must have been granted by the king. The colonists along the Atlantic seaboard introduced the English, and a few other mutton breeds. As a rule the flocks were not large, the main object in keeping sheep being to supply wool for making homespuns, and only incidentally to furnish a part of the family meat supply.

**The Embargo Act.**—In the year 1807, the people of the United States were forbidden by the Embargo Act to trade with foreign powers. Although this statute was frequently violated, its effect upon foreign trade in general was keenly felt. Among other things it so restricted imports that it caused a shortage of woolens, and American manufacturers found more demand for such goods than their supply of raw wool would satisfy. Moreover, because it turned many people in New England away from commerce into manufacturing, it still further increased the demand for raw wool. Men active in the affairs of the nation, realizing the need of more wool to supply the woolen mills, devoted both time and means to the task of getting more sheep into the country. Napoleon had ruined Spain's monopoly on Spanish Merinos. But years before this, Saxony in Germany, through a gift of a number of Merinos to her chief ruler from the king of Spain, had demonstrated that at least one other country besides Spain could grow Merino sheep and that she could even surpass Spain in the quality of wool produced. Saxony's success gave confidence to Americans who were interested in getting more fine-wooled sheep into their country. Merinos accordingly were imported, and soon they showed that they could thrive and produce wool of good quality in their new environment. There soon arose a craze for these sheep which continued from 1808 until about 1816, during which time quite impossible claims were made for them. Nevertheless they proved to be the type of sheep needed not only then but for many years afterwards, for they were adapted to grazing on undeveloped lands and to the production of that fine wool for which there was so strong a demand.

**Westward Movement of Sheep.**—The westward movement of

sheep began early in the nineteenth century during the period of mania for Merinos. Gradually flocks, mainly of Merino breeding, spread over the fertile, virgin lands of the Ohio Valley and of the Great Lakes region. When these lands became somewhat thickly settled and high in price, many sheepmen, desiring to operate on a large scale, moved farther west where range was cheap and extensive. It was chiefly because of vast stretches of cheap range in the West that certain of our sheepmen almost constantly kept on the march, first over the Appalachians, then across the Mississippi, thence west to the Rockies and southwest into Texas, and finally through all the Rocky Mountain Region.

**Changes in Centers of Sheep Population Shown by Census Reports.**—In 1840, as the census reports clearly show, the regions of densest sheep population were Vermont, New Hampshire, and New York. At that time there were no sheep in the far West except those of the Navajo Indians in northern New Mexico. In fact, the only state west of the Mississippi having sheep in considerable numbers was Missouri. Ten years later that part of Ohio lying south of Lake Erie was the region of densest sheep population. There was a noticeable thinning out in New Hampshire, Vermont, and New York, and a pronounced increase in southeastern Michigan, and in all of Indiana, Kentucky, Tennessee, and Illinois. Flocks had also made their way into southern Wisconsin and southeastern Iowa. The census of 1860 shows sheep in eastern Texas and the coast and central parts of California. Although the census report of 1870 does not show much new territory occupied by sheep in the Mississippi Valley and the far West, it does show with a great deal of significance a great increase in numbers in those regions and a great decrease in such eastern states as New York, Vermont, and New Hampshire. In 1880 southeastern Wisconsin, along with southeastern Michigan and much of Ohio, were the regions of densest sheep population. Such states as the Dakotas, Nebraska, Kansas, Colorado, and Wyoming, which ten years before were almost unoccupied, now showed a liberal sprinkling of flocks. By 1890 all the western states and territories were occupied and by 1900 the Rocky Mountain region had become the most important sheep section of the country. Of the sheep in the United States the western range area claimed over 58 per cent in 1910 and over 60 per cent in 1920 and 1935. (Figs. 5 and 6.)

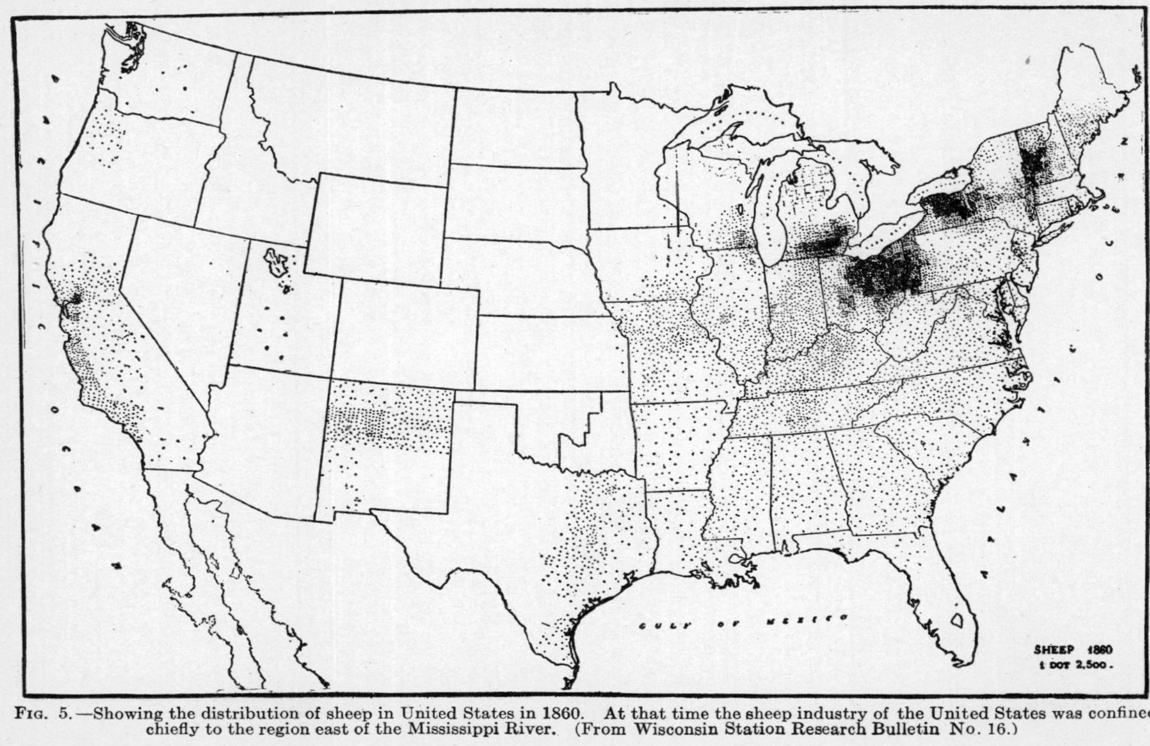


FIG. 5.—Showing the distribution of sheep in United States in 1860. At that time the sheep industry of the United States was confined chiefly to the region east of the Mississippi River. (From Wisconsin Station Research Bulletin No. 16.)

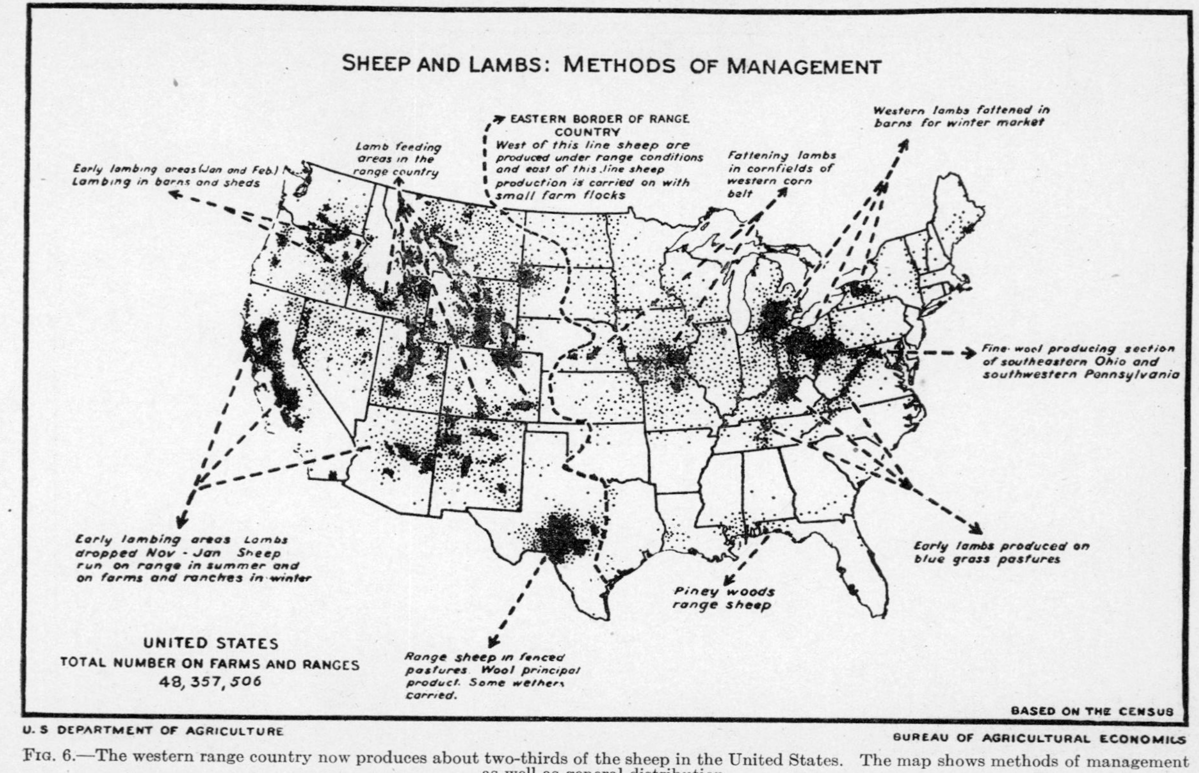


FIG. 6.—The western range country now produces about two-thirds of the sheep in the United States. The map shows methods of management as well as general distribution.

**Flocks in Farming Regions.**—When sheepmen first skimmed over the country with their extensive flocks their methods were somewhat similar to those of the large owners in the West to-day, who operate under what are called range conditions. That is, range or pasture was plentiful and in such states as Illinois and Iowa sheep were occasionally ranged in the open under the care of herders. But gradually the large flocks disappeared and in their place there arose small flocks which were kept in comparatively small, fenced fields. These became known as farm flocks, and they now typify the sheep industry of the United States in all but the western states.

**Mutton Blood.**—At first the Merino predominated in nearly all farm flocks, but gradually English mutton breeds were introduced until now nearly all such flocks are of mutton blood. The change to mutton blood was the result of the decline in the price of wool and the increase in the demand for mutton. The rise of land values also had an influence, for there came a time when the sheep yielding principally a fleece could not return a profit to the owner of high-priced land. For the same reason mutton blood has also been introduced in the far West, where range conditions still exist, but it will probably always be necessary to keep on the range sheep that carry a large proportion of Merino blood in order to preserve the close-flocking instinct and a fleece that will withstand semi-arid conditions.

**Increase in Value.**—The importance of the sheep industry in the United States now as compared with the past cannot be determined by merely comparing numbers. Sheep are considerably more valuable on the head basis than they were years ago, because the revenue from each sheep is much greater than in days of wool growing only. The breeding ewe yields not only wool but also lambs which are sold for mutton, and when she has passed her period of usefulness as a breeder or a wool producer, either on the farm or on the range, she still has a value as a mutton product.

**Sheep Raising in Australia.**—Prior to 1830, sheep growing in Australia had not attained commercial significance. Native sheep from the Cape of Good Hope were introduced as early as 1788, and the following year witnessed the coming of the Merino. In 1825 a group of English capitalists formed a land company and founded a large pastoral estate in Tasmania, which was then known as Van Diemens Land. Between 1825 and 1830 this company spent more than $145,000 in importing Merinos from

Saxony and some of the mutton breeds of England. The majority of the purchases were of the best Saxony types, descended from Spanish Merinos. A Mr. Warrington of Tasmania, in 1829, formed two separate breeding flocks from two noted families of Spanish Merinos.

England had long since ceased exporting wool and it is said that the original aim of the Tasmanian flock owners was to grow wool for England, and, ultimately, to render that country independent of Spanish, German, and other foreign sources of supply; but for many years their most valuable work was the breeding of Merino sheep for the rapidly multiplying "stations" around the coastal fringe of the Australian mainland. When wool from the Australian Merino flocks came into the hands of English manufacturers it met with a ready demand, and the growers were told that if they could supply such wool in bulk to the English trade, they would find a large and profitable market for it.

From 1830 on, the Australian wool growing industry made great progress. As owners found in the early days of sheep raising in our own country, so too the owners in Australia have found the wool type most profitable; and, largely because their country has been populated at a much slower pace than ours, they have been much slower to change to the mutton type than we. Merino blood still predominates in Australian flocks, although the mutton breeds are gradually gaining ground and the mutton qualities of the Merinos are being improved. As the supply of both mutton and wool in Australia far exceeds the home demand, sheep raisers are obliged to depend largely on foreign markets. Until recent years very little of the wool intended for export was sold before it left Australian ports. It was consigned to commission firms in England, who disposed of it by means of auction sales. But the custom of selling wool in Australian seaboard cities is now well established.

Australia disposes of her surplus mutton by shipping frozen carcasses to England. Until refrigeration for ocean liners was perfected, she had practically no outlet for surplus meat, and there was no incentive for encouraging the mutton sheep.

**Present Importance.**—Australia has no superior as a sheep country. It is a large country where pastoral agriculture has been emphasized for many years and sheep seem to have been the animals best adapted to her grazing lands. There has always been room for expansion; which fact, together with the demand for wool and mutton, has been the main factor in the steady growth of the sheep industry in spite of such difficulties as periodic drouths, ravages by rabbits, and lack of transportation lines extending far into the interior. The government is fostering the industry and farmers protect themselves against various pests and prevent excessive losses in years of drouth.

**Sheep Raising in New Zealand.**—Sheep were not taken into New Zealand until 1840, which was shortly after the first settlement established there by Europeans. Merinos exclusively were imported in the beginning, but as the needs of the trade developed, mutton breeds were introduced and it was found that they did unusually well. After 1882, the year in which the first shipment of frozen mutton was made from the country, the mutton breeds gained on the Merinos so rapidly that by 1910 the wool from Merinos formed three per cent of the total clip.

**Density of Sheep Population.**—New Zealand has less than twice the area of the state of Illinois, and yet in 1934 she reported 28,600,000 sheep. Think what a dense sheep population that is as compared with similar areas anywhere in our own country! Mutton is the staple meat in New Zealand. In addition to a large per capita consumption domestically, millions of lamb carcasses are exported annually to England.

Practically all sheep in New Zealand are managed under the "paddock," or "fencing," system. This is also true of Australia. Many of the fences are rabbit proof and cost about four hundred dollars per mile. As a general practice, the herding system characteristic of our sheep industry in the West ceased in Australia and New Zealand in the latter part of the last century.

**Sheep Raising in South America.**—At the time of the conquest of Peru there already existed a breed of supposedly indigenous sheep possessing enough good about them to be prized by the Incas Indians and by the conquering Spaniards. Gibson tells us that wool was first exported from the River Plate as early as the year 1600. However, the beginning of an extensive sheep husbandry in South America did not come until a much later time.

**Political Unrest in Leading Sheep Countries.**—The great sheep countries in South America are the Argentine Republic and Uruguay. In 1813 a shipment of pure Spanish Merinos arrived in the province of Buenos Aires. Upon this shipment was founded the first flock of improved Merinos in South America. Although the number of sheep in the Argentine Republic greatly increased after the founding of this flock, the progress of the industry was greatly hindered by the numerous political revolutions which were common throughout all of the River Plate region and sheep raising was later in attaining great commercial importance than in the United States and Australia.

**Importance of Merino Blood.**—Like each of the other countries mentioned above, South America found the wool type, or Merino sheep most profitable at first. Southdowns, the premier mutton sheep of England, were introduced as early as 1825, but because of their low yield of wool and predisposition to foot rot, they did not win wide favor. Then, too, the Merino had the gregarious instinct intensely developed, which was valuable to South American owners for the same reason that it is of value to any community where sheep are in the care of herders.

**Use of Mutton Breeds.**—Merino blood is still present in most of the flocks, but in many cases it is mingled with the blood of the English mutton breeds,—chiefly with the Lincoln and Romney Marsh. Both of these are long-wooled breeds which, when crossed with the Merino, produce a beautiful lustrous wool and a lamb that is suitable for the frozen carcass trade with England.

**Present Status of Sheep Industry.**—It has been said that there is probably no region where the shepherd's life is easier than in Argentina. Predatory animals are few. Except along the base of the Andes, no preparation of feed for winter is necessary, and, except in marshy regions, or in seasons of unusual rainfall, disease is rare. Nevertheless, in many parts the sheep industry has passed its meridian. The beautiful expanses of land, furnishing the plenty which has made life so easy for shepherds, are valuable for agricultural purposes, and the coming of cultivated fields is not only desirable but inevitable. While there is still some land that is not fully occupied by sheep, it seems improbable that Argentina will soon regain her former numbers, although sheep raising is now a profitable industry.

**Sheep Raising in South Africa.**—Although Merino sheep were imported into South Africa one hundred and fifty years before they were introduced into Australia, it is only recently that the wool markets of the world have begun to receive considerable amounts of pure and grade Merino wool from South African flocks. For various reasons the progress of sheep husbandry has been comparatively slow. Sheep scab has been very hard to contend with, and measures adopted by the Government have not yet proved adequate for keeping it under control. The black natives upon whom many sheepmen have had to depend for labor, have not been very reliable, and, therefore, because of the poor quality of labor, it has not been possible to produce as good mutton and wool as natural conditions would warrant. Further, predatory animals, jackals especially, have hindered the growth of the sheep industry by enforcing expense in erecting fences and by making it hazardous to keep sheep in certain sections. And finally, South Africa, like Australia, is subject to drouths which visit great hardships on sheep owners; in fact, they are the worst drawback to sheep raising. They are most pronounced in that part of the interior known as the Karroo, but periodically they also extend over the Transvaal, Orange Free State, and parts of Natal. Their effect is all the more severe because they usually come just after a period of such good feed in the veld districts that sheep owners have been tempted into overstocking. But in spite of the drawbacks, which after all every country possesses to greater or less extent, South Africa is making marked progress in wool production. Sheep owners are very much interested in breeding; they are giving much more attention to classing and grading wool for market than formerly, and in still other ways they are manifesting keen interest in sheep husbandry.

The tendency of recent years has been in favor of the big-framed robust-wooled type of Merino,—the Wanganellas and Rambouillet. Although the crossing of mutton breeds, such as the Southdown, Suffolk, and Shropshire, on Merino ewes has attracted attention, the sparse pastures have hindered this.

It is a significant fact that American breeders, more especially Ohio and Michigan men, annually exported a number of Rambouillets and Merinos to South Africa until the outbreak of the war in 1914. A few have been exported since 1918.

**The Important Sheep Countries.**—In the foregoing brief historical review of sheep raising the countries mentioned have each received separate attention, not only because they belong at the top of the list of the great sheep countries of the world, but also because they are the most important of the newer countries. Of course, other countries than these keep large numbers of sheep and the following tabulation shows the importance of sheep in various coun-

2

tries and it also gives some notion of where the world's supply of wool is produced[1] (Fig. 7, Chapter II).

*A—World Production of Sheep and Wool:*

| | |
|---|---|
| Sheep—approximate number | 691,000,000 |
| Wool—approximate number of pounds | 3,460,000,000 |

*B—Leading Sheep Countries*

| | Time of Estimate | Number of Sheep | Approximate Per Cent of World Total |
|---|---|---|---|
| Australia | 1934 | 109,900,000 | 15.9 |
| United States | 1935 | 48,357,000 | 7.0 |
| Argentina | 1930 | 44,400,000 | 6.4 |
| Union of South Africa | 1934 | 40,000,000 | 5.8 |
| New Zealand | 1934 | 28,600,000 | 4.1 |
| United Kingdom | 1934 | 25,000,000 | 3.6 |
| Russia (Europe & Asia) | 1934 | 47,000,000 | 6.8 |
| British India | 1933 | 25,270,000 | 3.6 |
| Spain | 1932 | 15,400,000 | 2.1 |
| Uruguay | 1932 | 20,600,000 | 3.0 |
| Turkey (Europe and Asia) | 1934 | 10,700,000 | 1.5 |
| China | 1932 | 45,000,000 | 6.5 |
| Peru | 1934 | 12,000,000 | 1.8 |
| Brazil | 1932 | 10,700,000 | 1.5 |
| Canada | 1934 | 3,421,000 | .5 |
| Mexico | 1932 | 3,674,000 | .5 |
| Chile | 1932 | 6,083,000 | .9 |
| France | 1935 | 9,600,000 | 1.3 |
| Germany | 1935 | 3,500,000 | .5 |

*C—Wool Production in Different Countries, According to Latest Estimates Available in 1936:*

| | Pounds | Approximate Per Cent of World Total |
|---|---|---|
| Australia | 1,031,000,000 | 29.7 |
| United States | 418,000,000 | 12.0 |
| Argentina | 348,000,000 | 10.0 |
| Union of South Africa | 210,000,000 | 6.1 |
| New Zealand | 306,000,000 | 8.8 |
| United Kingdom | 114,400,000 | 3.3 |
| Russia (Europe and Asia) | 167,000,000 | 4.8 |
| British India | 71,000,000 | 2.0 |

[1] Compiled from Bulletin 57 of the Empire Marketing Board, London, England, and reports of U. S. Dept. of Agr.

| | | |
|---|---|---|
| Spain | 67,600,000 | 1.9 |
| Uruguay | 107,000,000 | 3.1 |
| Turkey (Europe and Asia) | 13,800,000 | .4 |
| China | 78,000,000 | 2.2 |
| Peru | 11,900,000 | .3 |
| Brazil | 25,700,000 | .7 |
| Chile | 28,700,000 | .8 |
| France | 41,000,000 | 1.1 |
| Germany | 31,000,000 | .9 |
| Canada | 19,500,000 | .5 |
| Mexico | 5,250,000 | .2 |

## QUESTIONS

1. Where were sheep first domesticated? What uses were probably first made of sheep?
2. In what condition was sheep husbandry in Spain when Columbus discovered America?
3. How does Spain rank as a sheep country to-day?
4. How did England and Spain differ in methods of sheep raising?
5. What was Bakewell's contribution to the sheep industry of Great Britain?
6. What of the importance of sheep raising in North America at the time Bakewell lived?
7. What of the importance of wool growing in new countries?
8. When did significant expansion of sheep raising in North America take place and what were the circumstances that augmented it?
9. Recount the changes in the distribution of sheep in the United States between 1840 and 1910; the changes in the breeding of sheep during that time.
10. Of what importance was sheep raising in your state at the time it was admitted to the Union?
11. Compare the sheep industry of Australia with that of New Zealand.
12. What are the leading sheep countries in South America?
13. Name the countries which produce the bulk of the world's supply of wool.
14. Where do Australia, New Zealand, and South America market the bulk of their mutton and wool? How far are they from these markets?

## CHAPTER II

# PRESENT TYPES OF SHEEP RAISING IN LEADING SHEEP COUNTRIES

**Range Method, Using Herders.**—In the western part of the United States sheep raising is commonly carried on in the large flock or band under the care of a herder who keeps the sheep on a comparatively large area of unenclosed land—plains, foot-hills, and mountains. A band varies in number from 1500 to 3000, and besides the herder, requires the services of a camp tender, whose duties are to get provisions, move camp, select a new site where there is comparatively good feed, assist in cooking, and count the sheep (Fig. 8).

**Range Supplemented by Cultivated Crops.**—At first range sheepmen in the United States depended solely upon the wild growth of the land for their sheep feed. Aside from selecting as good natural range as possible no preparation was made for feeding in the stormy periods of winter when the snow covered the feed too deep for the sheep to get to it. Consequently many starved. But, now very few deaths result from lack of feed because the winter range is supplemented with such feeds as corn, cottonseed cake, barley, oats and alfalfa hay. The corn and cottonseed cake are shipped in, but the other feeds are raised in the West in dry farming and irrigated regions. Alfalfa ranks first in importance for it is used more extensively than any other feed in supplementing the winter range, and the practice of using it for summer range is increasing (Fig. 9).

**Ranging on Enclosed Lands.**—Many of the large flocks of Australia and New Zealand are kept on large tracts of enclosed land where no herders are required. It is claimed that the sheep can make much better use of the range under this system than they can under the herding system. Under the herding system each sheep regularly maintains a fairly definite position in the band. For example, certain sheep are always at the front while others are always in the rear. Those in the rear do not find as much to eat as those at the front; hence the band as a whole cannot be so uniformly fed as when it is kept within an enclosure because in the enclosure the band breaks up into a number of small flocks that live and feed more or less independently of each other. Then, too, the sheep in a band tended by a herder must be driven a great deal. They must be rounded toward camp and bedded down for the night; they must be kept from other bands of sheep; and frequently they must be driven to a watering place. All this driving is not so beneficial to the sheep as exercise taken at their own inclination.

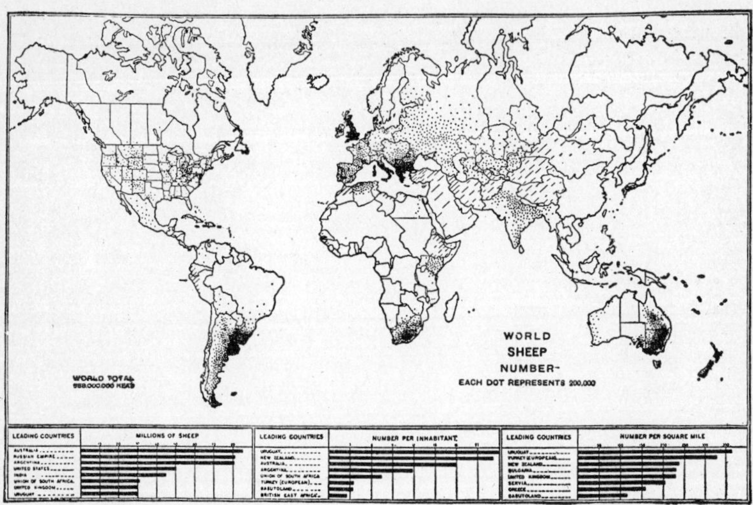


**Fig. 7.**—World distribution of sheep. It will be noted that there are six world centers of sheep raising, of which four, the South American countries, South Africa, Australia, and New Zealand, are new land with sparse population and are all located in the Southern Hemisphere. The two centers in the Northern Hemisphere are the Balkan States and Great Britain. In Asia Minor and in the Balkan States conditions of topography, climate, and the nomadic habits of the people in the recent past cause sheep to be important farm animals. In Great Britain many factors combine to make sheep raising a prominent industry in spite of high land values and extreme industrial concentration of population. The Russian Empire and the United States, although they rank high in total number of sheep, are, owing to large area, far down the list in number per square mile. (From U. S. Department of Agriculture.)

Still other advantages of the enclosure system are that the fences are said to cost less than the extra labor required in the herding system and to a large extent they are proof against animals that make sheep their prey.

In southwestern United States and in Australia and New Zealand, where both the herding and the enclosure methods have been tried, sheep owners favor the enclosure system.

Fig. 8.—On the open range the sheep are tended by a herder who may or may not be assisted by dogs. (From Forest Service, U. S. Department of Agriculture.)

**The Farm Flock Method.**—The flocks kept on the farms of the East, South and Middle West of the United States often contain fewer than 25 sheep and seldom more than 400 or 500. They are not under the care of special herders or shepherds, but of persons entrusted with other duties connected with the farm. As a rule these flocks are a factor of secondary importance in a scheme of diversified farming. Often they are kept for the purpose of destroying weeds, and they are commonly given the compliment of converting into mutton and wool what otherwise would be waste. But farm flocks

Fig. 9.—Supplementing the winter range with hay and other feed reduces the losses of old sheep, increases the vitality of the oncoming crop of lambs, and fills the udders of the ewes with milk for the lambs.

that are made to subsist mostly on weeds and waste are neither intelligently handled nor profitable. Since farm flocks represent the type of sheep raising followed in so many parts of the United States, much of the discussion which follows will be devoted to their selection, care and management (Fig. 10).

**The Hurdling Method.**—The hurdling method of sheep raising may be seen in its perfection in England, where thousands of sheep are kept within hurdles for several months in the year. It is also much in use in Scotland. It is a type of sheep raising extremely different from the range method. It is intensive, supporting several sheep on each acre of land.

As an appurtenance of sheep raising, hurdles are light, movable panels of fence which a man can carry with ease. With them the shepherd makes a temporary enclosure for his flock. The lambs are

FIG. 10.—The farm flock usually numbers less than one hundred sheep.

FIG. 11.—In Great Britain thousands of sheep are kept within hurdles which are moved often to furnish fresh feed.

usually permitted to go through creeps ahead of the ewes and in this way they get the best of the forage while their less fastidious mothers, having access to it a day or two later, make the most economical use of it by trimming it down close. As soon as a growth is eaten, the ground is turned and sown to another crop. Of course crops, like the grasses and clovers, are not treated in this way, but are left to grow up again.

The hurdling method aims not only at securing a maximum growth for sheep from a given area of ground, but also at furnishing almost a constant change of feeding ground. Sheep thoroughly enjoy a new feeding place, a fact which English shepherds have fully recognized as essential to successful flock husbandry. Anyone who has seen the sheep of England within hurdles cannot question

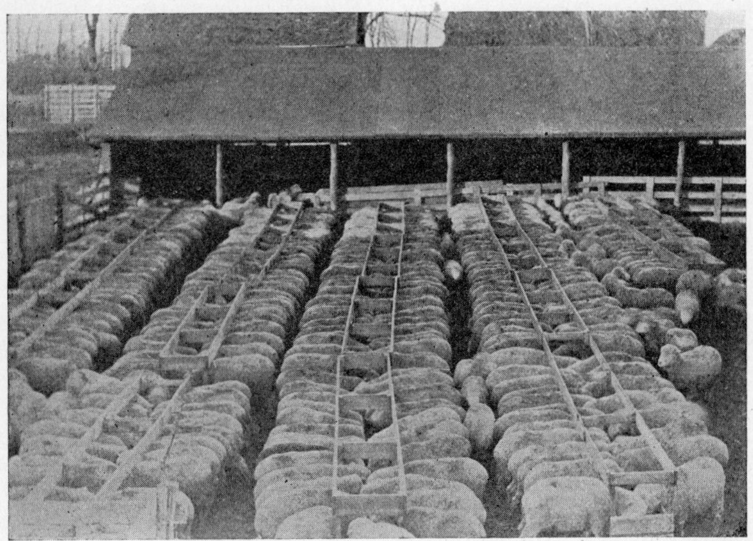

**Fig. 12.—Meal time for western sheep fattening on a corn-belt farm.**

the efficiency of the hurdling method for bringing sheep as nearly as possible to their perfection. Any type of movable fencing can be used in the hurdling method (Fig. 11).

**Pure-Bred Flock Method.**—Owners of pure-bred flocks have for their principal object the selling of breeding stock. They sell to the owners of commercial flocks who wish to use pure-bred rams but who do not care to keep pure-bred females, and of course, they also sell to each other. Since the object of the man who raises for breeding purposes is so different from that of the man who raises for the open market, it is natural to call his method of sheep raising a distinct type. He has to take certain things into consideration which do not enter into the operations of the owner of a commercial flock; for instance, the location of his farm, the study of individual sheep rather than of flocks or bands, the ability to make matings that will produce animals with great inherent possibilities, to feed so that these possibilities will be made apparent, and finally, the finding of a market for this product. In fact, the successful management of the pure-bred flock requires a proprietor of a special type with a special training.

**Sheep and Lamb Feeding.**—A great many western sheep and lambs are fattened for the market in the Middle West and in certain parts of the East.

These western sheep and lambs are purchased in the autumn when large numbers are reaching the central markets. In such states as Illinois, Iowa, and Missouri they are usually allowed to run first in the fields, where they feed on pasture stubble, corn stalks, weeds, and in some cases, soybeans and rape. They accomplish what may be termed a general "cleaning up" of the farm, and many farmers depend on them for this as others depend on the small flock for the same function. Before the fattening process is finished it is almost always necessary to supplement the feed of the fields with grain and hay. Further east, as in Ohio, Michigan, and New York, feeding sheep and lambs are not often given a run in the fields, but are placed in the barns immediately after their arrival at the farm and are fattened on various harvested feeds. In a few sections of the country sheep and lambs are still fed in large plants especially constructed for the purpose. This kind of feeding is very largely a speculative business as both the animals and the feeds used have to be purchased (Fig. 12).

## QUESTIONS

1. Name the types of sheep raising commonly practiced in the prominent sheep countries.
2. Which type is followed in your community?
3. In your opinion which type requires the most labor per sheep? Which gives the greatest returns per sheep?
4. Which types are most likely to be followed in communities where land is very fertile and costly?
5. Which types are likely to become more general in the United States than at present?

## CHAPTER III

# PROBLEMS IN THE IMPROVEMENT OF SHEEP

**Appearance of Unimproved Sheep.**—In countries practicing modern methods of breeding and feeding, the domestic sheep (*Ovis aries*) is markedly different in appearance from its unimproved kind. Judged according to our conception of right proportions, unimproved sheep are ill-shaped, with long, thin legs, long necks, and narrow bodies. As a rule their wool is coarse, characterless, admixed with hair, variable in color, and does not extend well over the lower parts of the body. It may be of good quality on the shoulders, but coarse and very little different from hair on the thighs, and in color it may be white, brown, gray, or black on different individuals, or sometimes two or more of these colors appear in the same fleece. The sheep belonging to the Navajo Indians of New Mexico and Arizona furnish the most interesting study of unimproved strains to be found in North America (Fig. 13).

**Breeding Problems.**—When man first started to domesticate sheep, he probably recognized certain valuable characteristics in them, and he likely bred for these, or it may be that he recognized some of their more valuable characteristics before he began the work of domestication; for Shaler says that man attains some of the mechanic arts before he begins to domesticate animals. Weaving, a very old art, was supplanted by the practice of pressing moist wool into a felt, which itself was an advance over the custom of using skins with hairy or woolly covering for clothing and shelter.

**Improvement of Wool.**—From all we can learn it would appear that the problem of improving wool must have early attracted the attention of sheep owners. Probably the first step consisted in getting a longer, heavier growth of wool more nearly free from an admixture of hair. Very likely such improvement was sought to make the wool easier to handle in the process of weaving, which was a considerable task among the nomads whose raiment, tents, and beds were woven from wool and hair.

**Fine Wool.**—As the art of weaving developed and as the people cultivated a taste for fine raiment and furnishings, wool of fine quality undoubtedly began to be prized. The Romans went to much trouble to produce this kind of wool. They kept their sheep covered with cloths and confined in barns in order to make the wool fibers fine and soft. At frequent intervals they washed their sheep, combed their fleeces to keep the wool from matting, rubbed fine oil into their skins, and moistened their fleeces with wine. By selecting rams with fine fleeces they succeeded in developing breeding stock which possessed very fine wool.

The production of fine wool has been a problem of considerable importance ever since the time of the Romans, if not before. Breeders in Spain, Germany, France, and England have worked at

FIG. 13.—Sheep and goats belonging to the Navajo Indians. The sheep are ill-shaped and not uniform in color.

it and it still receives attention in leading sheep countries such as Australia, New Zealand, South Africa, North America, and South America.

**Color of Wool.**—In improving wool, color has received careful attention. Variety of color was perhaps regarded favorably in early times, but when various dye stuffs came to be used, white wool was preferred, because none but a black dye can be used on wool which is black, brown, or gray. It may be that white sheep were once uncommon, for after Spain attained prominence as a wool-growing country her wool was reported as being black. But in all countries where improved methods of sheep husbandry are practiced, the constant elimination of blacks, browns, and grays has been so effective that color scarcely enters into the problem of wool improvement at the present time, although in a few breeds some difficulty is experienced in preventing a light scattering of dark fibers in the fleece (Fig. 14).

**Combining Various Properties of the Fleece.**—The problem of associating length, strength, and weight with quality of fleece has caused improvers of wool a great deal of effort. Length combined

FIG. 14.—The Mouflon—a wild sheep. Note the lack of uniformity in color. Exterior of coat is hair.

with quality and strength became very important within the past century when fine worsteds, fabrics requiring long, fine, strong wool, came into fashion, and it was the desire to make wool growing pay that led to increase in weight of fleece.

**During the past 125 years** Saxony in Germany, Australia, and the United States have contributed most to improvement in wool growing. Experts in Saxony studied the wool of breeding rams in minute detail, and made great improvement in fineness of fiber and in uniformity of the quality of the fleece. Vermont and Ohio breeders taught the world a great deal about growing strong, fine fiber and fleeces of exceptional weight. Australian breeders contributed much in combining quality, length and weight and by determining the types of wool suited to different environments; in fact they have led the world in the general merit and integrity of their wool product.

Although sheep breeders have by no means ceased to pay attention to wool, yet it is perhaps safe to say that the day of improvement, as characterized by an attempt to get into the fleece the maximum of fineness, length, and weight, has begun to wane. Great changes have come about in the manufacturing processes of wool. Long, fine wool, although still much sought after, is not so valuable, relatively, as it once was because combs have been invented which will comb comparatively short wool. Manufacturers have learned to make all sorts of blends in order to meet the demands of fashion and it seems that they are capable of meeting almost any demand likely to be made. The world product is easily brought to their doors and they can combine quality, length, and strength through mechanical devices more cheaply than the grower can through breeding. The rise in the importance of mutton has resulted in a large amount of cross-breeding in countries where the bulk of the wool was formerly produced by pure Merinos. Reports of the great wool sales in Bradford, England, show enormous increases in amounts of cross-bred wool in recent years. This is a pretty sure indication of either a check to progress in wool improvement through breeding, or of a readjustment of the notions of wool improvement. In the writer's opinion it is an indication of the latter (Fig. 15).

**Improvement of Mutton.**—Although the flesh of sheep has always been used for food, it seems that the improvement of the mutton qualities was a much later problem in sheep breeding than was the improvement of wool. Whether the first object in improving mutton was to secure a more palatable product or a cheaper one is not altogether clear, but the weight of evidence is in favor of the latter, for it was said of Bakewell that when he was confronted by a man who told him his sheep were so fat a gentleman could not eat them, he declared that he was not breeding sheep for gentlemen, but for men. More mutton,—on fewer acres, produced in less time, to furnish more to eat with less waste,—was the object, rather than to tickle the palate of the epicure. But before economy of produc-

Fig. 15.—Cross-bred sheep and lambs. The wrinkles and folds on neck and body indicate Merino blood, while the dark hair on face and legs and thickness of body indicate mutton blood.

tion had gone very far, palatability was joined with this primary object, so that the epicure, too, can now make his selection of a mutton joint from the improved mutton breeds.

**Changes.**—Mutton improvement has involved changes in form, quality, fattening properties, age at maturity, feeding capacity, milking function, and prolificacy. With the possible exception of the last two, these factors are so interdependent that they all had to be considered at the same time. And it is clear that mutton improvement could not go very far without considering milking properties because the making of a good mutton lamb depends in large part on its getting plenty of milk. But sheep's milk was a human food in very early times, hence the milking function may have received considerable attention before the era of mutton improvement, still it was woefully neglected in flocks of fine wool sheep in Italy and Spain.

**Prolificacy** has to do entirely with the economic phases of production and whether or not an attempt is made to increase it depends on conditions. Until mutton became important as a commodity for sale, there was certainly no great incentive to try to fix such a thing as the twinning habit because it was possible to keep up the size of flocks for wool production by a rate of increase of one lamb a year from each ewe. Even where mutton is an important consideration, the supply of feed must be liberal before breeders attempt to encourage great prolificacy, because ewes with twins must not only have the tendency to milk well, but they must have plenty of feed so that they can produce enough milk to grow their lambs well. Partly on account of a lack of a liberal supply of feed, there are places devoted to the production of mutton and wool in which single lambs are much to be preferred to twins, but in places where ewes can easily take good care of two lambs, marked prolificacy is usually desired.

**England was the center** of mutton improvement. Beginning with Bakewell, conditions were favorable for encouraging English farmers to effect this improvement. They had the climate and crops necessary to grow sheep well; they received a fair remuneration for their efforts, and numerous livestock shows created keen competition in the effort to secure perfection of animal form and finish. A great amount of improvement was effected in a comparatively short period, so much in fact, that many English breeders of the present time doubt whether significant further improvement has been made in the last quarter or half century.

**Combining Mutton and Wool.**—Combining mutton and wool qualities became a problem after mutton attained importance. Obviously this problem did not arise at the same time in all the large sheep-growing countries because mutton did not become important in all of these countries at the same time. For example, Australia and New Zealand had comparatively little demand for mutton until the inception of ship refrigeration in 1882 permitted them to engage in the exportation of frozen carcasses. And in the United States, the West had little use for mutton sheep until transportation facilities were developed so that the live sheep could be sent to the large central markets.

Until Bakewell began mutton improvement, he was disposed to give the wool no attention. Perhaps the size of his task in the field of mutton betterment justified him in this attitude, but his successors saw the folly of it if continued, and hence they did not fail to give wool attention commensurate with its importance.

When the production of mutton became profitable in the newer sheep countries such as North America, South America, and Australia, there was a sheep stock that had been maintained primarily for its wool, and the wool from this stock was still too valuable to be altogether disregarded. Under such conditions the real problem of combining mutton and wool qualities began. Crossing wool breeds with mutton breeds was the first step, and with a few exceptions progress has not gone much further than this. In New Zealand a new type has been fixed from crosses between Merinos and the English long-wool mutton breeds. In the United States progress has been made in improving the mutton qualities of some of the wool breeds.

A desirable combination of mutton and wool is still a large breeding problem on the ranges of the United States. As yet a type possessing what is desired in wool and mutton properties, together with certain other characteristics, has not been fixed, but the Federal government is directing work along this line.

**Adaptability.**—Adaptability always has been, and without doubt always will be a problem in sheep breeding. When sheep were in a wild state their adaptability was measured by their ability to live and procreate their kind. When they came under domestication they had to be able, with the aid of man's protection, not only to live and procreate but also to produce something which man desired. Moreover, they had to produce the thing he wanted at a cost he was willing to pay and in such a way that he got it with less trouble than he could have secured it, or an equally desirable substitute, from other known sources.

Man may not have demanded much from sheep and he may not have removed them far from their natural habitat in the early stages of domestication. Hence, adaptability may not have been a serious problem at first. But as they were moved out of their natural environment under the guidance of man into lands different in altitude, soil, climate and vegetation, and as the demands on them for such products as wool, milk, and meat become greater than what they had yielded in the wild, then undoubtedly the serious side of the question of adaptability arose; then attention had to be given to such things as constitution, hardiness, and fecundity.

In Italy, fine-wool sheep were developed, but at the sacrifice of a high degree of adaptability, for the ewes were very poor mothers and the lambs were delicate. The ewes often had difficulty in parturition; they were very deficient in the milking function, and they frequently refused to own their lambs. To a certain extent the Merinos of Spain possessed the same faults, for it was said that frequently a percentage of their lambs were deliberately killed in order to allow each remaining lamb to suckle two ewes. In both Italy and Spain conditions seemingly were such as to permit the sheep industry to prosper with this low degree of adaptability, but the fact that it is recorded in history shows that it received some attention. Spanish owners seemed to think that much travelling added to the hardiness of their sheep, and undoubtedly dropping along the wayside lambs unable to make the marches, helped to keep up a stronger race for the conditions to which their flocks were subjected.

At an early time in England severe winters, scarcity of feed in winter, and foot rot weeded out the weak sheep, and frequently conditions were so severe that many of the very strongest animals died. Dealing with adversities, the English sheep farmer thoroughly learned the importance of constitution and hardiness, and if he has neglected these characteristics at any time he has done so with his eyes open. He has done a great deal, indeed, in finding or evolving breeds adapted to different altitudes. Though England is a small country, the breeds on mountains, hills, and lowlands are markedly different and in such a way as to show that adaptability is the main cause.

**Neglecting Adaptability.**—In seeking certain desirable characteristics in their sheep, breeders have often been guilty of at least temporarily overlooking adaptability and hardiness; or, as may have been the case in Italy and Spain, they have been willing to sacrifice these things to a certain extent in order to gain the characteristics especially desired. Bakewell's Leicesters lost in fecundity and hardiness; breeders of Shropshires allowed their sheep to lose in constitution in order to gain extreme covering with wool on head and legs; following the Civil War Merino breeders in America sacrificed stamina in their sheep for the sake of extreme weight of fleece in proportion to body weight.

Whether or not adaptability should be sacrificed, to a certain extent depends on the degree to which it is present and on the importance of the thing involved in making the sacrifice. Italy and Spain certainly were not in position safely to sacrifice further the mother instinct and milking function of their ewes even though this would have gained for them in a per head return; American Merino breeders in the period mentioned above went too far in reducing the stamina of their sheep, and Shropshire breeders made an economic mistake by permitting a loss in constitution for the sake of extreme covering of head and legs with wool.

**Importance of Adaptability in the United States.**—As a problem, adaptability in sheep breeding or finding the right type is important in the United States for the following reasons: First, it has not received sufficient attention generally. With a few exceptions, breeders of pure-bred mutton sheep in this country continue to import breeding rams and ewes from English flocks; this goes to show that little has been done toward developing mutton types suitable to American conditions. Second, consumers are changing and may continue to change with respect to the kind of mutton and wool they want. Third, in many localities agricultural practices are changing and probably will continue to change for some time to come and hence the type of sheep suitable in a certain community at the present time may be out of date in a few years. The future will see more attention given to adaptability in sheep breeding in this country because, as the land comes to be more and more intensively handled the crops grown on it, both plant and animal, will have to be more and more efficient and any crop that does not fit well will have a hard time to retain a place.

## QUESTIONS

1. Enumerate the problems that have been involved in the improvement of sheep and indicate which pertained to the products yielded by sheep; which to the sheep themselves.
2. What are the important problems in breeding at the present time in the United States?
3. Show how breeding problems have changed in the United States.
4. Why would you expect British breeders to excel American breeders in mutton improvement?
5. Why did breeders in Australia first give attention to the improvement of wool rather than mutton?
6. When does high degree of prolificacy become a breeding problem? Early maturity?

## CHAPTER IV

## METHODS OF IMPROVEMENT

**Feeding and Shepherding.**—Good feeding and shepherding have played an important part in the making of the modern breeds of sheep. The providing of better feed through bringing the root and clover crops to England helped to pave the way for the breed improvement that came later. Evidently Bakewell recognized the value of good feed and care, for he kept about him faithful old herdsmen and grooms who were very painstaking in the feeding of the animals under their care. Doubtless he and other great breeders since his time would say that any method of breeding conducted with poorly nourished animals will fall short of marked results, for if the animal is not well fed, it cannot exhibit its maximum possibilities and these must be seen if substantial progress is to be made.

**Methods of Breeding.**—Selection has been the keynote in breed improvement no matter what the method followed may have been, and the success of great breeders has been traceable, in no small degree, to their superior judgment in selecting breeding stock.

**Mass Breeding.**—Selection without special reference to ancestry, or what has been termed mass breeding, was one of the first methods of breeding to be employed in the improvement of sheep. Breeders took the native sheep in their community and began their work by breeding what they considered the best. Perhaps some of the less desirable females were rejected, but mass breeding, as practiced in earlier times, extended little farther than the selection and use of what were judged to be the best rams. The Spaniards must have improved the wool of their sheep by this method. They also kept flocks pure within themselves, but their reason for so doing was that each of the large breeders considered his flock the best in the kingdom and believed that the introduction of blood from other flocks would cause retrogression rather than improvement. In England some improvement was made by selecting the best of the native stock for breeding purposes, but before Bakewell's time, unwarranted emphasis was often placed on very minor points. For example, in a certain community breeders would have nothing to do with rams whose horns did not curve in front of their ears, while in another community they insisted that if rams did not have horns curving back of the ears they were unfit for breeding. It was Bakewell's good common sense in singling out points of utility for improvement quite as much or even more than his insight into laws of breeding that made him invaluable to livestock improvement.

As a method, mass breeding possesses a great deal of merit and the amount of selection it involves is about all that is practiced at present by those breeders who raise sheep merely for the wool and mutton they produce.

**A Study of Matings.**—When men became thoroughly absorbed in the problem of sheep breeding, they doubtless began to study the animals to be mated, and this naturally led to attaching a history of the parents or an ancestry to an animal, for men soon learned that the physical make-up of the offspring was not dependent solely upon the appearance of the immediate parents. So far as is known, it was Bakewell who first studied matings closely, and unquestionably this study contributed, in no small way, to the far-reaching results of his work. At the present time the most skillful sheep breeders are close students of matings. A few years ago, the writer, while visiting a prominent breeder in England, was shown records which contained both pedigrees and carefully worded descriptions of all the rams that had been used in the flock. In each breeding season these records were brought into use as a help in determining matings. Before time for breeding, each ewe was studied critically, then reference was made to the breeding and appearance of the sire, grandsire, and perhaps great grandsire. The decision as to the ram with which to mate her was not final until all of this study had been made. The flock bore ample evidence of the value of exercising such care in mating.

A careful study of mating stimulated the tendency to observe associations which, when correctly noted, became a means of assistance in the selection of rams and ewes for breeding purposes. For example, when breeders observed that rams having suitable wool and body conformation, and strong, bold features about the head and neck sired stronger and better offspring than rams having similar wool and body conformation, but lacking in strength and boldness of features, an important association in the degree of development of characters was discovered which has since been a useful guide in breed improvement. It is perhaps erroneous to say that all associations were entirely ignored until matings were studied closely. Boldness of features in males and refinement of them in females undoubtedly attracted the attention of the very earliest breeders, but there were many important associations overlooked until matings became a matter of close study. When they were recognized and seized upon as an agency in selection, there was often a tendency to exaggerate them and to declare that they existed when in reality they did not.

**Pedigree or the ancestral history** of the animal is really an outgrowth of the study of matings. When pedigree is not over-estimated, it serves as a valuable agent in helping to direct constructive breeding. But often when depended upon at all, too much reliance has been placed on pedigree and not enough on individual excellence. Too often it has been assumed that animals identical in pedigree are alike in breeding powers, but we now know that this is not necessarily true. Although two sheep may be twins, and hence alike in pedigree, it does not necessarily follow that they have inherited equally from each of their ancestors. One may have the stronger dose of inheritance from the ancestors in the sire's line and the other a stronger dose from those in the dam's line; or, one may inherit strongly from the grandsire on the side of the dam and the granddam on the side of the sire, while the other may inherit in converse manner. Many combinations are possible, and hence the possibility of animals as closely related as twins being unlike in the degree of the development of characters is relatively large. And any breeder makes a mistake who practices selling the better of a pair of twins and retaining the poorer for breeding purposes, thinking that the latter will breed just as well as the former.

Then, too, pedigree is frequently over-estimated in another way. It is not uncommon for breeders to take a fancy to an animal because a certain great individual of the breed appears in its pedigree. This great animal may be as far removed as great grandparent and the individuals closer up in the pedigree may have been at best only average specimens. If such is the case, the animal in question should be of outstanding merit in order to draw marked attention, and even then he (in case it is a ram) should not be used extensively until his capacity as a breeder is determined from an examination of his offspring. But too often faith in a pedigree containing a celebrity, even though he be two or three generations removed, goes far toward offsetting the commonness in an animal.

**In-and-in breeding,** such as breeding sire to daughter, son to mother, or brother to sister, was another step forward in methods of improving sheep through breeding. Undoubtedly this practice occurred long before Bakewell's time, but, as far as we know, he was the first to employ it as an agency for improvement. We do not know whether he deliberately resorted to in-breeding or whether he took it up because he did not know where to procure animals that would better serve him in accomplishing his desired ends.

As is well known to breeders with experience, in-breeding is a means by which the degree of development of characters is intensified and fixed. Manifestly, then, it cannot be a means for doing good until there has been a careful study of matings, because it intensifies and fixes the bad as well as the good in an animal, and any breeder who does not possess keen judgment had better not try to make use of it.

**Line Breeding.**—Line breeding which involves breeding together animals of the same family or strain, but less closely related than those used in "in-breeding," has appealed to sheep breeders as being less erratic in behavior than in-breeding. It has been a great agency for improvement, especially among the English flocks, and perhaps it has been depended upon more than any other method in developing and fixing the type of the various breeds prominent in that country. Among great Shropshire breeders in England it has been the prevailing practice for a breeder to select a strain from which he draws his rams year after year, and it is only now and then that he uses a ram that could be considered foreign to the strain adopted. Rams belonging outside of the adopted strain are almost invariably used with caution, and if they do not combine and recombine, "nick" well, as breeders would say, with those characters already prevalent and desirable they and all their offspring are immediately discarded.

**Cross Breeding.**—The first step in the making of many of the most prominent mutton breeds of the present time consisted in crossing one breed upon another. It was the improvement secured by crossing the Southdown upon the old Cannock Chase and Morfe Common sheep around Shrewsbury, England, that gave impetus to the formation of the Shropshire breed. When Southdown rams were bred to the old Wilts and Hants ewes in South England the initial step had been taken in the making of the Hampshire. Bakewell's Leicesters were used on the old sheep of the Cotswold Hills and the outcome of this crossing was the modern Cotswold. The Hampshire when bred to the modern Cotswold produced the foundation from which the Oxford has been developed, and it is possible to continue, if necessary, with the enumeration of still other breeds that have had their beginning from a cross between breeds.

Apparently promoters of such breeds were inclined to consider origin through crossing a discredit to the breed, for frequently they attempt to prove that they did not originate in this way. Presumably they believe that any breed which traces back to a cross will not breed as true to type as one developed by selecting and breeding together the best of a type or breed long common in a community, as was the case with the Southdown. But this view is not necessarily true. A type which undoubtedly breeds true, as we understand the term, can be developed from animals resulting from crossing distinct breeds. It takes time, however, to do this because the hereditary material handed down by the original parents is capable of coming together in so many different combinations. Characters which seemingly have been eliminated reappear and breeders become discouraged over the behavior of the strain they are trying to "fix" so that it will be worthy of being called a breed. When Shropshires were first shown at the annual show of the Royal Agricultural Society of England they were markedly lacking in uniformity. This was in 1857, but 15 years or more before the close of the century they were breeding true to type, and when crossed on other breeds their characteristics were sufficiently impressed on the offspring. What may be said of the Shropshire may also be said of other breeds that trace to a cross between breeds.

One of the latest breeds to be developed from a cross is the Corriedale. In New Zealand three long-wool mutton breeds, Lincoln, Cotswold, and Leicesters, were crossed on Merino ewes. The cross-bred animals were bred together and by eliminating the undesirable types a breed has been evolved in the last 50 or 60 years which is very popular with those New Zealand and Australian breeders who wish to grow sheep for both mutton and wool.

In the western part of the United States cross breeding has helped sheepmen to solve the question of adaptability and at the same time to meet the demands of the market. It has been found, however, that mere crossing is a temporary expedient and that when regions as a whole adopt it there is no economical way to breed in order to get desirable breeding ewes. Therefore, western breeders are now casting about for a way to get breeds which possess the good points of the cross-bred animals they have been producing. Corriedales are being "tried out," and there is some tendency to develop a breed or breeds by a method similar to that pursued in evolving the Corriedale.

Cross-breeding is still extensively practiced in England by breeders who plan to sell their lambs for mutton. It is likely, too, that it will be resorted to, to greater or less extent, in all countries recognized as being important in the production of mutton, because the cross-bred lamb is, as a rule, unusually vigorous and in many regions breeders find it to their advantage to keep ewes of such breeding that a foreign breed must be crossed on them to get the best possible market lambs from them.

## QUESTIONS

1. What part has better feeding had in the improvement of sheep?
2. Enumerate the different methods of breeding by which improvement has been effected.
3. What are the methods followed in mass breeding?
4. What were some of the effects from the early study of matings?
5. What can be said of the importance and limits of pedigrees?
6. Explain the meaning of in-and-in breeding.
7. Of line breeding.
8. What may be some uses of cross breeding?

# PART II

## STRUCTURE AND JUDGING

# CHAPTER V

## STRUCTURE OF THE SHEEP

**Position in the Zoological Scheme.**—The following outline, according to Lydekker,[1] shows the position of the domesticated sheep in the subkingdom of *Vertebrata:*

Subkingdom *Vertebrata*—Vertebrates, or Back-boned Animals.
  Class *Mammalia*—Mammals.
    Order *Ungulata*—Hoofed Mammals, or Ungulates.
      Suborder *Artiodactyla*—Even-toed Ungulates.
        Section *Pecora*—Typical Ruminants.
          Family *Bovidæ*—Hollow-horned Ruminants.
            Subfamily *Caprinæ*—Sheep and Goats.
              Genus *Ovis*—Sheep.
                Species *Ovis aries*—The Domesticated Sheep.

**The Sheep a Ruminant.**—The sheep chews its cud; that is, it brings its food back from the stomach to the mouth for thorough mastication. This characteristic distinguishes it as a true ruminant. It belongs to the family of ruminants termed *Bovidæ,* of which the ox (*Bos*) is a typical representative. Besides cattle and sheep the family *Bovidæ* includes such classes of animals as goats, muskoxen, chamois and antelopes, but sheep represent a distinct genus for which the name *Ovis* has been adopted, and as a species the domesticated sheep has been given the name *Ovis aries.*

**How the Sheep Differs from Other Animals in Its Family.**—Although very much alike in general structure the sheep and ox present some interesting differences, the most marked being in size and nature of hairy covering. The sheep carries its head higher, and its cranium is relatively broader and higher at the center and much narrower toward the extremities. Instead of having a broad, naked, undivided muzzle like the ox, its muzzle is narrow, covered with short hairs, and divided by a vertical cleft. Owing to the fact that its muzzle is so much narrower and its lips more mobile, the sheep can graze much closer than the ox.

---

[1] R. Lydekker, "The Sheep and Its Cousins," p. 12, Pub. by E. P. Dutton & Co., New York, 1913.

Sheep are different from any other class of animals belonging to the family *Bovidæ* in that they possess suborbital face glands, and glands in the groin and between the two main toes of the feet. All of these secrete sebaceous or fatty substances. The suborbital face gland is situated in a shallow depression called the lachrymal pit in the lachrymal bone of the skull. In the live animal its location is indicated by a furrow in the skin extending downward from the inner corner of the eye (Fig. 16).

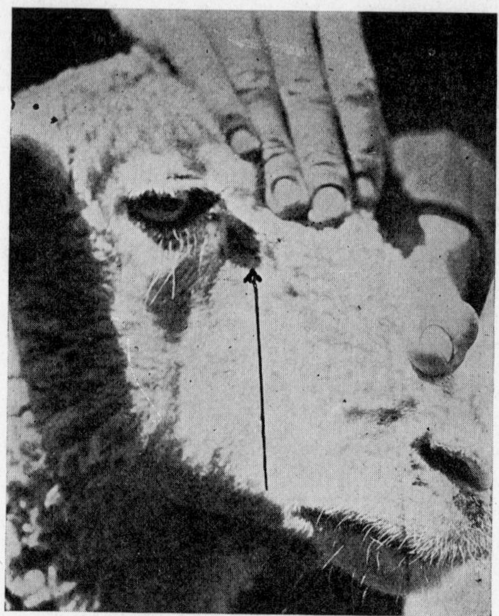

Fig. 16.—Furrow in skin over lachrymal pit.

The secretion from the foot-gland or interdigital pouch is carried to the surface of the skin through a small duct called the interdigital canal, the round opening of which is to be found near the top of the triangular depression on the front of the pastern, a little above the hoof (Fig. 17). This opening is large enough to be seen easily with the naked eye and is often referred to by sheepmen as the hole in the foot.

Different functions have been ascribed to the foot glands. It is thought by some that they secrete a substance that scents the ground over which sheep pass and thus assists members lost from the flock to trace their fellows. It is also thought that the secretions are waste products which if not eliminated will cause inflammation and lameness. The likelihood of plugging the hole in the foot and thus preventing the escape of the secretions is regarded as one important reason why sheep should not be made to walk through mud.

In sheep, the foot glands are present in all four feet. They are usually absent in goats, but sometimes small glands appear in the fore feet.

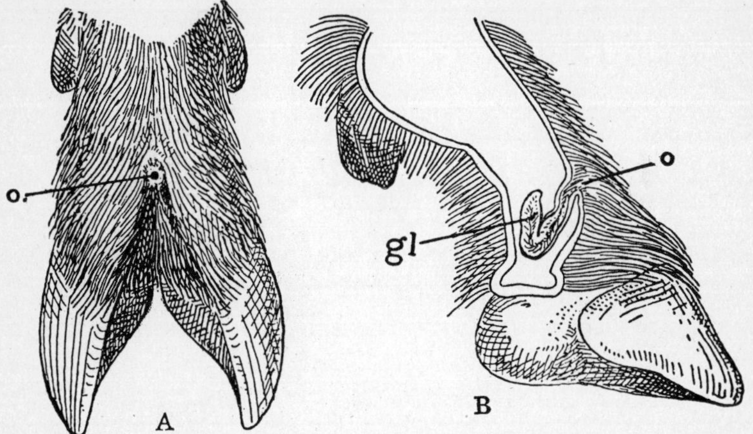


Fig. 17.—The interdigital pouch. (From "Sheep and Its Cousins," Lydekker. Courtesy of E. P. Dutton & Co.)

**The Skeleton.**[2]—The vertebræ forming the spinal or vertebral column are grouped as follows: 7 cervical, 13 dorsal or thoracic, 6 to 7 lumbar, 4 to 5 sacral, and 3 to 24 coccygeal. The last are not perfect vertebræ, as the spinal canal does not extend through them (Fig. 18).

With the exception of the cervical vertebræ all of these groups vary in the number of bones they contain. There are usually 13 vertebræ in the thoracic group, but occasionally there are 14, and more rarely, only 12. In the lumbar group the occurrence of 7 vertebræ is almost as frequent as 6, but the reduction to 5 seldom takes place. Seyffurth indicates that there may be 4 or 5 sacral

[2] See Sisson, "The Anatomy of the Domestic Animals," 1914.

vertebræ, but Sisson recognizes only 4. With the exception of the last vertebra, these are fused into one bone in the adult animal. The number of coccygeal vertebræ present largely determines the length of the sheep's tail, and that this number varies is apparent to any one who has handled a large number of lambs before their tails have been cut off.

**The Ribs.**—Ordinarily the sheep has 13 pairs of ribs, 8 pairs being sternal or true ribs, 4 pairs asternal or false ribs, and one pair floating ribs. True ribs are distinguished from false ribs by the fact that the cartilaginous bars extending from them articulate with the sternum or breast-bone, while those of the false ribs overlap and are attached to each other, forming what is known as the

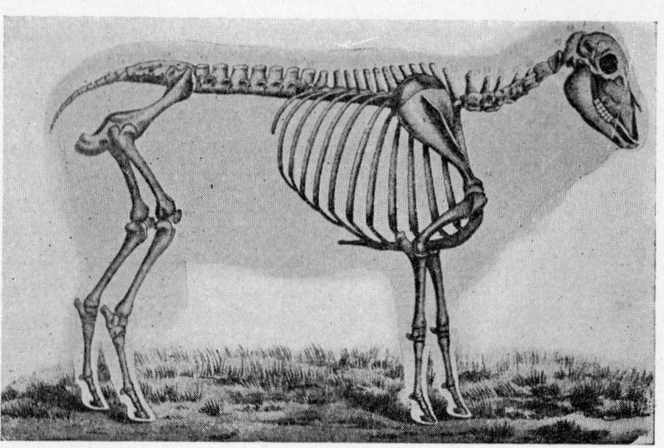

Fig. 18.—Skeleton of sheep. (Courtesy of Wm. R. Jenkins Co.)

costal arch. The cartilages extending from floating ribs are unattached. Sometimes there are 14 pairs of ribs, in which case the fourteenth rib is also floating.

**The sternum,** or breast-bone, is composed of 7 segments (sometimes only 6) and there are indentures in the sides for the reception of the cartilages extending from the ribs.

**Effects of Variations in Skeletal Structure.**—No attempt will be made to describe the bones of the skull and of the thoracic and pelvic limbs because the chief object of discussing the skeleton in this connection is to show how the external form may be influenced by differences in those regions of the skeleton subject to variation in number of parts. Undoubtedly many sheep which are relatively longer than others have more than the average number of vertebræ forward of the coccygeal group. When a sheep is unusually long in the middle, speculation as to whether it possesses an extra rib is quite justifiable, and if the space between the last rib and the junction of the ilium (hip bone) with the spine is abnormally wide there is basis for assuming that there is an extra vertebra in the lumbar group. If, on the other hand, the sheep has a short middle and if the space from the last rib to the hip is also very short, it may be that the lumbar vertebræ are reduced to 5 in number (Fig. 19).

Fig. 19.—A long and a short sheep, illustrating the probable variation in the number of vertebræ in the spinal column.

Aside from the variations noted, little is known of how much sheep vary in skeletal arrangement. Judging from exterior form, some individuals seem to carry a wider and higher arch to their ribs than others, but just how much of the difference is due to thickness of flesh and fat, and how much to the actual shape of the ribs has not been definitely determined. The processes extending upward from the vertebræ in the region of the shoulders seem longer in some sheep than in others, or else the top of the blade is set lower down, for in certain instances the spinal processes are so prominent that any amount of fattening will not cover the shoulder top. In practically every improved breed there are occasional specimens

FIG. 20.—Rump well carried out.

FIG. 21.—Rump drooping. Variation between Figs. 20 and 21 probably due to difference in skeletal position of sacral vertebræ and pelvic bones.

having low-set tails and sharply drooping rumps. Surely the sacral and coccygeal vertebræ and probably the pelvic bones are not in the same position in these specimens as in those whose rumps carry out almost level to the dock from the surface between the hips. And there can be no doubt as to the variation in the shape, position, relative length and size of the leg bones (Figs. 20, 21, and 22).

FIG. 22.—Showing variation in length of leg bones.

**The Skin and Its Appendages.**—The skin of sheep varies in extent, thickness and color. According to Sisson, the variation in thickness is from one-half to three millimetres. In Merinos there is a great expanse of skin due to numerous wrinkles and folds, and as a rule their skin is thick, thus making a great weight of pelt in proportion to body weight. In the English mutton breeds, because the skin covers the body smoothly, the weight of pelt is relatively less. Rams have considerably thicker skins than ewes of the same breed.

In all improved breeds producing white wool except those with very dark faces and legs, the skin, if healthy, is bright pink or cherry in color, but in the exceptions noted and in sheep bearing dark wool it is often bluish and in some cases almost black. In nearly all breeds the naked skin around the muzzle is black.

The skin [3] consists of the cutis or skin proper and its epidermal appendages, the hair, wool, hoofs, and horns. The cutis is composed of two layers, the epidermis, a superficial epithelial layer,

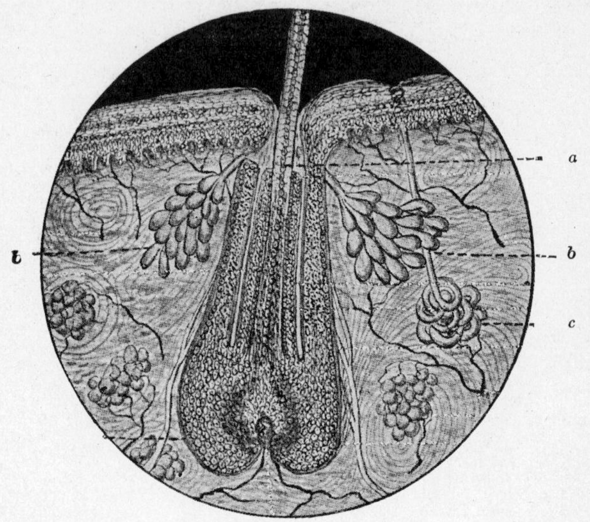


Fig. 23.—Diagrammatic section of skin, showing (*a*) shaft of hair arising from the follicle, (*b*) sebaceous glands and (*c*) sweat glands. (From "Structure of the Wool Fibre," Bowman. Courtesy of The Macmillan Co.)

and the derma or corium, a deep, connective-tissue layer, which is supplied with blood vessels and nerves and contains glands and hair-follicles.

**The hair-follicle** is a modification of the skin and, according to Sisson, may be regarded as an invagination or a folding-inward of the epidermis. It seems, however, that the follicles of the larger human hairs contain both epidermal and dermal elements [4] (Fig. 23).

**The hair** originates at the bottom or base of the hair-follicle from an extension of the corium called a papilla, to which the

[3] See Sisson's "Veterinary Anatomy," 1911.

[4] Bailey, "Text Book of Histology," 1916.

materials necessary for the growth of the hair are supplied. Being a development of the epidermis, the hair is composed of epithelial cells, and these are arranged in three layers. From within outward these are medulla, cortex and cuticle (Fig. 24).

Bailey gives the following description of these layers:

(1) "*The medulla* occupies the central axis of the hair. It is absent in small hairs, and in large hairs does not extend throughout their entire length. It is from 16 to 20 m.[5] in diameter, and consists of from two to four layers of polygonal or cuboidal cells with

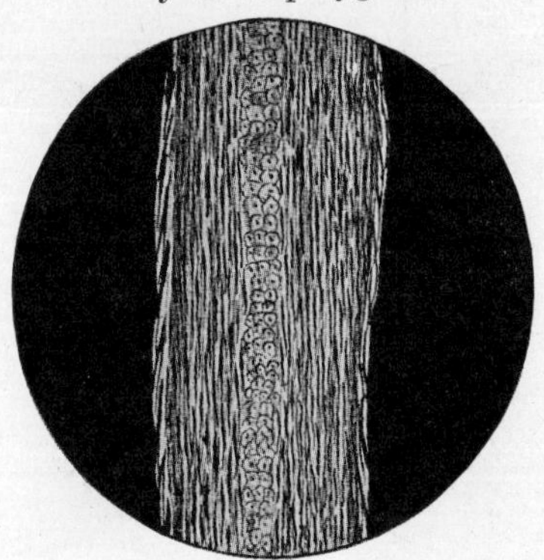

FIG. 24.—Longitudinal section of a human hair. (From "Structure of the Wool Fibre," Bowman. Courtesy of Macmillan Co.)

finely granular, usually pigmented protoplasm and rudimentary nuclei.

(2) "*The cortex* makes up the main bulk of the hair and consists of several layers of long spindle-shaped cells, the protoplasm of which shows distinct longitudinal striations, while the nuclei appear atrophied. As these striations give the hair the appearance of being composed of fibrillæ the term 'cortical fibers' has been applied to them. In colored hair pigment granules and pigment in solution are found in and between the cells of this layer. This pigment determines the color of the hair.

(3) "*The cuticle* has a thickness of about 1 m. and consists of clear, scale-like, non-nucleated epithelial cells. These overlap one another like shingles on a roof, giving to the surface of the hair a serrated appearance."

---

[5] M. refers to a micron which is 1/1000 of a millimeter in length, and the millimeter is 0.03937 part of an inch.

**Structure of Wool.**—The structure of wool is similar in many respects to that of hair. Both grow from hair follicles in the skin; both are nourished in the same way; both consist of epithelial cells arranged in three layers, but the medullary layer may be absent in wool. The striking and essential difference between them is in the cells forming the outer layer or cuticle. In hair these cells are rather rounded in form and smooth along the edges, while in wool they tend to be pointed and irregular along the edges.[6] In the hair the overlapping cells are attached to the under layer up to the very

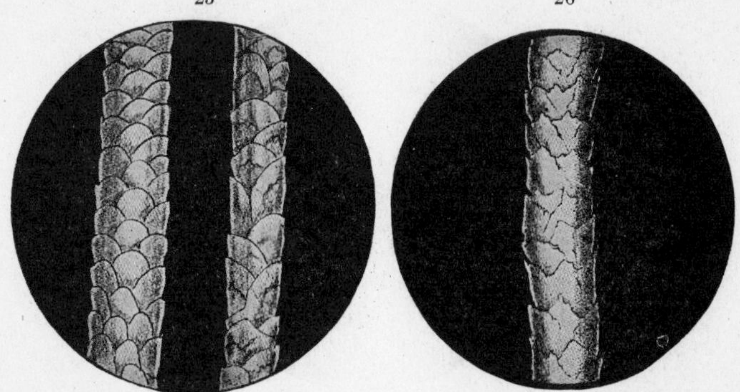


Fig. 25.—Coarse hairs, showing regular scales unsuitable for interlocking or felting.
Fig. 26.—Typical wool fiber, showing irregular scales. Such fibers felt easily. (From "Structure of the Wool Fibre," Bowman. Courtesy of The Macmillan Co.)

margin of the cell, while in wool they are free for about two-thirds of their length and they turn slightly outwards. Because of their shape, position and manner of attachment to the cells beneath, the cuticle cell of wool fibers will interlock, but those of hairs will not to any marked degree. It is this property of interlocking, called felting, that makes wool so much more valuable than hair in the manufacture of fabrics (Figs. 25 and 26).

As a rule wool is smaller in diameter than hair, and in white wool, as in white hair, there is little if any pigment or coloring matter in the cortex layer. Wool is also more wavy than hair, the waves in the finer wools being so short and distinct as to be called crimps.

**Function of Wool.**—Wool is a protective covering for the animal. The cuticle cells point outward from the skin and serve to keep out foreign substances such as dirt and chaff. Sheep with fairly dense, oily fleeces are less subject to *colds* than those having

[6] Bowman, "Structure of the Wool Fibre," 1908.

more open fleeces. The reason for this is that the wool is a non-conductor of heat and hence protects against variation in temperature, and when it is dense and oily it prevents the rain from penetrating to the skin.

**Variations in Hairy Covering.**—With the exception of the Barbadoes breed, all of the domesticated breeds in the United States are covered with wool over all parts save the head, legs, armpits and groins. In nearly all of these breeds wool extends partly over the head and legs, and in the Merinos it is not uncommon for it to grow over the surface of the armpit and most of the groin.

Breeds exhibit marked variation in length, fineness and density or thickness of wool. Density may vary from 600 to 1500 fibers to each square inch of skin; fineness from one three-hundredth or more to one three-thousandth of an inch in diameter; and length attained in twelve months from less than one inch to fifteen inches or more. As a rule the shortest wool is the finest and densest. White wool prevails among the domesticated breeds of the United States and of other countries giving special attention to the production of wool, but the color of the hair on face and legs varies, the most common shades being white, reddish brown, light soft brown, and deep brown or black. In various parts of the world there are domesticated breeds, in most cases not highly improved, however, that grow gray, brown and black wool.

Wool is rarely if ever uniform in length, fineness and density over all parts of the sheep. The finest and densest wool is in the regions of the shoulders, about midway between the top and bottom lines of the body; the coarsest wool grows on the outer thighs and at the dock; and the shortest wool is to be found on the belly.

**The horns and hoofs** are modifications of the epidermis. Most of the modern breeds are hornless; in a few breeds only the males have horns, and in a few others they appear in both sexes, but the males always have them much more strongly developed than the females. Males unsexed while young resemble the females of the breed in the degree of development of the horns. Hoof tissue and also horn tissue, if present, are white only in those breeds in which the naked skin at the muzzle is pink.

**Glands of the Skin.**—The sweat glands, secreting water and potassium salts, and the sebaceous glands, secreting a fatty or oily substance, are the most important glands in the skin. Their combined product, less most of the water secreted by the sweat gland, is the yolk. This functions in various ways as a preservative of the wool. The sweat glands are distributed throughout the skin, but the sebaceous glands are usually connected with the follicles and they pour their secretion around the wool fibers just beneath the surface of the skin. It is said that there is no relation between the

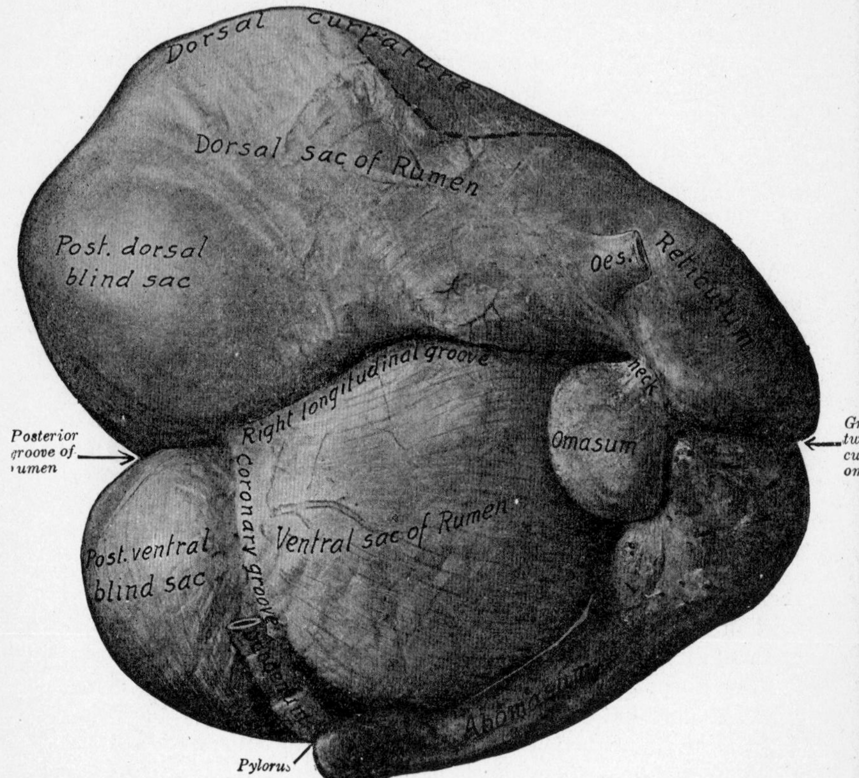


FIG. 27.—Stomach of sheep; right view. ("Anatomy of Domestic Animals," Sisson. Courtesy of W. B. Saunders Co.)

size of the gland and the fiber connected with it, the smallest fibers often being associated with the largest glands. Also, the thicker the fibers on the surface of the skin, the greater the number of glands. These observations suggest why the wool of Merinos is more oily than that of breeds bearing coarser, less dense wool (Fig. 23).

**The Digestive Tract.—Teeth.**—Sheep grow two sets of teeth; the first or temporary teeth number 20, and the second or permanent teeth number 32; of the permanent teeth, 8 are incisors, 12

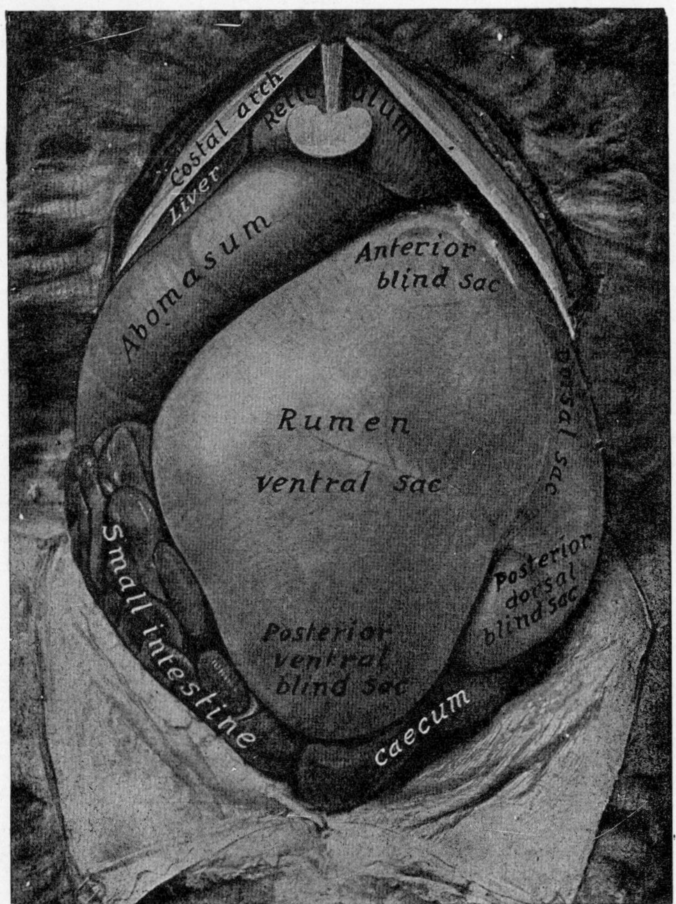


Fig. 28.—Abdominal viscera of sheep; superficial ventral view. ("Anatomy of Domestic Animals," Sisson, W. B. Saunders Co.)

premolars and 12 molars. There are no teeth in the front part of the upper jaw in either lambs or sheep, but instead a cartilaginous pad, on which the incisor teeth of the lower jaw impinge. As a rule, the lamb has some of its teeth when it is born, and by the time it is a few weeks old it has all of the temporary set. The permanent teeth begin to replace the temporary teeth when the lamb is about one year old. More will be said about the teeth in the next chapter in connection with the indications of age in sheep.

**Stomach.**—The stomach has four compartments: the rumen, the recticulum, the omasum, and the abomasum. The first three, of which the rumen is by far the largest, serve as places for storing and softening or macerating the food, while the fourth, the abomasum, is the compartment in which most of the digestive processes characteristic of the stomach occur. According to measurements made by the writer, the capacity of the stomach of a fat sheep weighing from 175 to 180 pounds is about 21 quarts. Sisson, however, gives it as 16 quarts, and Henry and Morrison as 31.3 quarts. Based on Henry and Morrison's figures, the capacity of each of the various compartments is as follows: Rumen, 24.7 quarts; reticulum, 2.1 quarts; omasum, 1 quart; abomasum, 3.5 quarts; the total being 31.3 quarts (Fig. 27).

**Intestines.**—As given by Henry and Morrison, the small intestine of the mature sheep is about 85.9 feet long and has a capacity of 9.5 quarts; the large intestine is approximately 21.4 feet long and has a capacity of 5.9 quarts. Digestive processes take place in both the small and large intestines (Fig. 28).

## QUESTIONS

1. What distinguishes the sheep as a ruminant?
2. How does it differ from the ox; from all other classes of animals belonging to the family *Bovidæ?*
3. Enumerate common variations in the skeletal arrangement of sheep.
4. How may variations in skeletal structure affect the form of the sheep?
5. How are wool and hair different in structure?
6. To what extent do sheep vary in hairy covering?
7. How many temporary teeth have sheep? Permanent teeth?
8. What large glands pour their secretions into the digestive tract of sheep?
9. What is yolk in wool; where does it come from?
10. Of what advantage is the rumen or paunch to wild sheep? To domestic sheep?
11. Gently pressing a wool fiber, draw it back and forth between the thumb and forefinger. Can you distinguish which way the cuticle cells are pointed?

## CHAPTER VI

# THE NATURE OF SHEEP

**The Life of a Sheep.**—Most sheep are fully grown at eighteen to twenty-four months of age. The manner in which they are fed has some influence on their rate of development; sheep that are forced by heavy feeding may at one year of age show indications of being two years old. As a rule, the Merino breeds are later in developing than the mutton breeds, but whether this later development is altogether a breed characteristic is not wholly clear. The method of growing Merinos generally in vogue may be different enough from that employed in growing the mutton breeds to cause some of the difference in rapidity of development. But the early improvers of the mutton breeds apparently sought early maturity more persistently than the early improvers of the Merinos. It is, therefore, only fair to assume that the mutton breeds are disposed to develop at a more rapid rate.

In general, sheep are old at five or six years of age. But there are many exceptions to this rule, so many, in fact, that the flockmaster ought to be his own judge as to when his sheep are old. On the ranges in the western part of the United States where the flocks are very large, it is common practice to discard ewes when they become five or six years old solely on account of their age, because they usually begin to decline in yield of wool after their fifth year. But the owners of small flocks can afford to base their discarding on a study of individuals, for not infrequently seven- and eight-year-old ewes when members of a small group, produce quite as well or even better, than younger ewes.

Unfavorable environment and improper care, exposure, and poor feed often hasten the approach of old age. In dry, sandy countries, sheep may become old at a comparatively early age through the teeth being worn down short by the excessive amounts of sand both in and on the vegetation. Then, too, a scanty supply of feed on the range may require the sheep to do so much travelling when it is not adequately fed that physical decline sets in prematurely.

It frequently happens that sheep which have become too old for one set of conditions are moved into more favorable surroundings where they prove profitable for two or three more years. In England and Scotland ewes which are too old to be kept in the hills where feed is rather scarce, are often moved into the lowlands where there is an abundance; here they thrive and produce two or three crops of lusty lambs, and are finally fattened for market.

Sheep normally inclined to develop slowly do not, as a rule, begin to break down until well along in years. Thus the Merino breeds are perhaps longer lived than the mutton breeds. Undoubtedly, longevity of life has its advantage, but the usefulness of a breed cannot be determined on this alone.

FIG. 29.—Old sheep; prominent Shropshire prize winners when in their prime. They were each eleven years old when photographed. Their lean necks and general lack of flesh were due to advanced age and not to poor care.

**Indications of Age.**—(1) **Teeth.**—One of the best indications of the age of a sheep is the teeth. The temporary or lamb teeth are small; the permanent teeth are broader and longer. If a lamb develops normally, the two temporary teeth in the middle of the front part of the lower jaw are replaced by permanent teeth at about twelve months of age. Therefore, when a sheep shows two broad teeth with small teeth on either side, it is an indication that the animal is a yearling; if there are four broad teeth, that it is two years old; if there are six, that it is three years old. At four or five years of age all of the eight temporary teeth in the front part of the jaw are likely to be replaced by permanent teeth and it is impossible to determine the age with any degree of accuracy.

It should be borne in mind that the teeth indicate the degree of

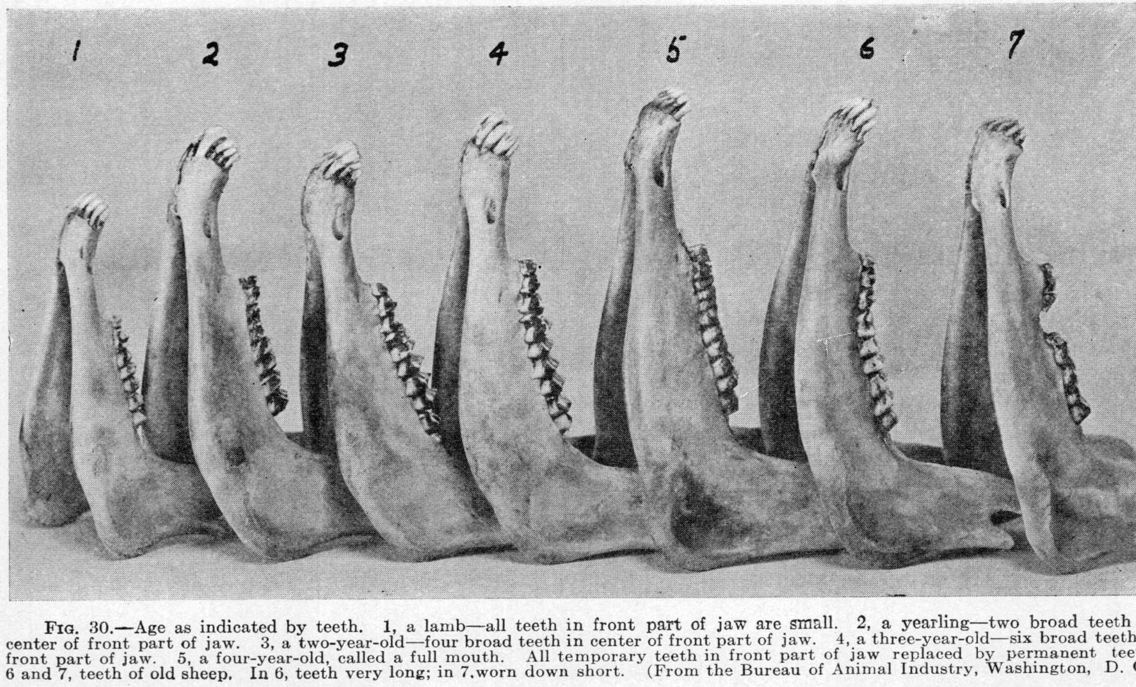


Fig. 30.—Age as indicated by teeth. 1, a lamb—all teeth in front part of jaw are small. 2, a yearling—two broad teeth in center of front part of jaw. 3, a two-year-old—four broad teeth in center of front part of jaw. 4, a three-year-old—six broad teeth in front part of jaw. 5, a four-year-old, called a full mouth. All temporary teeth in front part of jaw replaced by permanent teeth. 6 and 7, teeth of old sheep. In 6, teeth very long; in 7, worn down short. (From the Bureau of Animal Industry, Washington, D. C.)

development rather than the absolute age of the sheep in calendar months; hence, they are not infallible indications of age. If development is slow, the first permanent teeth may not appear until the sheep is fifteen or sixteen months old; if it is rapid, they may appear at ten months of age. A yearling sheep that has been forced by heavy feeding may have four broad teeth in front instead of two (Fig. 29).

The teeth of an old sheep are likely to be spread apart, missing, or worn down short. Other indications of advanced age are a sunken appearance over the eyes, a comparatively short fleece with sunken places on the surface, and a general lack of fullness of body outlines (Fig. 30).

(2) **The Break Joint.**—On our large livestock markets, an index often depended upon for determining whether an animal belongs in the sheep or lamb class is what is known as the "break joint." This is the temporary, or epiphyseal cartilage located immediately above the pastern joint. Without it bones could not elongate and hence it is present until the lamb is pretty well along in body development. It can be distinguished best on the live animal by rubbing up and down on the foreleg just above the pastern joint with the thumb and forefinger. If temporary cartilage has not disappeared, a great deal of prominence will be felt; if it has, the bone will be comparatively round and smooth (Fig. 31).

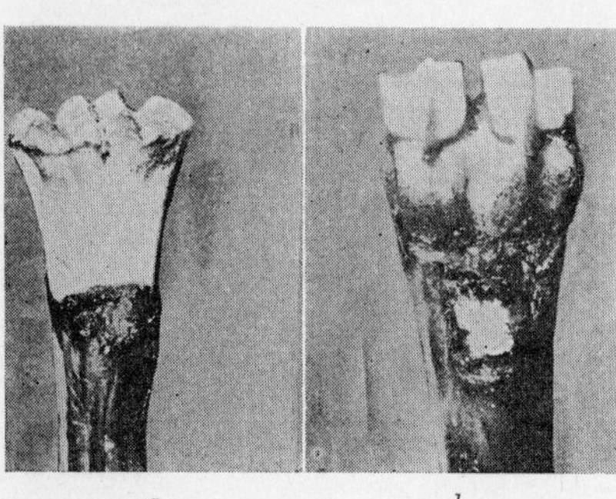

*a* *b*

Fig. 31.—(*a*) The break joint; when an immature sheep is slaughtered its forelegs are severed at this joint—its presence being a sure indication that the animal was young. (*b*) The regular articulating joint below the break joint; the forelegs of mature sheep are severed at this joint.

**Feeding and Drinking Habits.**—Being ruminants, sheep are adapted not only to the consumption of grain, but also of bulky feeds, such as grass and hay. They eat all of the grasses except the very coarsest varieties and are very fond of the cultivated leguminous plants. They eat most of the weeds common to farms, and in the West, weeds on sheep ranges are considered very valuable feed. Sheep feed on young tree growth more than any other of our domestic animals except goats.

Sheep prefer short herbage on an extensive range to a rampant growth on a limited area. When placed on a tall plant growth they nip off the ends of the plants and trim off the leaves, but usually leave the stems standing. They are structurally adapted to feeding on short herbage, because of their very mobile lips and sharp incisor teeth. The upper lip is very mobile, which is in part due to the vertical fissure in the center which permits one-half of the lip to move somewhat independent of the other half.

FIG. 32.—The paths or terraces to the left and high up on the hillside were made by sheep while grazing. (From Morris and Kirby, Chinook, Montana.)

The inherent love which sheep have for change of feeding ground is well known, and is always plainly indicated in the eager and playful way in which they feed just after they are turned into a fresh pasture.

It is thought that the native home of the domesticated sheep was in the high, treeless plateaus and mountains. Most sheep especially enjoy feeding on the high places in their pastures, but some of the modern breeds have been kept on low, level lands so long that it is doubtful whether they would take to the hills from choice. It is interesting to note how sheep feed on hills. In a hilly country, where sheep are grazed in large numbers, the traveller is sure to see along the hillsides many sheep paths which look like little terraces, indicating that in grazing, the sheep do not pass over the hill, but rather along the side, gradually working to the top (Fig. 32).

Sheep are able to exist without water longer than most domesticated animals. Craig says that this is probably due to the fact that they have unusually large salivary glands; very likely it is also due in part to still other physiological characteristics. It has often been thought that sheep do not need to have daily access to water, but such an assumption is erroneous, for even in cold weather they will drink from two to four quarts daily. They prefer running to still water.

Fig. 33.—The little lamb aspires for heights affording wider outlook upon the world.

**Folding Habits.**—Sheep that have been allowed to choose between shelter and the open, prefer to lie out of doors on high places. This may not be true, however, of sheep that have been raised in barns. Their preference for high, well-drained, and airy resting and sleeping grounds is very marked, for it is only in the severest of winter weather that they abandon such spots for lower, wind-protected places. After the lamb is a few hours old it constantly seeks some eminence, such as its mother's back, a bale of hay, a log, or a rock. It has been observed that young sheep seek high places more readily than do the older ones; yearlings will feed higher up on a hillside than old ewes (Figs. 33 and 34).

**Breeding Habits.**—Most domesticated breeds of sheep are monoestrous. That is, the ewes come in heat (œstrus) in but one season of the year, which, in the United States, is in the autumn and early winter months; hence, it is not possible to have lambs born at any time in the year. But there are a few breeds, such as the Tunis and Dorset Horned, for which it is claimed that the ewes will breed to produce lambs at the time desired by the owner. Such breeds are especially useful to those who desire to grow fancy lambs out of season in order to supply a high-priced commodity to a limited few. If, as it seems, ewes are induced to a certain extent to come in heat by the cool of the autumn nights, it may be that there are localities in which climatic conditions will cause ewes to breed out of their normal season and perhaps twice a year. Summer nights in the hills may correspond to the autumn nights on the plains and by moving ewes from the plains to the hills, one may succeed in breeding them out of normal season.

Fig. 34.—Sheep enjoy being on high places.

A ewe remains in heat for about two days; if she is not bred, or if she fails to get in lamb from the service of the ram, the period of heat, or œstrus, recurs in approximately sixteen days. On this point there is variance of opinion and some writers mention twenty-one days as the length of time between œstrus periods. In the Middle West of the United States, however, the intervening time, although varying all the way from twelve to twenty-eight days, is most often sixteen days. In case the ewe is not bred, she is likely to recur in heat regularly for three or four months, beginning in late summer or early autumn and continuing until late December.

About one hundred and forty-six days is the normal gestation period for ewes. At the Illinois, Wisconsin, and Ohio Stations, it has been observed that the period of gestation for Rambouillet and American Merino ewes is more frequently one hundred and fifty-two than one hundred and forty-six days. And one hundred and forty-four days has been given as the normal period for Southdowns. From this it would seem that breed may be the cause of some variation in the length of the period of pregnancy.

It is common for each ewe to give birth to one or two lambs. Occasionally a ewe has three lambs at one parturition period, and there are instances of even more, but since the ewe has but two teats that function (in rare cases there are four), she is not well

Fig. 35.—A capacious, matronly type of ewe capable, as the photograph shows, of taking good care of a pair of lambs.

prepared to take care of more than two lambs. By carefully selecting parent stock, promoters of certain breeds have succeeded in developing ewe stock having a marked tendency to produce twins (Fig. 35).

**Recognition of Young.**—A ewe recognizes her new-born lamb wholly through the sense of smell, but in a few days she can distinguish it at sight. In cases of perplexity, however, she always relies on her nose for recognition. Apparently the odor by which a ewe identifies her newly-born offspring is due to something coming from her, for in case she refuses to own her lamb she may be induced to receive it (but not always), by placing some of her milk on its rump, the point where she usually sniffs at the lamb to recognize it.

**Gregariousness.**—Sheep have the gregarious instinct; that is, they like to keep together. The flocking instinct is not so pronounced in some breeds as it is in others, but there is no breed or variety known that does not possess it. Of the well-known breeds, the Merinos have this trait most strongly developed, for, as stated in Chapter I, they stay close together whether grazing or resting. On range where herding is practiced this statement applies to the whole of a large band. On the other hand, nearly or quite all of

Fig. 36.—Following the leader. (By courtesy of The Country Gentleman, Philadelphia.).

the English mutton breeds are less inclined to stay close together while grazing. Flocks of any of the mutton breeds seem to prefer to spread out over a rather large area while feeding, yet if something frightens them, as the bark of a strange dog, they show their gregarious instinct by bunching up as fast as they can. One of the breeds least inclined to close flocking is the Black-faced Highland, a mountain breed of Scotland. In their native country, one may see the hill or mountain sides dotted with small groups consisting of from three to ten of these sheep picking at the heather, apparently oblivious of their flock-mates more than half a mile away.

The flocking instinct is so strongly implanted in sheep that when an individual is separated from the flock, it is an indication that something unusual has happened. The first thought of the trained shepherd when he sees a sheep alone and some distance from its mates is likely to be that it is ill or has been injured.

The instinct to flock in large numbers is of great value where herding is practiced, as in the western part of the United States. In extensive, unfenced, and undeveloped lands any herder would lose large numbers from his band through straying and through the attacks of predatory animals if his sheep were not disposed to continue in a rather compact body.

Closely associated with the gregarious instinct of sheep is its instinct to follow a leader. There is an old saying, "Where one sheep goes, all others will follow," which really is not an exaggeration. If the leader passes on, the others will take a chance on a long leap, a narrow path, or even a plunge into the water in order to follow (Fig. 36).

**Timidity and Defenselessness.**—In the presence of foes sheep are sadly lacking in ability to defend themselves and they become so frightened that they run wildly hither and thither. Although they fear all animals disposed to prey upon them, their worst enemies are the wolf and kindred animals, such as the coyote, the dog, and the jackal. The jackal furnishes trouble for the sheepmen of South Africa; the dingo, a wild dog, makes depredations on flocks in Australia, and the wolf and particularly the coyote, seriously handicap sheep raising on the western ranges of the United States. In farming communities the dog is the worst hindrance to the keeping of flocks. While any of these animals may kill outright, their attacks are almost as deadly if they only chase and bite because the sheep are badly frightened and run so hard that a physical breakdown is likely to follow. In case they are bitten, death may result from infection of the wound. Other predatory animals in the western part of the United States are the bob-cat and mountain lion. In New Zealand and Australia the kea (a parrot-like bird) often attacks sheep on the back in the region of the kidneys.

Being easily stampeded by fear, sheep really encourage dogs to chase them, for if a dog full of vigor and eager for exercise, but with no intention of mischief, enters a field where sheep are feeding or resting, the entire flock may dash away at top speed at the sight of him. Their action stirs the dog to the depths of his desire for the chase, and he is after them in what he considers a rollicking good game, but it means disaster to the owner of the sheep.

Horned breeds of sheep are said to be less afraid of their enemies than hornless breeds. Strong, masculine rams are also more aggressive and somewhat less afraid than ewes; but spirited ewes with lambs at side will defend their young. Both ewes and rams, in their attempt to scare away the enemy, have a habit of vigorously stamping the forefeet.

**Non-Resistance to Disease.**—Sheep do not show much evidence of illness until they are very sick, and this is perhaps the reason for the oft-repeated statement, "A sick sheep is as good as dead." A careful and observant shepherd, however, takes many a sick sheep in hand in time to save it and any sheep raiser to be successful must learn to discover that something is wrong with his sheep before they are "as good as dead." Certain breeds apparently resist disease better than others; hence it seems probable that general hardiness may have been more or less disregarded in the development of some of our modern breeds.

## QUESTIONS

1. Can you tell how a healthy sheep acts when it is separated from its fellows? A sick one?
2. Why are the attacks of predatory animals so injurious to sheep?
3. Do you know what parts of the sheep's body are most frequently bitten by dogs?
4. By what may the age of a sheep be estimated?
5. Compare the period of growth in sheep with that in man.
6. Can you give reasons why sheep select high, well-drained places for sleep and rest?
7. Do sheep prefer extensive or limited range?
8. How do they graze over hills?
9. Do you know how a goat grazes over a hill?
10. In what seasons are lambs born in the United States?
11. How many lambs can a ewe conveniently nurse?
12. What proportion of lambs to ewes have you observed?

## CHAPTER VII

## TYPES

**The term type** as applied to sheep is used in various ways. Breeds developed primarily for mutton are grouped under the mutton type, and those developed especially for wool belong under the wool type. As regards development for mutton and wool, a few breeds are dual in type, but the term dual-purpose type has not yet been widely applied to sheep. An acceptable specimen of a breed possesses what are termed breed characteristics. These constitute breed type and serve to distinguish the specimen from individuals of other breeds and of no breed. Sexes differ in other characters than sex organs, so there is what may be termed sex type. There exists a market type which coincides in most respects with the mutton type, but, because of special emphasis laid on certain points, is somewhat different.

**The Mutton Type.**—The ideal type, which is sought in all of the prominent mutton breeds, consists of a relatively broad and deep body and such a development of head, neck, legs and body parts that the whole conformation suggests symmetry, thickness, compactness, and quality. This is regarded as the most suitable type for producing growth and finish economically and for yielding the kind of carcass the consumer wants (Fig. 37).

**Head.**—As between the different breeds, the head varies more in shape and size than any other part of the animal, but in general it is short and wide, and its various features are developed and proportioned so as to suggest hardiness and strength. The mouth is large; the nostrils are well expanded; the eyes are large, round and bright; the nose is short, rather wide, and varying in profile from slightly dished to pronouncedly Roman, and both the eyes and the ears are wide apart. The ears harmonize in size and quality with the other features of the head and are set so as to contribute to the carriage and style characteristic of the breed to which the animal belongs.

**The neck,** though free from coarseness, is strongly muscled and joined neatly to both the head and shoulders. It is comparatively straight underneath from the junction with the jaw to the brisket, and there is no depression on the top just in front of the shoulders. Breeds differ with respect to length and set of neck, but in general a short neck is preferred provided it carries the head stylishly. In no case should the neck be placed so that the head is carried lower than the top of the body.

**The body,** consisting of the fore quarters, hind quarters, and middle or barrel, possesses lines and dimensions which indicate sub-

FIG. 37.—The mutton type—wide, deep, compact, evenly developed in form.

stance, capacity, and vigor. It is broad, deep, and of medium length and its lines are comparatively straight. Low and full flanks and a short space between the last rib and the hip contribute to the thick, compact appearance of the body.

The fore quarters, which include the shoulders and the brisket, fit up smoothly with the neck in front and with the middle behind them. The shoulder blades come snug to the spine and level with it, thus forming a smooth, compact, wide top which is covered with flesh and fat. The sides of the shoulder also are well covered and free from prominence of bone. The brisket is wide, full, and extends well in front of the legs, and its anterior contour is rounding rather than pointed. In fat sheep there is no depression between the brisket and the lower part of the shoulder.

The parts forming the middle or barrel of the body are the ribs, back, loins, and flanks. The ribs are long and widely arched, a conformation that gives pronounced width to the back, which extends from the shoulders to the loins, and also forms a deep, wide, capacious chest indicative of stamina and constitution. The back extends from the shoulders to the last ribs and the loins from the last ribs to the hips. Besides being wide and level, both are covered with firm flesh and fat to such an extent that the processes of the spine are scarcely noticeable to the touch. Since the back and loins contain valuable cuts, their extreme development is always sought. The floor of the body is wide and slightly convex.

The parts of the hind quarters are hips, rump, thighs, and twist. The hips are level, wide in proportion to the width of the body, and free from prominence at the points. The rump, which extends from the hips backward, is long, level, wide, and thick at the dock. Sheep with this conformation of rump produce more mutton, and the ewes have slightly less trouble in giving birth to their young than those with peaked or drooping rumps and with low-set tails. The thighs, which join the rump a few inches below the top line, are full and wide at the top, while down toward the hocks they stand out boldly, indicating sturdiness and strength. The twist, formed by the meeting of the thighs at the rear of the body, is wide, low, and relatively firm to the touch. If the rump, thighs, and twist are not well developed, a leg of mutton from the carcass cannot be first class in form nor up to proportionate weight.

**The legs,** both in front and behind, are straight, strong, free from coarseness at the joints, and placed far apart, with the pasterns strong and the toes neither close nor sprawling. In front the arm is full and heavily muscled. Behind, the hocks are straight and placed so that they neither bow outward nor come in close to each other. In a ram, particularly, either sickle-shaped or badly placed hocks are serious faults because they are likely to render him incapable of service.

**Quality.**—Although some of the mutton breeds have large, strong bones and rather large, bold head features, quality receives important consideration in each and every breed. In all cases coarseness, as characterized by rough legs with large joints, fat heads and faces, coarse, staring hair on the face and legs, and soft tallowy flesh, is to be avoided.

**Skin, Wool.**—In general, pink skins of fine texture are preferred because they indicate health, quality, and disposition to make good use of food. The wool of the mutton breeds varies greatly in length and fineness, but in all breeds clean, white wool free from kemp and dark fibers is sought after.

Fig. 38.—The extremely developed wool type—with large wrinkles on all parts of the body. The pelt (skin and wool) of this sheep constitutes a large per cent of its total weight.

**The Wool Type.**—Fineness, density, and weight of fleece have been the prime objects of those who have developed the wool-type breeds and in these particulars breeds of other types do not equal them. Because of dissimilarity in form, skin, and wool, the extreme wool type is markedly different in appearance from the mutton type of sheep. But increasing consideration is being given to mutton form and quality in breeds belonging to the wool type; hence the difference between the two is not quite so pronounced as it once was (Fig. 38).

**Comparison with Mutton Type.**—As compared with the mutton type, the wool type lacks in straightness or evenness of lines, fullness of outline, and disposition to lay on a great deal of external fat. It is common for the spine to project considerably above the shoulder blades, for the back to sag slightly, for the ribs to be flat, and for the rump to droop sharply. Often, the body as a whole lacks in width or thickness, the ribs being rather flat, the shoulders thin, and the thighs hollow. Since the floor of the body lacks width, the legs in most cases are close together and frequently very close at the knees and hocks. As a rule, the face of the wool type is proportionately longer than that of the mutton type and the same can be said of the neck. Less stress is laid upon the smooth junction of neck and shoulders and frequently there is a depression in the neck just in front of the shoulders. Although sheep of the wool type differ so much from the mutton type in form, they are nevertheless hardy, and quite as carefully bred for what they are intended as any of the breeds belonging to the mutton type.

**Folds and Wrinkles.**—In the wool type, there are usually parts of the body on which the skin forms wrinkles or folds, thus giving proportionately more surface on which to grow wool than in the mutton type. Sometimes the wrinkles extend over nearly all parts of the body, but there is an increasing tendency to eliminate them almost altogether from the body proper and to permit of only a few large wrinkles or folds on the neck and perhaps one on the body just behind the shoulders and one or two more at such places as the thigh, dock, and rear flank. Although high-class specimens possessing very many wrinkles are still rather numerous the owners of commercial flocks are finding less and less use for them, and unless demand changes so as to make the production of wool relative to the production of mutton much more profitable than it has been during the past two decades the preference for smooth bodies will continue and it will sooner or later prevail in determining type.

**Breed type** is determined by considering, in connection with the general type to which the sheep belongs, the standard adopted for the particular breed in such matters as size, style or carriage, general quality, color of skin and hair, size and shape of head, length of legs, and the wool with respect to length, fineness, and extension over various parts. When a sheep is judged as a representative of a breed it should not be favorably considered if it is very poor in either general type or breed type. In a breed belonging to the mutton type, such as the Shropshire, an individual having a bare, narrow, sagging back should not be rated high no matter how nearly perfect it may be in those features characteristic of the Shropshire breed. On the other hand, should it be perfect in mutton type, but markedly deficient in features pertaining solely to the Shropshire breed, it should not receive favorable consideration as a Shropshire sheep. And a fault in breed type may be such as to disqualify an animal as a breed representative. No enlightened judge would permit a sheep with a pure white face to take a place in a ring for Shropshires because the typical face color for this breed is deep, soft brown.

**The general type and the breed type** are inseparable and a problem constantly arising in judging is to know just how far perfections in the one recompense faults in the other. It is easy for the student fresh in the study of judging sheep to ask such a question as how much should the shape of head be sacrificed for filling at the twist, but only a few, if any, of long experience would attempt to give him a definite answer.

**Constitution** is weighted most when considered in connection with breeds, and is, therefore, closely associated with breed type. To properly estimate constitution the whole make-up of the sheep must be considered. Were a low-headed, wobbly-gaited, flabby sheep perfect in spring of rib and extension of brisket, it would not be rated high by a competent judge because he would know that such a specimen is lacking in stamina. Compactness of build, strong, well-placed legs, large, firm muscles, wide loins, and a properly molded head are quite as important in determining constitution as a deep, wide chest.

**Objectionable Points.**—In considering breed type it is very necessary to know what supporters of the breed are trying to get rid of. Dark skins are discriminated against more in some breeds than in others; kemp (structureless fibers) is very objectionable in the fleeces of the fine wool breeds, and vestiges of horns are not tolerated in certain breeds.

**Sex Type or Sex Character.**—Whenever a sheep is judged as a breeding animal, the development of certain of its features, aside from sex organs, should clearly indicate the sex to which it belongs.

This development is known as sex character or sex type; in rams it is called masculinity and in ewes femininity.

Pronounced masculinity is indicated by boldness and ruggedness of head features; strong, thick neck, massive development in the fore quarters; a proud, stylish, active, and bold carriage which suggests domineering disposition. In general, a ram with a truly masculine head has a fairly large mouth; big, round, well-expanded nostrils; a pronounced spread of nose (commonly called the knob) just above the nostrils if the animal is mature; wide-open, bright, prominent eyes; and pronounced width between the eyes and ears. The strongly masculine neck sets to the shoulder so that the head can be carried well up. The neck is very thick at the junction with the shoulders, so thick, in fact, that there is scarcely any depression between it and the shoulders. On the top of the neck just behind the head there is usually a rise or prominence which really appears more like a feature of the head than of the neck. Comment on the massive development in front is hardly necessary, but perhaps it is well to call attention to the full, strong forearm which should accompany the wide, deep chest, and the full, rounding, well-extended brisket (Fig. 39).

In order to have an active, bold, or fearless carriage, the ram must have a deeply-muscled body supported by strong, well-placed legs. When one touches a ram possessing outstanding masculinity, there is the sensation of having in hand an individual with the fibers and sinews of a giant. The study of such an animal is never finished, for there is something present which defies accurate measurement with the hand, and the whole make-up of the animal suggests something which is beyond the estimate of the eye.

No ram is really masculine if his sex organs are not well developed. Undersized testicles indicate sex weakness, and when they are less than normal size the animal is usually lacking in strength of features about the head. English shepherds often comment on a ram having a deep bleat as a sheep with a real ram's voice. In the breeds in which the males have horns, the development of horn should be in harmony with the other features of strength about the head.

**Importance of Masculinity.**—Experienced breeders usually select rams showing much masculinity because they believe such individuals will impart more vigor and transmit their characters to their offspring in greater degree than rams that are weak in mas-

*a* *b* *c*

FIG. 39.—Studies showing pronounced masculinity. *a*, Dorset Horned ram; *b*, Shropshire ram; *c*, Hampshire ram.

culinity. Several years ago, while visiting various pure-bred flocks in Great Britain, the writer was greatly impressed by the unusual masculinity of most of the stud rams he inspected. It seemed to him then, as well as now, that the English sheepbreeder places higher value on masculinity than the American breeder. This is a matter to which American breeders should give careful consideration, with a view to determining whether they or the British breeders are more nearly right.

**Femininity** is manifested by refinement of features, matronly appearance, and relatively great development in the hind quarters. All of the above characteristics combine to produce an effect which is quite the opposite of that produced by masculinity. The truly feminine ewe has proportionately less substance in her neck and front of body than the masculine ram, her features are much less rugged and her body lines are more gracefully turned. But the refinement characteristic of femininity is not over refinement to the point of delicateness. At this point the breeder needs to exercise care. Strong bone, provided it shows quality, size of body, or roominess, with features to match do not necessarily indicate lack in femininity, but rather that very essential development of characters which should be associated with it (Fig. 40).

Mild expression has often been spoken of as indicative of femininity in ewes. If this term implies meekness and submissiveness, then it is wrongly applied, because the desirable breeding ewe possesses vigor and snap. She is upheaded, alert and conscious of what is in progress around her almost to the point of appearing to be nervous. She may be of retiring disposition so long as she is not a mother, but with her young at the side she is courageous and stands between her young and what she senses as danger with defiant fearlessness. In parturition such a ewe is very nervous, apparently so anxious to see her lamb that she cannot wait for it to come; but when it does come she usually not only protects it, but also feeds it well.

Successful breeders discard masculine or "staggy" ewes because usually they are not profitable as producers. Often they do not breed at all. When they do, they may have trouble in lambing; and they are usually poor both in maternal instinct and milking properties.

**Wethers** (castrated males) if unsexed when only a few weeks old, tend to resemble ewes in the various characters influenced by

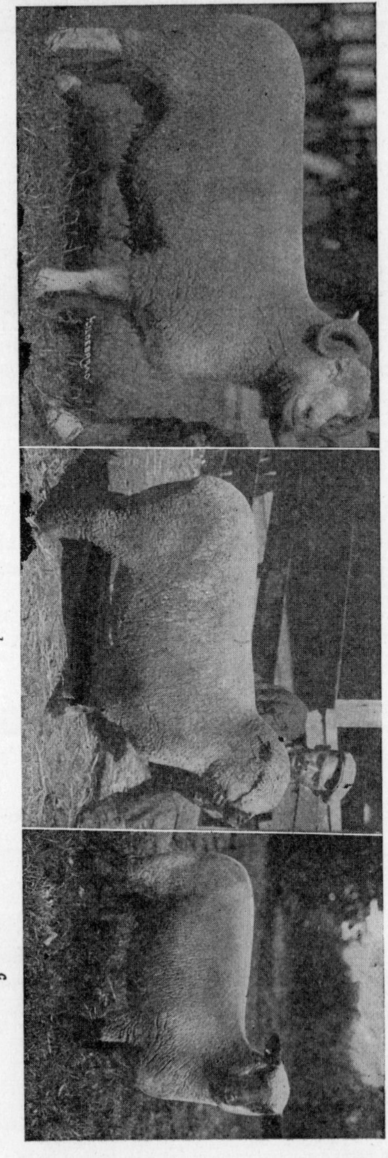


FIG. 40.—Studies in femininity. *a*, Dorset Horned ewe; *b*, Shropshire ewe; *c*, Hampshire ewe.

Fig. 41.—A wether. Not so strongly developed in the head and neck as a ram, but coarser in these features than a ewe should be.

sex. But a wether cannot be said to possess femininity; in fact, it is decidedly uncomplimentary to a ewe to say that she looks like a wether. That is, the wether retains a little of the masculine in his various features (Fig. 41).

**Market Type.**—The mutton type approximates closely the market type. But in fat sheep the market puts more stress on condi-

Fig. 42.—Market sheep carrying the degree of fatness desired by American consumers of mutton.

tion, quality, and weight than on form. Market quality consists in freedom from coarseness and from undue weight of pelt (skin and wool combined), while in the mutton type a heavy fleece is not necessarily a criticism against quality. Ideal market condition requires an even, firm covering with fat, but it does not call for excessive fatness such as is expected of breed specimens and fat wethers in classes for single sheep at large exhibitions. The fact is that show specimens are often made too fat. The weight desired of market sheep is a matter that varies with the different classes, lambs, yearlings, wethers, and ewes; it is also a matter that varies somewhat with the different seasons (Fig. 42).

**In selecting feeder sheep,** condition, quality, weight, form, and thrift are the factors to be considered. The ideal feeder should not be fat, neither should it be so thin as to seem lacking in vigor and health. Its quality should correspond with that of the fat sheep and it is best in form when it corresponds to the description of form given under mutton type, but perfection of form cannot be expected in a sheep that is not fat.

## QUESTIONS

1. Which is easier to determine, general type or breed type? Why?
2. List the large differences between the mutton type and the wool type.
3. Which would grade the higher on the market, the wool type or the mutton type? Why?
4. Compare the head of a ram with that of a ewe of the same breed.
5. How are the differences noted to be accounted for?

6

## CHAPTER VIII

## JUDGING SHEEP

**Preparation for Judging.**—Regardless of whether judges are born or made, skill in judging sheep is attained at the expense of much practice. The men who judge best are nearly always at it, not in the arena, of course, but wherever they see sheep. It is this irresistible tendency constantly to compare and contrast animals that builds up in the mind of the judge a rich store of experiences which serve him well, and in fact come to his rescue when he is making awards where competition is keen and close. These experiences mold his standard and set it out in bold relief. Organized class study, although of great help, is after all only one step toward proficiency in judging. It is a step which many of the best judges have never taken, and one which is not used to proper advantage unless it is supplemented by extensive practice in field and fold (Fig. 43).

**Examining the Sheep.**—Capable judges, realizing the importance of careful examination, first look the sheep over from a distance and then go over it with their hands. It does not make any difference which view of the animal is noted first so long as the examination is thorough and systematic. The writer prefers to begin with the front of the sheep, then observe its sides, and lastly its rear, for the reason that in handling he examines the rear first.

**Looking the Sheep Over.**—Following this plan, there are certain points which should be noted from each view.

(1) *The front* view gives the best opportunity to study the make-up of the head, the width and depth of brisket, and the length, shape and placing of the forelegs. Very close attention should be given to the head because its quality is indicative of the quality of the animal and in breed specimens it reveals a great deal of what is known as breed type. The stamina or constitution of the animal is also indicated in the way certain features of the head are developed.

(2) *Side.*—In taking a side view, the size, style, and general lines of the sheep attract attention first. Then comes an analysis of the general impression thus gained which takes note of the

length and depth of body, the carriage of the head, the length and setting of the neck, the extension of brisket, the evenness or trueness of top and bottom lines, and length and shape of legs, and

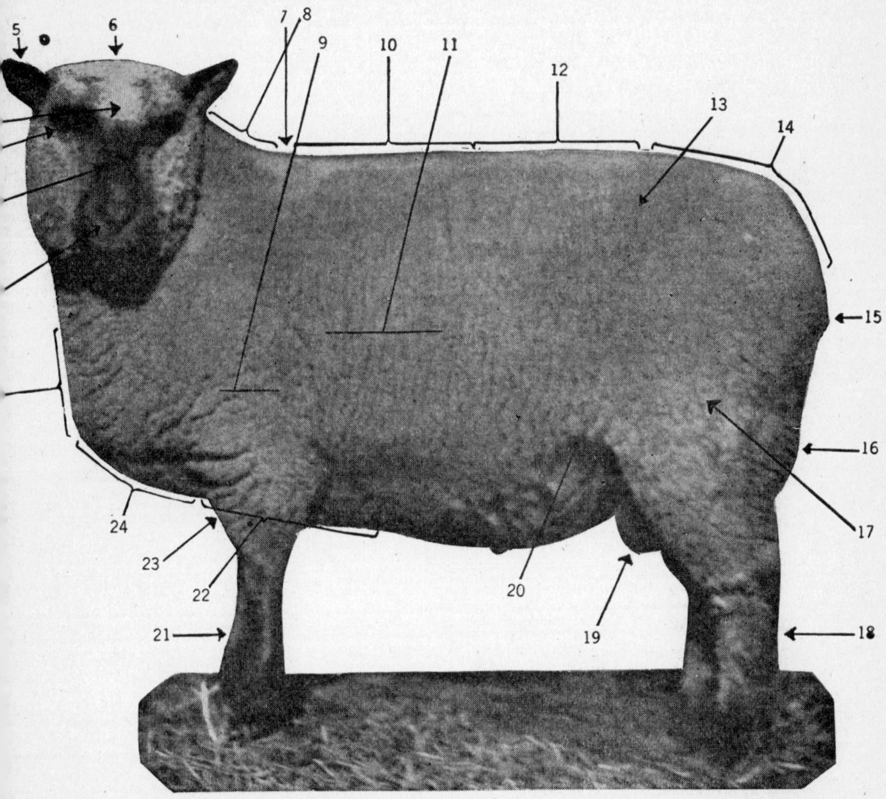


FIG. 43.—The external parts of a sheep. 1, muzzle broad, lips thin, nostrils large; 2, face short, features clean-cut; 3, eyes large and clear; 4, forehead broad; 5, ears alert and not coarse; 6, poll wide; 7, top of shoulder compact; 8, neck short, thick, blending smoothly with shoulder; 9, shoulder thickly covered with flesh; 10, back broad, straight, thickly and evenly covered; 11, ribs long, well sprung, and thickly covered; 12, loin broad, thick, and well covered; 13, hips wide and smooth; 14, rump long, level, and wide to dock; 15, dock thick; 16, twist deep and firm; 17, thighs full, deep, and wide; 18, legs straight, short, and bone smooth; 19, cod or purse in wethers, scrotum in rams, udder in ewes; 20, flank full and deep; 21, forelegs straight, short and strong; 22, chest deep, wide, and full; 23, forelegs wide apart and forearm strong; 24, brisket full and rounding in outline; 25, breast well extended.

lastly, the relation of neck, shoulder, middle, and rump, in turn, to total length.

## Sample Score Card Useful as Beginning Step in Judging

MUTTON SHEEP MARKET

| SCALE OF POINTS | Perfect Score | Student Score 1 | Student Score 2 | Corrected Score 1 | Corrected Score 2 |
|---|---|---|---|---|---|
| **GENERAL APPEARANCE—37 per cent.** | | | | | |
| 1. Weight, pounds | | | | | |
| 2. Form, straight top and underline; deep, broad, lowset, compact, symmetrical | 12 | | | | |
| 3. Quality, hair fine; bone fine but strong; features refined but not delicate; pelt light | 10 | | | | |
| 4. Condition, deep, even covering of firm flesh. Points indicating finished condition are: thick dock, thick covering over loin, back, ribs and shoulders, fullness between shoulder and brisket | 15 | | | | |
| **HEAD and NECK—9 per cent.** | | | | | |
| 5. Head, features clean cut; mouth, large; lips, thin; nostrils, large; eyes, large, clear; face, short; forehead, broad; ears, alert, not coarse, considerable width between ears | 5 | | | | |
| 6. Neck, short thick, full at junction with shoulder | 4 | | | | |
| **FORE QUARTERS—10 per cent.** | | | | | |
| 7. Shoulders, covered with flesh; compact on top, smoothly joined with neck and body | 8 | | | | |
| 8. Brisket, rounding in outline and well extended | 1 | | | | |
| 9. Legs, straight, short, wide apart, strong, full forearm, bone smooth | 1 | | | | |
| **BODY—18 per cent** | | | | | |
| 10. Chest, wide, deep, full | 2 | | | | |
| 11. Ribs, well sprung, long, close and thickly covered | 4 | | | | |
| 12. Back, broad, straight, thickly and evenly covered | 6 | | | | |
| 13. Loin, thick, broad well covered | 6 | | | | |
| **HIND QUARTERS—17 per cent.** | | | | | |
| 14. Hips, far apart, level, smooth | 1 | | | | |
| 15. Rump, long, level, wide to dock thick at dock | 5 | | | | |
| 16. Thighs, full, deep, wide | 5 | | | | |
| 17. Twist, plump, deep, firm | 5 | | | | |
| 18. Legs, straight, short, strong, bone smooth | 1 | | | | |
| **WOOL—9 per cent.** | | | | | |
| 19. Quantity, long dense, even in density and length | 3 | | | | |
| 20. Quality, crimp distinct and even throughout fleece | 3 | | | | |
| 21. Condition, slight amount of yolk, foreign material not excessive | 3 | | | | |
| Total | 100 | | | | |

STUDENT..........................................................

DATE..........................................................

(3) *Rear.*—From the rear the width and evenness in width of body are to be noted; then the development of rump, thighs and twist, and the placing of the hind legs.

**Handling the Sheep.**—After surveying the animal in this systematic manner the judge is ready to verify his visual impressions by handling. This is necessary because the wool may cover defects in form and handling is the only sure way to determine the amount and quality of flesh. In the show ring it is a common practice to

FIG. 44.—Laying the hand on deliberately and firmly with the fingers together is the best way to measure the amount and quality of flesh.

trim the wool in order to conceal defects in form. Then, too, the wool and skin should be inspected at close range (Fig. 44).

The proper way to handle a sheep is to keep the fingers together and lay them down flat on the animal except where it is necessary to grasp the parts, as is the case with the lower thighs. This manner of handling gives the most accurate impressions and does not disarrange the wool. Correct touch is a matter of study. The hands should be laid on deliberately and firmly, but without undue pressure, and pounding or clawing are entirely out of order. At the same time the judge must keep his mind with his hands, comparing the information they give him with the impression he already has of the animal. If he really has his mind on just what he is doing there is no possible excuse for anything but a correct touch (Fig. 44).

After looking the sheep over as is suggested here, the logical place to begin handling is at the rear, and a right-handed judge should stand on the left side of the sheep.

(1) *The Rear, Including Thighs, Twist, Dock, and Rump.*—The first thing to investigate with the hands is the development of

Fig. 45.—Left hand on back of thigh, right hand at rear flank to measure the lower thighs.

the lower thighs. This is done by putting the left hand at the back of the thigh and the right at the rear flank (Fig. 45). In this way the amount of flesh on both the outer and inner thighs can be ascertained. Next, the right hand should press upward on the twist to estimate the amount and firmness of flesh at that point. The development of the upper thighs is determined by placing the hands flat on them and pressing the hands toward each other. Instead of doing this, many judges press one hand against the thigh while resting the other on top of the rump (Fig. 46).

After finishing with the thighs, the judge may either examine the rump or pass one hand along the entire top of the sheep to get an idea of its levelness and covering. The first movement in judging the rump is to grasp the dock with one hand and note its size and fullness. A wide, thick dock is taken to indicate deep, strong muscling along the spine (Fig. 49). A good filling of fat on either side between the dock and the rump indicates high condition; hence a great deal of importance is attached to this part of the investigation. The next thing is to determine the width at the hips and

Fig. 46.—Determining the amount and firmness of the filling at the twist and the depth from the top of the rump to the lower boundary of the twist.

the evenness with which this width carries back. This is done by pressing one hand on either side of the rump from the hip points to the dock (Figs. 47 and 48).

(2) *The Middle, Including Loin, Back, and Ribs.*—The loin is examined for width and thickness by placing one hand straight down on either side of it. This movement is often difficult for beginners, who are unable to hold the hands straight and who have considerable difficulty at first in correctly estimating width. Experienced judges often get an idea of width and thickness of loin by reaching across it with one hand. The covering of loin is judged by placing the fingers flat over the spine and noting whether the

Fig. 47

Fig. 48

Fig. 47.—Pressing the upper thighs between the hands.
Fig. 48.—Pressing the rump between the hands to note how the rump carries in width from the hips to the dock.

bones are prominent or cushioned over with flesh and fat.

The back may have been examined already for levelness and covering, but re-examination will do no harm. Width of back, a good point in any breed, seems to depend mainly on long ribs, arching high and wide as they leave the spine, and special attention should be given to the degree of arch, or rather of width, just back of the shoulders (Fig. 51). There are two ways of ascertaining this: First, place the fingers of the hand on one side of the spine and the thumb on the other; or, second, place one hand on either side of the spine. The spring of the last rib should also be noted carefully as the width of a properly shaped barrel or body increases gradually from the shoulders back to the last ribs (Fig. 50).

In addition to being long and arching well, the ribs should be covered with firm flesh and fat, and the spaces between the ribs

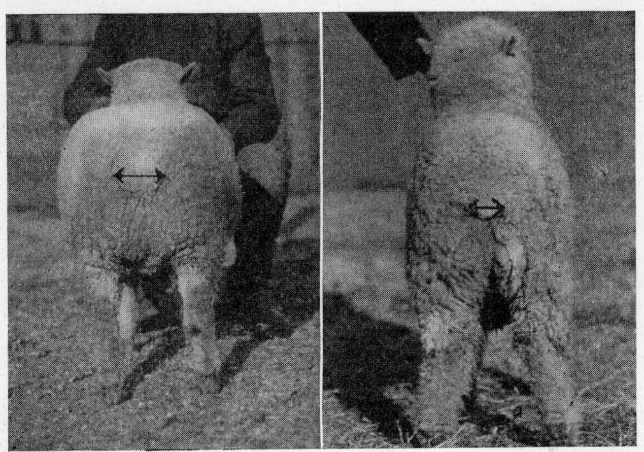

Fig. 49.—A wide dock; a narrow dock. A wide dock indicates deep muscling along the spine; a dock well cushioned over with fat indicates that the animal is in high condition.

should be well filled and firm. These points can be determined by rubbing the hands back and forth over the ribs. If they are prominent to the touch and if the flesh and fat are soft, the covering is poor in both extent and quality. In examining the ribs the hands should also be placed over the fore flanks to proximate the width of chest (Fig. 52).

(3) *The Front, Including Shoulders, Chest, Brisket, Neck, and Head.*—By placing one hand on top of the shoulders it is possible to learn how compactly the shoulder blades are set up against the spine and how well these parts are covered with flesh (Figs. 53 and 54). Next, the hands should be placed first on the sides of the shoulders to examine the depth of flesh, then they should be moved

Fig. 50

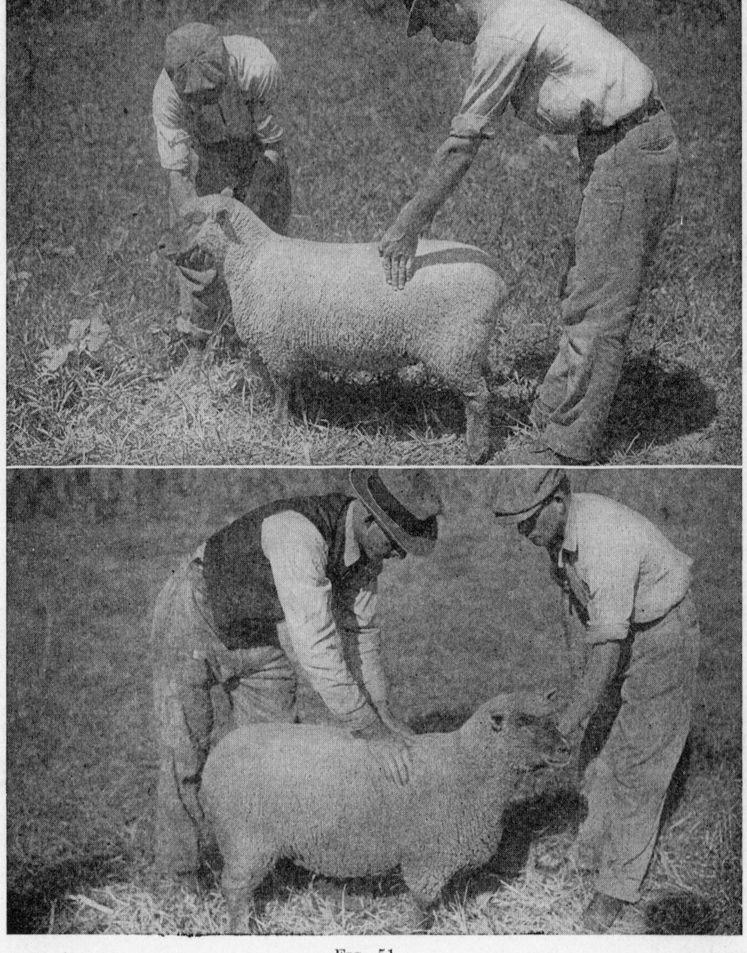

Fig. 51

Fig. 50.—Examining the loins for width and depth.
Fig. 51.—A hand on either side of the spine just back of shoulder to note whether the ribs spring high and wide from the spine.

forward to the neck vein to determine whether the neck blends smoothly with the shoulders as fullness here indicates both high condition and well-muscled neck. The lower points should next be touched to note whether or not the bones are unduly prominent and coarse. Finish or high condition is estimated by placing the hands just in front of the lower points where the brisket joins the lower part of the shoulders. At this point there is a noticeable depression in the thin animal which is scarcely discernible in the fat one. One hand should be passed on down to the floor of the brisket and chest to examine width. By keeping the other hand on the top of the shoulders, a notion of the depth of chest can be gained. The front

FIG. 52.—Placing the hands on the ribs to determine the depth and firmness of covering.

of the brisket should be touched for the purpose of getting an idea of its extension and contour (Fig. 55).

A good way of determining the setting and size of the neck is to grasp it on top, with one hand, just in front of the shoulders at the neck vein. With the thumb on one side and the fingers on the other, a good idea can be gained of its fullness, both at the top and on the sides. A similar grasp should be made just behind the ears to ascertain whether the neck is coarse or smooth where it joins the head (Fig. 56).

It is not necessary to handle the head much, but in woolly-headed breeds handling helps in estimating the width of head, and

Fig. 53.—Handling top to note whether the shoulder blades and spine are so related as to make a smooth even top.

Fig. 54.—Handling side of shoulders to determine smoothness and covering with flesh and fat.

touching the various features assists in determining quality. In judging rams of the hornless breeds, it is always advisable to place the fingers in the horn holes to note whether there is any growth of horn. Most judges practise parting the lips and looking at the teeth for the purpose of estimating age. This is necessary even though the teeth do not proximate age closely. While handling the head it is a good thing to examine the eyes closely.

(4) *Fleece and Skin.*—After the conformation of the sheep has been determined, the fleece and skin must be examined. Since the best wool grows on the side of the shoulder or just behind it, the fleece is first opened in that region. This should be done by laying the hands down flat on the surface of the fleece and gently forcing it to part so that the density, quality, color, luster, and condition of the wool,[1] and the color of the skin can be noted (Fig. 57).

Similar examination should be made at mid-side and on the thighs in mutton breeds, and in wool breeds at the points mentioned and wherever else the judge deems necessary, but especially along the spine, at the hip point, dock, and on the belly. In breeds in which dark fibers in the wool and dark spots on the skin are likely to be present, the fleece should also be parted on the top of the head just behind the ears, on the fore part of the shoulder, and just above the hocks.

(5) *Noting Defects.*—In connection with the handling of rams it is advisable to note whether the scrotum is normally developed. Occasionally the testicles are very small. When this is the case, the features about the head usually lack masculinity. Again one testicle

[1] Density of fleece is determined when the wool is parted. The smaller the amount of skin exposed the denser the wool. Or density can be estimated fairly well by grasping a portion of the fleece between the thumb and fingers; if the wool feels compact and fills the hand well, it is likely to be dense. Quality of fleece is indicated by the waves or crimps in the wool fibers. If these are short, carry regularly from the skin to the outer tips of the fibers, the wool is fine and even in quality. Luster is a factor in the quality of luster wools. It is a brightness, similar to that of polished metals and its presence depends on the size and shape of the cuticle cells or scales forming the outer layer of the fibers. It is most marked in the longer, coarser wools, and least in the fine, short wools. Condition of fleece refers to color, yolk, and the foreign material in the wool. To be in good condition the wool should be bright, not dingy; it should be practically free from dirt, chaff, and burrs; and the yolk should be evenly distributed.

Fig. 55.—Placing one hand on the shoulders and the other between the legs to note depth of chest.

Fig. 56.—Grasping the neck at head to note development.

Fig. 57

Fig. 58

**Fig. 57.**—Examining the wool and skin.

**Fig. 58.**—Detecting overdone condition **which is characterized by soft, flabby fat that can be shifted by pressure with the hand.**

may be abnormally small or not let down in the scrotum sack. Such defects are to be discriminated against largely according to their intensity. The testicles may be so small that the judge feels confident that the ram is not a breeder, in which case he should not be awarded a prize. In judging ewes, it is well to examine the udder. If it is hard or otherwise defective some discrimination should be made. There are also such defects as large, lumpy growths under the throat, which because the wool is trimmed closely or because it hangs over them in large mases as in the long-wool breeds, may not be discovered except by handling. Wrinkles under the throat in breeds not supposed to have them are often so well concealed by close trimming that they can be discerned only by touch.

Soft, blubbery fat, due to "overdone" condition, often escapes the notice of beginners in judging. There are two places on the body where this fat is present in largest quantity; namely, on the fore ribs and on the rump. A good way to get an estimate of this soft, blubbery fat is to place one hand near the top of the animal and the other lower down and push them toward each other. In the United States and Canada it is not customary to award a prize to sheep in badly "overdone" condition (Fig. 58).

The judge should always know the sex of the animal he is examining.

**Faults of Beginners.**—Beginners especially possess the fault of viewing too little and handling too much. Before getting a good impression of the animal they pounce upon it and begin to handle. Defects easily discovered by viewing may be entirely overlooked. It is hard for the beginner to understand why viewing before handling is of importance, because many experienced judges appear to lay all of the emphasis on handling, but the old judge sizes the animal up quickly and he is soon ready to see whether handling will confirm his impression of it.

## QUESTIONS

1. From what view can you best determine whether a sheep has strong or weak pasterns? Sickled hocks? Sprawling toes?
2. From viewing how would you determine whether a sheep has a narrow chest?
3. Describe the difference in feel between a bare and a well-covered back.
4. Determine the difference in width between a wide and a narrow sheep.
5. Handle a sheep carefully along the top and determine whether the wool is uniform in length at all points.
6. Handle two sheep over the ribs and describe the difference you note.
7. Write up a comparative study of the heads of two sheep, noting differences in ears, eyes, profile of face, nostrils, mouth, width between ears, and between eyes.

# PART III

## BREEDS

# CHAPTER IX

## THE MUTTON BREEDS

ALL of the mutton breeds kept in the United States, excepting the Tunis and Corriedale, were developed in Great Britain. Beginning with Bakewell the era for evolving these breeds covered almost a century. Roughly speaking, they were evolved from two general types. One of these was a large, coarse, slow-maturing sheep, growing long, coarse wool and yielding a fleece weighing from seven to twelve pounds. With the exception of a few dark spots, the black hoofs and black skin around the nostrils, its face and legs were white. It was kept principally on the low fertile lands in the counties of Lincoln, Leicester, and on the hills of Gloucester. The other type, being smaller, was suited to the hills and lighter soils. It grew short, fairly fine wool and produced a fleece weighing from two to five pounds. Some strains had black faces and legs; others were white in their markings, and still others had speckled or gray faces and legs. As a rule the sheep belonging to the smaller type were good travellers and were adapted to herding on the commons or downs in fairly large numbers. A rather common practice was to fold them on the arable land at night in order to get the manure for field crops, and to drive them several miles out during the day to feed on the downs.

From the large, coarse-wool type such breeds as the modern English Leicester, the Border Leicester, Cotswold, Lincoln, Romney Marsh, Devon Long Wool, South Devon, and Wensleydale have been developed. From the smaller type producing short and fairly fine wool we have secured most of the down breeds, such as the Southdown, Shropshire, Hampshire, Suffolk, and also such breeds as the Dorset Horn and Ryeland. In a few cases a breed has been developed by crossing improved sheep descended from each of the old types. A notable case is that of the Oxford Down, produced by crossing the Hampshire with the Cotswold.

British breeders are thoroughly grounded in the belief that different environments demand different types of sheep. In their opinion sheep adapted to the lowlands are not profitable in the hills and on the mountains. And the soils in regions of similar elevation

FIG. 59.—The native homes of various English breeds.

may be so different as to demand different types. Consequently many breeds have been developed as is indicated by the fact that twenty-five breeds, all native of Great Britain, have been given a place in the premium lists of the annual show of the Royal Agricultural Society of England (Fig. 59).

## QUESTIONS

1. Why were so many different breeds developed in Great Britain?
2. When did Bakewell live?
3. Was he interested in other classes of livestock besides sheep?
4. Make a list of the breeds of sheep kept in the United States.
5. Which were developed in Great Britain?
6. Where were the others developed?

## CHAPTER X

## THE SOUTHDOWN

**History.**—Of the widely distributed improved mutton breeds, the Southdown, next to the Leicester, is the oldest. John Ellman, who lived in southeastern England near Lewes, Sussex County, on the hills known as the South Downs, began to improve the old Southdowns or native sheep of Sussex in the latter half of the eighteenth century, and Arthur Young, who saw this flock in 1776, pronounced it the best in the country. Forty-five years later (1821) Jonas Webb, living 100 miles further north in a more fertile country, near Cambridge, purchased Ellman sheep and further improved them. Although other men had something to do with the improvement of the Southdown, most of the credit for developing it to its present state of mutton perfection is usually given to Ellman and Webb (Fig. 60).

The Southdowns are low, chalky hills which Ellman described as being twenty-six miles long and five miles wide. In his day about one-half of the land was arable and the other grass land. Wheat, oats, barley, clover, vetches, or tares, and roots were some of the more common crops cultivated, while the grass land grew a short, fine, sweet herbage. The vegetation which was not rampant was better suited to a small active breed such as the old Southdown was than to a larger, heavier breed. Ellman most likely recognized this fact and probably it had some weight in his choice of the stock he selected for improvement. He took note of the hardiness of the old Southdown, of its ability to thrive when the land was heavily stocked; of its fine fleece; and of its good leg of mutton. On the other hand, he clearly saw its two worst faults, an ill form and a light fleece.

**The Old Type.**—As a type the old Southdown was small, with long, slim neck, light fore quarters, bowed back, narrow body, low-set tail, coarse bone, and thick leg of mutton. The fleece, though fine, was short, thin, and did not extend over the lower parts of the body. In face and leg markings there were variations ranging from white-brown mottled to solid deep brown or almost black.

**Improvement by Ellman.**—Long before Ellman began his work there was a widespread conviction amongst sheep raisers on the Southdowns that fine fleeces and ill forms were closely associated, and hence that in order to grow fine wool ill-formed sheep had to be tolerated. But Ellman did not believe this and he proposed to make out of the old Southdown a better sheep by improving both its form and fleece. In connection with the improvement of mutton form he also sought more fattening power and quality with respect to the percentage of offal in dressing. He rapidly attained

Fig. 60.—Southdown ram exhibited by Robert McEwen, Byron, Ontario. The thick, compact body, combined with the quality denoted by the trimness about the head are characteristic of the breed.

considerable improvement and, so far as is known, entirely by selection, although it is probable that the selections he made resulted in inbreeding or line breeding. He selected the best for his purpose wherever he could find it, but always within the native Sussex breed. He fixed a type which was shorter in neck, thicker in fore quarters, more nearly level on top, wider sprung in the rib, and better in fleece with respect to length, quality, density and extension than the original stock from which he started.

Mr. Ellman's career as a breeder extended over a period of 54 years or more. In 1829 he dispersed his flock of about 1400 head. He died in 1832.

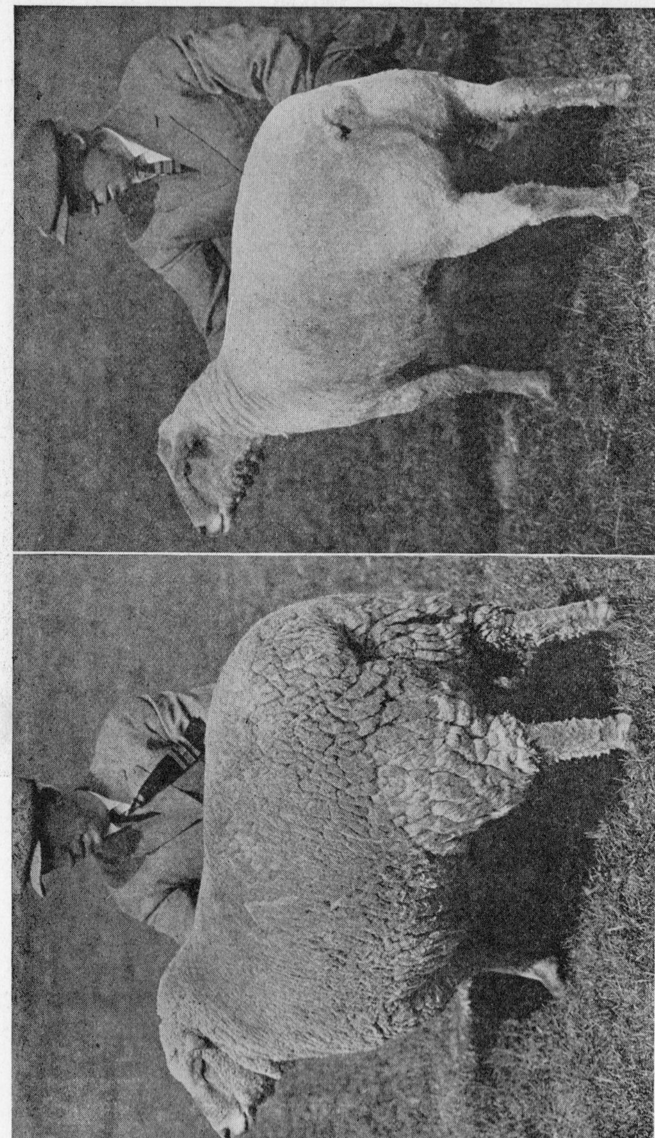

Fig. 61.—A good Southdown ram bred by the U. S. Department of Agriculture.

Fig. 62.—It is clearly shown here that a typical Southdown is thick in thighs and twist.

**Improvement by Webb.**—Mr. Webb, who carried on the improvement of Southdowns from the point where Ellman left it, studied matings closely and never allowed price to keep him from buying the best rams. Being in a country where the soil was more fertile and where the liking for large sheep was more pronounced than in Mr. Ellman's region, he bred for more size. He practically perfected the breed as regards mutton conformation and quality.

Fig. 63.—Southdown ewe bred and exhibited by Robert McEwen, Byron, Ontario. This ewe, shown at leading fairs in Canada and the United States in 1915 and 1916, was defeated but once.

Fortunately he lived to reap the fruits of his good work, for his ram lettings and sales became noted events in the world of animal breeding. He was also very successful in the show ring and, being of persuasive personality, he did much to popularize the breed. His flock was dispersed in 1862 at a memorable auction sale (Figs. 61 and 62).

**Description.**—*Form and Weight.*—The best specimens of the present-day Southdown closely approximate the ideal mutton type in form. The body, which is oval on top, is wide, deep, low set and evenly covered with deep, firm flesh. The neck is short, thick, and placed to the shoulders so that the head is carried just a little above them. The legs are placed far apart, thus giving to the body width at the bottom about equal to that at the top. The arch of rib, the smoothness at hip and lower shoulder point, the fullness at fore-arm, thigh and twist suggest a rotund rather than a rectangular conformation. A compact, symmetrical block of mutton fittingly summaries Southdown form. Mature rams in breeding condition weigh from 185 to 220 pounds; ewes from 135 to 155 pounds.

*Features.*—The features are neither refined nor coarse, but are developed to harmonize with those of the body. The mouth and nostrils are fairly large and the lips somewhat thick as compared

Fig. 64.—Southdown ewes bred by the University of Illinois. Note the width and compactness, both typical of the breed.

with the development of other features. In ewes the profile of the nose or face is slightly dished; in rams it is almost straight. The eyes are large, round, bright, and prominent, suggesting alertness. The ears are short and erect, giving an expression of smartness. The legs are short and straight. As a rule the bone of the fore legs is a little more nearly round than in the other mutton breeds (Fig. 63).

*Markings, Wool, and Skin.*—The color of face and legs varies from light steel gray to a light soft brown, frequently referred to as a mouse brown. The face should not approach black in color nor be speckled with white. Clear, pink skins are preferred, as sheep having dark skins are regarded as hard feeders. The weight of fleece ranges from 5 to 8 pounds and in twelve months it attains a length of about two inches. In addition to covering the neck it extends as clean white wool over the head to form a cap on the forehead and a covering on the cheeks, but it does not extend down over the face much below the eyes. Below it extends to the knees in front and to the hocks behind. Frequently a downy, incipient growth of wool runs down on the hind legs to the pasterns.

**Disqualifications.**—The English Flock Book publishes the following reasons why judges should not at breeding stock shows award a prize to otherwise good sheep:

(a) Horns or evidence of their presence.

(b) Dark poll.

Fig. 65.—Southdown lambs bred by the University of Illinois. These lambs won first prize in the competition for pen of four Southdown lambs at the 1917 International Live Stock Show, Chicago.

(c) Blue skin.

(d) Speckled face, ears, and legs.

(e) Bad wool, probably meaning decided departures from typical Southdown wool (Fig. 64)

**Properties.**—The Southdown is preëminent among mutton breeds for the quality of its mutton. It is famous for the fine-grain, firmness and juiciness of its lean and for the whiteness, flakiness and sweetness of its fat, which is not excessive in amount. Whether it is consumed as baby lamb, ordinary lamb, or mature mutton, these qualities are present to the satisfaction of the most exacting epicure.

**Hardiness and Feeding Qualities.**—On the whole the Southdown is considered hardy, but it is not adapted to the rigorous conditions under which some breeds are able to live. At birth the lambs weigh about eight pounds and, as a rule, they are strong, active, eager for feed and disposed to grow from the start. Both the mature sheep and the lambs take kindly to all well-known sheep feeds and they are especially fond of grazing on pasture grasses, to which they are perhaps somewhat better adapted than to luxuriant forage crops. Under average conditions with respect to feed and shepherding, it is characteristic of the mature sheep to remain plump and in good condition through practically all seasons, and the lambs early attain plump form and a firm, ripe condition which give them distinction as a prime baby lamb product. The lambs do not attain weight as rapidly, however, as do those of some of the

Fig. 66.—Grade Southdown lambs bred by University of Illinois. The granddams—the western ewes in Fig. 148. These lambs, two crosses removed from Western ewes, possess the characteristics of Southdowns to such extent that none except expert judges could distinguish them from pure breds.

other breeds, but unquestionably they make good use of the food they consume. In America they weigh approximately 50 pounds when three months old (Fig. 65).

**Breeding Qualities.**—In Southdown flocks, the per cent of lambs born to the number of ewes bred ranges from 125 to 150. The ewes are good mothers; they seldom disown their lambs and they suckle them well. When in the lambing fold, the ewes, although smart and alert, are not wild, nervous or reckless to the detriment of their lambs.

In cross-breeding and in grading up, Southdown rams are extremely prepotent. No matter what kind of ewes they are mated with, their offspring bear unmistakable resemblance to the Southdown breed not only in external appearance, but also in manner of feeding and growth, and in quality of mutton. For this reason Southdown rams are especially suited to crossing on Dorset Horned and Merino ewes when early or winter lambs are desired for special markets (Fig. 66).

**Distribution.**—The Southdown has been introduced into practically all countries where the production of mutton has received attention. But in spite of its trimness, which is always a delight to the eye, and its superior quality of mutton, it has not become the prevailing breed in many regions outside of its native home. In America, and in various other countries as well, England excepted, its distribution is characterized by occasional flocks. The reason for this is that it is not big enough and its fleece is too light in weight to suit the average sheep raiser. But unquestionably there are many places in the United States where the grain and grass crops are admirably suited to the Southdown, and since the American markets always welcome neat, tidy lambs, there is no good reason why pure and grade Southdown flocks should not be more numerous.

Both in England and in the United States societies have been organized for the promotion of the breed. The English society, which succeeded the English Southdown Sheep Breeders' Association, organized in 1890, is known as the Southdown Sheep Society and it annually publishes a volume entitled "The Southdown Flock Book."

The American society was incorporated in 1882 as the American Southdown Association. It was reorganized in 1922. The publication of its pedigree volumes, which had been suspended for a number of years, has now been resumed.

## QUESTIONS

1. Compare the work of Ellman and Webb.
2. What desirable features did the old Southdowns possess?
3. What undesirable features?
4. Enumerate the superior points of the Southdown as a mutton sheep.
5. What criticisms have been made against the Southdown?
6. On what kind of land do you think Southdowns would return as much or more than any other breed?
7. On what kind of land do you think it would be inadvisable to keep them?
8. Would you gather from the history of the Southdown that it strongly impresses its characters when crossed with other breeds?
9. What can be said of the prolificacy and milking qualities of Southdown ewes?

## CHAPTER XI

# THE SHROPSHIRE

**History.**—*Old Types.*—The Shropshire was developed into a distinct breed in the counties of Shropshire and Staffordshire, in central western England. Because of extensive areas of pasture on both hill and cultivated lands, flock husbandry was a prominent feature in the agriculture of these counties long before the time of modern Shropshire. Certain types of sheep were confined to different parts, the more important of these being Morfe Common, Cannock Chase, Long Mynd, and Whittington Heath. The sheep were named after the locality to which they belonged, and, although they bore an unmistakable resemblance to each other, they were somewhat different and were regarded as separate types. It is also probable that they were not markedly unlike the old stock on the Southdown Hills from which the Southdown breed was developed. They were active, hardy, accustomed to running at large without a shepherd, and little subject to scab or foot rot. They yielded from two to three pounds of wool, which was graded with the choicest produced in England. As a rule, they matured slowly and when fatted at two or three years of age, weighed from 75 to 110 pounds. Lack of width and a drop behind the shoulders were their most pronounced faults in conformation. They varied in face and leg markings from spotted to dark brown or black, and with the exception of the Cannock Chase, they were horned (Fig. 67).

**Method of Development.**—Writers are not agreed as to the way in which the Shropshire was made. Some maintain that it was formed by selecting and mating the best from the old native breeds of the two counties, while others say that it came into existence through the crossing of improved Southdowns, Leicesters, and Cotswolds on the native stock. Alfred Mansell, Secretary of the English Shropshire Sheep Breeders' Association, and a leading authority, states that there are no reliable records showing how improvement in size, in uniformity of character, and in value and weight of fleece was effected. He further says: "In the early days, some historians say that the Southdown ram was introduced for this purpose, whilst others equally well qualified to express an opinion assert that uniformity of character and perfection of form are the result of selection from home-bred sheep of the best type. Speaking from personal knowledge far back into the last century, I am in a position to assert that no one who has achieved any success as a breeder or exhibitor has deviated from a line of pure breeding for the past 60 or 70 years" (Fig. 68).

There seems to be a preponderance of evidence, however, that cross breeding was practised prior to and during the time the breed was coming into existence. Wilson, Plymley, Tanner, Melden,

Fig. 67.—Shropshire ram, Tanner Royal. First prize, two shear ram, English Royal and International Show in Chicago, 1913. Bred by Alfred Tanner, England. A great sire in the flock of Arthur Broughton and Sons, Albany, Wis.

Clarke, Spooner, and Wrightson are practically agreed on this point. John Algernon Clarke states that two of the most celebrated founders of the breed, Samuel Meire and George Adney, practised crossing, the former using both Southdown and Leicester blood, and the latter only the Southdown cross. W. C. Spooner in an article on cross-breeding, published in volume 20 of the Royal Agricultural Society Report, quoted the following as a part of a speech that M. J. Meire made before a farmers' club in Shropshire County: "It is not attempted to be denied that the Shropshire is a cross-bred sheep; the original breed was horned, and the first attempt at improvement was to get rid of these incumbrances, and there is little doubt that this was effected by the cross of the Southdown. This sheep was well adapted for the Downs, but for the enclosures of Shropshire something more docile was required, consequently recourse was had to the Leicester." It is altogether probable that most, if not all, of this crossing was done before there was a conscious movement toward the formation of a new breed, and it is certain that selection has been the great agency in the improvement of the breed. The leading breeders have been thorough students of blood lines, and in the main

Fig. 68.—Corston Illini. Third prize yearling Shropshire ram. International show. Bred by Thos. A. Buttar, Scotland; owned by University of Illinois. A smooth, low-set, thick type that has helped to develop popularity for the Shropshire.

they have practised closely restricted line breeding. Except from the standpoint of historical interest it little matters how the breed was developed because it is a notable fact that at the present time it breeds true to a uniform type (Fig. 69).

**Coöperation of Breeders.**—A comparatively large number of farmers, with a few leading, worked together to bring the Shropshire into prominence. As stated elsewhere, a certain Samuel Meire and a George Adney were two of the earlier and more prominent improvers. These two men did their most effective work in the early fifties of the nineteenth century, although, according to the "Farmers' Magazine," Adney's flock must have been founded as early as 1820. Other early improvers of note were Messrs. Henry Smith, J. and E. Crane, Green, Horton, Farmer, W. O. Foster, G. M. Kettel, H. J. Sheldon, Thomas Mansell, John Coxon, Thomas Harley, John Stubbs, E. Thornton, Sampson Byrd, Colonel Dyott, and Mrs. Annie Baker. Others coming into prominence a little later were Messrs. Henry Mathews, Pryce, W. Bowen, J. H. Bradburne, R. H. Masfen, Joseph Meire, Maddox, John Preece, John Stubbs, C. R. Keeling, William Grindle, J. B. Green, T. C. Whitmore, Edward Thornton, Lord Wenlock, and still others. This large group of breeders worked together for the perfection and advancement of the breed and that they succeeded is a well-known fact. One thing

Fig. 69.—Stud Shropshire rams in field condition. Property of Thomas Buttar, Coupar Angus, Scotland. These sheep, although not in pretty show-yard bloom, possess the characteristics Shropshire breeders desire in their breeding rams.

they did which displayed farseeing and intelligent coöperation was to petition the Council of the Royal Agricultural Society to appoint well-known judges to act for a term of years at the Royal Show for the purpose of fixing the true type and character of the Shropshire. The Council took heed of this petition and the decisions of the judges it appointed were studiously noted. With the awards in mind, breeders returned to their homes and carefully determined the good and bad points in their own sheep and the direction in which their efforts in breeding should be turned. No other group of breeders has done a more significant thing than this in its bearing on uniformity of type (Fig. 70).

**Recognition as a Breed.**—Shropshires were first exhibited at the Royal Show of England in 1845, but no class was made for them at that time. In 1853 they were placed in a special class for short-wooled sheep, not Southdowns, and they were given a class of their own in 1859, which was the first time that any of the short-wooled breeds broke up the classification, "Short-wooled sheep which are not Southdowns." Their rapid rise in prominence at the shows can

Fig. 70.—Shropshire ewe. Bred by T. S. Minton, England, and exhibited by J. C. Andrew, West Point, Indiana. Female champion of the breed at the International Live Stock Show, Chicago, 1916. The extension of white wool over the face and legs, the turn of the neck, smoothly set high on the shoulders, and the rounding line of the body are desirable.

be appreciated by a statement of the entries at the Royal Show in 1884. At Shrewsbury, the center of the home of the breed, 875 Shropshires from fifteen counties were on exhibition, while the total of all other breeds was 420. This exhibit further stimulated home breeding and created a strong foreign demand.

**Description.**—The Shropshire is the result of great skill and judgment on the part of breeders during the past sixty years and it is very different from the most typical specimens that appeared at the English shows between 1850 and 1870. Speaking of the show-yard celebrities of that period, Mansell says: "They were for the most part brown with speckled legs, fine in the bone and devoid of wool, with bare bellies, and too often sickle-hocked, and crooked spines were the rule rather than the exception. The head of the males lacked masculine strength and character, and carried little or no wool on the poll, and the sheep generally stood on much longer legs than the modern Shropshire. Little attention at this early date had been paid to the wool, which was generally of a soft open character and greatly lacking in that density, length of staple

**Fig. 71.—Fitted Shropshire ewes adorning the pastures of J. C. Andrew, West Point, Indiana.**

and fineness which is now one of the leading attributes of breed" (Fig. 71).

**The Present-Day Shropshire.**—*Form and Weight.*—The Shropshire is similar to the Southdown in build of body and length of legs, but considerably different in various other features. The neck is longer and more arched; the head is carried higher and is proportionately broader between the ears and eyes, slightly longer and stronger in face profile; the ears are attached a little lower down on the sides of the head and are not quite so nearly erect; the hair on nose, ears, and legs is a darker shade of brown, being called a deep, soft brown, and the wool is lo- ger, not as fine, and extends farther over the face and legs. Shropshires are larger than Southdowns, mature rams weighing from 200 to 250 pounds; ewes from 150 to 180 pounds.[1]

*Style.*—In style and show-yard finish the Shropshire is impressive and it leads the mutton breeds in drawing attention and admiration at American livestock exhibitions. With its head set proudly upon a gracefully turned neck, and with its smoothly turned symmetrical body, and its picturesque extension of downy, white wool over the face and legs, it possesses an air of grandeur rather than of smartness and nattiness which is characteristic of the Southdown (Fig. 72).

Fig. 72.—Eleven typical Shropshire ewes sired by "Senator Bibby," a famous stud ram in the flock of Geo. McKerrow & Sons, Pewaukee, Wisconsin.

*Wool.*—In twelve months Shropshire wool attains a length of from two and one-half to three inches and fleeces average between 8 and 10 pounds in weight. The wool is fairly fine and sufficiently dense to protect the animal well from unfavorable weather. No other mutton breed equals the Shropshire in extension of wool over the face and legs. With the most typical specimens all of the face except the nose or muzzle is covered with white wool and the legs are covered to the pasterns. Also the ears are often covered with

[1] Weight standards are hard to fix and at best only an estimate can be made. For the Shropshire and all other breeds discussed in this volume the weights given apply to sheep that are in fairly high condition, but not exceedingly fat.

wool. In most cases the leg covering is not complete, particularly on the forelegs, and frequently it is not clear white. White wool should extend to the knees and hocks, however, and on the hind legs it should extend on down from the hock to the pasterns, but between these points a slight admixture of dark wool is permissible. Dark wool also often appears on the head and face, the places of its most frequent occurrence being the horn holes and the regions just above the eyes. In show sheep such wool is objectionable, but if present to only a slight extent it is largely overlooked in flock specimens (Fig. 73).

Fig. 73.—Shropshire lambs bred by Henry Wardwell, Springfield Center, New York. Few animals are as winsome as four-month-old Shropshire lambs covered with baby fat and encased with downy white wool from nose to toes.

Breeders attempt to grow white wool on the head and legs of their sheep for two reasons: first, pure white wool on the extremities almost invariably indicates freedom from dark fibers in the body of the fleece; second, the sharp demarcation between white wool and deep brown hair has a much more pleasing effect than the merging of dark wool and brown hair. Dark wool in the body of the fleece detracts from its value because white wool admixed with dark fibers can not be dyed to a pure color other than black. For this reason any Shropshire having a noticeable amount of dark wool anywhere above the knees and hocks and back of a line drawn from ear to ear should be discarded as a breeding animal. Regarding the covering of head and legs with wool, it should be stated that it is seldom uniform in extent through all seasons of the year. Breeding ewes particularly are likely to begin shedding it a few weeks after they lamb and both sexes are likely to lose some of it during the hot summer months.

*Markings and Skin.*—Although a deep soft brown is the most typical color for the hair on the nose, ears, and legs, considerable variation exists and is permissible. Bluish or steel gray markings are not objected to by many American breeders, as they are regarded as indicative of robustness, easy feeding qualities, and pure white fleeces. Rusty brown or faded out brown, particularly when associated with very thin short hair on the nose and ears, are undesirable shades of color, and spotted markings, characteristic of crossbred or grade down sheep, are undersirable to such extent that they usually disqualify the animal.

The skin of the typical Shropshire is a bright pink or cherry red. No other group of breeders of dark-faced sheep has been so exacting

Fig. 74.—Shropshire ewe lambs, eight months old, bred by the University of Illinois.

with respect to the color of skin as the Shropshire men. In spite of this fact, however, bluish skins and pink skins with numerous bluish spots are not uncommon. Pink skins are thought to indicate easy feeding qualities and freedom from a tendency to grow dark wool (Fig. 74).

Horns or evidence of their presence are regarded as a disqualification. They never appear in females, but in males their presence or absence should always be determined by the examiner.

**Properties.**—The mutton of the Shropshire is of high quality, being fine grained, firm, and of desirable color both in lean and fat. The lambs when well finished and weighing about eighty pounds are of especially high quality and rank with the best as lamb mutton.

**Hardiness and Feeding Qualities.**—In ability to withstand hardship and disease the Shropshire is no hardier than most of the mutton breeds, but it is unusually well adapted to average conditions with respect to feed and care. It responds well to rich pastures, but it also does well where the grazing is of only average quality. The Shropshire thrives on forage crops and it takes kindly to the dry lot if soiling crops are available. Whether in the north or south, on lowlands, hills, mountains, or semi-arid plains, it grows into a pretty good Shropshire and satisfies the demand for a good mutton sheep. Although the lambs grow at a fairly rapid rate, they are not inclined to be as plump and firm at an early age as the Southdown, one reason being that so many of them are

FIG. 75.—Lambs by Shropshire ram in Fig. 150 and out of western ewes shown in Fig. 148. These lambs are the kind that command top prices at the market.

twins. At three months of age they average about fifty pounds in weight.

**Breeding Qualities.**—In prolificacy the Shropshire is unsurpassed by any other widely-distributed improved breed of sheep. A flock of one hundred breeding ewes will often average from one hundred and fifty to one hundred and seventy-five lambs, and even a larger percentage is not uncommon. Undoubtedly this marked prolificacy is due in no small degree to the attention given it by the early improvers of the breed. At birth the lambs weigh about eight pounds. As a rule the singles are considerably heavier, but the average birth weight is cut down materially by the great number of twins. The ewes suckle very well and the lambs are fairly strong at birth. In the selection of breeding ewes most American breeders need to emphasize the practice of retaining females that are able to produce strong lambs and grow them well. Unless this is done there is danger of marked prolificacy being a hindrance rather than a help to the breed. There was a time when Shropshire breeders would sacrifice too much, in such essentials as constitution and ability to make rapid growth, for the sake of extreme wool covering. Distinctive and picturesque as are Shropshires with woolly heads and legs, they do not conform to the "rent-paying" idea early conceived by improvers if they do not possess the power of growing strong,

Fig. 76.—A group of yearling Shropshire ewes, bred and owned by University of Illinois.

lusty, sappy lambs. It is better to have only a moderate wool covering than to be without this power, a fact which all Shropshire breeders should keep in mind.

Shropshire rams, because they impart their mutton qualities uniformly to their lambs, have been widely used in the United States and elsewhere in cross-breeding and grading up. Their offspring from either pure or grade Merino ewes develop into splendid market lambs (Fig. 75).

**Distribution.**—Because of inherent good qualities and efficient promotion, the Shropshire breed has been widely distributed. It is more nearly a cosmopolitan than any of the other mutton breeds; exportations have been made from its native home to all of the leading sheep countries and to many others of lesser importance. In the farm flocks of the United States and Canada there is more Shropshire blood than that of any other breed; it has also been widely distributed over the range regions of these countries. In England the members of the Shropshire Sheep Society have coöperated in making their breed prominent, chiefly by making large and attractive displays of their sheep at the leading shows. The volumes published yearly since the organization of the society contain much interesting material concerning the breed. The American Shropshire Society, organized in 1884, is the largest separate sheep society in the world. It had published thirty-two volumes containing 486,299 pedigrees up until the year 1922. Since that time the publication of these volumes has been suspended. At the close of 1936 more than 840,000 pedigrees of Shropshire sheep had been recorded by the society (Fig. 76).

## QUESTIONS

1. In what direction and about how far is the native home of the Shropshire from that of the Southdown?
2. Contrast the method of developing the Shropshire with that of developing the Southdown.
3. When were Shropshires first recognized as a distinct breed at the Royal Show of England?
4. Compare a typical Shropshire with a typical Southdown.
5. What properties of the Shropshire have had an influence on its distribution?
6. Discuss the prolificacy of the Shropshire.

## CHAPTER XII

# THE HAMPSHIRE

**History.**—*The Old Stock.*—The Hampshire breed originated on the rolling, chalky, light land of south central England in the county of Hampshire, the southern border of which touches the English Channel. Early in the nineteenth century the Southdown, as improved by Ellman, was extensively used by the farmers in the general region of Hampshire for crossing on the old Wiltshire and Berkshire Knot breeds. The old Wiltshires have been described as white-faced, large, imposing looking animals with long legs, high withers, sharp spines, big heads, Roman noses, and curling horns. Their wool was moderately fine and the fleeces from ewe flocks averaged from two to two and one-half pounds. Originally they were kept primarily for their wool and dung. They were well adapted to folding on the arable land and to travelling out several miles each day for their feed on the closely cropped downs. Before the introduction of Southdown blood, the Wilts farmers were increasing the size and improving the conformation of the Wiltshire to such extent that they were accused of breeding for beauty and not for utility. With the exception of dark faces and legs, the Berkshire Knots resembled the Wiltshires (Fig. 77).

In many cases pure Southdowns replaced the native sheep of both Wiltshire and Hampshire and crossing with Southdowns became so general that the native types were merged into the old Hampshire, which was a sort of modified Southdown but not sufficiently uniform in type to deserve the distinction of being called a breed. According to James Rawlence the last flock of the old Wiltshire horned breed disappeared about 1819. Probably the Southdown, with its superior quality and attractive character would have entirely replaced the old breeds had it not been that Wiltshire and Hampshire farmers awakened to the indispensable value of the hardiness, early maturity, and large size which the flocks carrying some of the blood of the old sheep possessed. The value of these characteristics became apparent not long after the down lands were enclosed, treated with artificial manures and planted to such crops as turnips, rape, vetches, clover, rye, and Italian rye grass.

Fig. 77.—Field Hampshire ewes. Property of H. C. Stephens, England. The uniformly dark color of face and legs is characteristic of the breed.

These crops, secured at considerable expense, had to be fed to sheep capable of handling large quantities of rank forage and of turning off big wether lambs rather than yearling or two-year-old wethers (Fig. 78).

**Work of Humphrey.**—By 1835 Hampshire sheep, according to Wrightson, had taken their general form, but there yet remained the task of reducing them to a uniform type with the power of transmitting their characters regularly to their offspring. In this work Mr. Humphrey, of Oak Ash, near Wantage, in Berkshire, led all others to the extent that he is generally credited with giving the breed its present character and position. He attained his success by carefully selecting those ewes which in his judgment were the best of the old Hampshire Downs, then known as West Country

Fig. 78.—Hampshire ewes in England cleaning up a growth of forage, which has been partially consumed by their lambs.

Downs, and mating them with Southdown rams from the flock of Jonas Webb. His method of procedure is well brought out in his historic communication to W. C. Spooner in 1859.

"About twenty-five years since, in forming my flock, I purchased the best Hampshire or West Country Down ewes I could meet with. Some of them I obtained from the late Mr. G. Budd, Mr. William Pain, Mr. Digwee, and other eminent breeders, giving 40 shillings when ordinary ewes were making 33 shillings, and using the best rams I could get of the same kind until the Oxford Show of the Royal Agricultural Society. On examining the different breeds exhibited there, I found the Cotswolds were beautiful in form and of great size, and, on making inquiries as to how they were brought to such perfection, I was informed that a Leicester ram was coupled to some of the largest Cotswold ewes and the most robust of the produce was selected for use. The thought then struck me that my best plan would be to obtain a first-rate Sussex Down Southdown sheep to put to my larger Hampshire Down ewes, both being the Short-woolled breed. . . . With this object I wrote to Mr. Jonas Webb to send me one of his best sheep, and he sent me a shearling of his favorite sheep Babraham. I went down the next two years and selected for myself, but the stock did not suit my taste so well as the one he sent me, and I did not use them. I then commissioned him to send me the sheep which obtained the first prize at Liverpool, and from these two sheep, the first and last, by mark-

FIG. 79.—Twenty-two thousand Hampshires in pens made with hurdles, Salisbury Fair, England.

ing the lambs of each tribe as they fell, then coupling them together at the third and fourth generation, my present flock was made" (Fig. 79).

Some time after Mr. Humphrey began his work he drafted twenty-five ewes from a purchase of one hundred, made in conjunction with his neighbor, Mr. Rawlence. This was the only time he introduced outside blood through females. Before using any of his rams extensively he tested them on a selected few of his ewes and if they did not breed to suit him, they were sent to the butcher. His greatest difficulty was the loss of size which was overcome by regularly disposing of his smallest ewes. In fact, his skill as a breeder was due in large part to his diligence in weeding out animals that did not promise to contribute to the end he had in view. After his death, in 1868, his flock was sold at auction. Mr. James Rawlence, of Bulbridge, who from time to time purchased stock of Mr. Humphrey, proved to be a worthy successor as a leader in still further improving and promoting the breed. In founding his flock his method was just the opposite of that of Mr. Humphrey; he selected Southdowns for his female stock and mated them with Hampshire rams (Fig. 80).

Fig. 80.—A prominent prizewinning Hampshire ram lamb, weighing 225 pounds before one year of age. Bred by Mt. Haggin Land and Livestock Co., Montana. Massiveness of body, heavy bone, thoroughly masculine features in the head, and a strong neck raising rather high where it joins the head are desirable characteristics of a Hampshire breeding ram.

**Cause of Early Maturity.**—Among Hampshire breeders most of the rams in flock service are lambs, and the belief that the early maturity of the breed has been brought about by the consistent continuance of this practice is prevalent. That it has been a contributing cause is altogether likely, but E. P. Squarey and J. E. Rawlence, in their history of the Hampshire Down as it appears in the first volume of the English Society, maintain that early maturity was characteristic of the old Wiltshire (Fig. 81).

**Description.**—*Form and Weight.*—The Modern Hampshire is a bold, massive, thick-fleshed, hornless sheep with a long, deep, symmetrical body, heavy bone, and striking head features. Mature rams in breeding condition weigh from 250 to 300 pounds; ewes from 180 to 225 pounds. The head is large and the face profile is slightly Roman in females and distinctly so in males; the ears are long, fairly wide and thick and attached so as to fall slightly outward and forward when the animal is at attention. The neck,

Fig. 81.—Hampshire ewe. The ears are typical of the breed—rather long, set almost horizontal to the head with the inside turned frontward.

although rather long, is thick and muscular and set to the shoulders so as to permit the sheep to carry the head above the body rather than horizontal with it. The legs, being of medium length are properly proportioned to the large body that they support.

A fault rather common in the Hampshire about twenty years ago was a falling away behind the shoulders, but this defect has been almost eliminated.

*Wool.*—Hampshires, when properly cared for, yield approximately eight pounds of unwashed wool, which is about two and one-half inches long, fairly dense, and a trifle coarser than Shropshire wool. To be typical the fleece must be all white, but an admixture of dark fibers is not uncommon. Pure white wool extends over the head, cheeks, and forehead to a line a little below the eyes. Of late years breeders, especially those in the United States, have been inclined to favor an extension of wool over the face, and lambs with almost as much face covering as Shropshires have appeared at shows. On the legs white wool should extend to the knees and hocks. Most show specimens, however, have the wool carried down almost, or

Fig. 82.—Hampshire ewes in show bloom: Two to left are yearlings; two to right are lambs and are almost as large as the yearlings.

quite, to the pasterns. Some American breeders have observed that the woolly-faced ewes are not as heavy milkers and as a result do not grow their lambs as well as the open-faced ewes (Fig. 82).

*Markings and Skin.*—The color of face, ears, and legs, is a very rich, dark brown approaching black, which makes a sharp but pleasing contrast with the white wool on the head, forehead, cheeks and legs. Breeders are particular about color. A dark tinge in the head wool is sure to give an animal a low rating in a high-class show and a bar of light brown or gray hair across the face, just below the wool cap, is unfavorably regarded in rams.

The skin of the typical Hampshire is pink, but there is a strong tendency toward very dark or bluish skins. Horns or evidence of their presence amount to a disqualification (Fig. 83).

**Properties.**—*Rate of Growth.*—Hampshires are famous for their size, rapid rate of growth, early maturity, and ability to thrive on forage crops between hurdles. When liberally fed they are without an equal in rapid rate of growth. In England, where they are kept between hurdles a great part of the time, the lambs often make more than a pound of gain per day through periods of one hundred days or more. They attain what seem like preposterous weights before they are a year old. Eight- and nine-month lambs can be made to weigh two hundred pounds and even more. As a pure-bred

Fig. 83.—Present-day Hampshires are fast growing but are lower set and more compactly built than the Hampshires of 25 years ago. They also have more quality.

sheep they undoubtedly belong in a system where liberal feeding is practiced; otherwise their most valuable properties cannot function. The ewes winter well on roughage.

In quality of mutton the Hampshire shows its Southdown inheritance; the lean meat is fine-grained and firm and as large mutton it has no superior (Fig. 84).

**Breeding Qualities.**—Hampshire ewes are prolific, strong in maternal instinct, and good milkers. The lambing record of thirty-seven English flocks was kept by the English Society in 1903; 15,482 ewes raised 18,462 lambs or 119.17 per cent. Numbers considered, this speaks well for the prolificacy and hardiness of the breed. At birth the lambs are large, weighing around ten pounds, and they begin at once to grow rapidly. As pure breds they do not come to market finish at as light weight as Southdowns and Shropshires, it being necessary for them to grow to eighty pounds

FIG. 84.—Hampshire ewes and lambs on western range.

or more before they are sufficiently firm and ripe to be a first-class lamb product. This is not the case with the cross breds, however, and both in England and America the Hampshire ram is in demand

FIG. 85.—Lambs sired by the Hampshire ram in Fig. 153 and out of Western ewes shown in Fig. 148. Lambs of this cross grow rapidly and are very popular on various Western ranges.

for crossing purposes. In Idaho, Washington, and Montana, Hampshires crossed on range ewes produce ideal market lambs. On the mountain range they grow big, fat, and ripe and ready for slaughter without ever having received grain (Fig. 85).

**Distribution.**—The wide distribution of the Hampshire indicates its importance. In England it is to be found in many different counties, but it is kept in greatest numbers in the region of its native home. At the great summer and autumn fairs or sale days in Hampshire and Wiltshire, the numbers penned at a single fair run from 20,000 to 100,000 head. Exportations have been made from England to all of the important sheep countries. In the United States they are now well distributed although they are found in greatest numbers in the range areas where the rams are used in many flocks for market lamb production.

Hampshire Sheep Breeders' Associations were organized in both England and America in 1889. The English Association published the "Hampshire Down Flock Book," and the American Association, the "Flock Record of Hampshire Down Sheep," in which approximately 360,000 Hampshires have been recorded up to the end of 1936.

## QUESTIONS

1. Secure a map of England and locate the native home of the Hampshire. In what direction is it from the native home of the Southdown?
2. What has the nature of the soil in the native home of the Hampshire to do with the way sheep are handled there?
3. Who was the greatest improver of the Hampshire? Tell something of his methods.
4. Give the most marked difference between Shropshires and Hampshires.
5. Would you feed Hampshires and Southdowns together?
6. Describe the markings of the Hampshire; the bone; the head.
7. What sections of the United States do you think best adapted to Hampshires?

## CHAPTER XIII

# THE OXFORD DOWN

**History.**—The Oxford Down or Oxford, as it is commonly called, originated in the county of Oxford in central England. Oxford County is the meeting ground of the strongholds of the Hampshire just south, and of the Cotswold immediately west. The Oxford sheep was made by crossing these two breeds. Mr. Samuel Druce, of Ensham and several other Oxfordshire farmers began to breed Cotswold rams to Hampshire ewes in 1833 or thereabouts. Druce and William Gillet also used Southdowns to some extent in the early days before the Hampshires were settled to a uniform type by Humphrey, when Hampshire breeders, themselves, occasionally used Southdown rams. Cross-breeding probably continued for a number of years. Wrightson quotes C. S. Read as saying: "The (flock) owner formerly divided his flock into three parts, putting the half-bred ram to the ewes that were about right, a Cotswold to the small ones, and a Down (Hampshire Down) to the coarser sheep." Drawing upon the words of someone else, Wrightson further says: "Mr. Druce early found that good qualities can better be secured by employing the cross-bred animals on both sides than by using the first cross." Gradually the breed type evolved from a more or less heterogeneous group of cross-breds. After 1854 pure-breds from either of the parent breeds or from any other breeds were no longer employed (Fig. 86).

Beginning in 1840, J. T. Twynam did much to draw the attention of the public to the new breed. It was given a place as a distinct breed by the Royal Agricultural Society at its show at Battersea in 1862.

**Description.**—*Form and Size.*—The Oxford is a large, somewhat upstanding sheep with strong bone and a high, graceful carriage of head which it doubtless inherits from the Cotswold. The top of the body is very wide and in contour approaches the rectangular, rather than the oval characteristic of the Southdown and the Shropshire. The head and ears are a trifle smaller and the face profile less inclined to be Roman than in the Hampshire. Mature rams in breeding condition weigh from 275 to 300 pounds and ewes 200 pounds or more (Fig. 87).

FIG. 86

FIG. 87

FIG. 86.—Oxford-Down ram. A noted prize winner owned by Iowa State College, Ames, Iowa. The Oxford-Down has a longer fleece than other Down breeds. (Upper figure.)

FIG. 87.—Oxford-Down ewe, a prominent winner. Property of George McKerrow and Sons, Pewaukee, Wisconsin.

*Wool.*—There is a little more of the face covered with wool in the Oxford than in the Hampshire; the growth on the forehead is long enough to form a distinct top knot which is intensified in show specimens by leaving the forehead wool long at shearing time. In twelve months Oxford wool grows to a length of from three to four inches; it is strong and lustrous and ranks with Hampshire wool in fineness. Unwashed fleeces average from ten to twelve pounds in weight. As a producer of wool no other Down breed equals the Oxford.

*Markings and Skin.*—The color of the face, ears and legs in the Oxford is a lighter brown than in the Hampshire. In fact the typical Oxford brown has no suggestion of black about it, as there is in the case of the Hampshire and Shropshire. Breeders allow

Fig. 88.—A group of four Oxford lambs, prize winners at many shows including the 1933 International. Owned by W. Bartholomay, Jr., Marellbar Farm, Libertyville, Illinois.

considerable variation in color markings, however, and shades ranging from steel gray to dark brown pass as being typical. Oxford breeders prefer sheep with bright pink skins to those with spotted or bluish skins. Dark wool either on the head or body is objectionable. The breed is hornless; hence, any evidence of horns in rams is undesirable (Fig. 88).

**Properties.**—Great size, outstanding weight and quality of wool for a Down breed, prolificacy and deep milking properties are attributes which Oxford breeders claim for their sheep. In addition it may be said that although the mutton is hardly as fine in quality as that of the Southdown, it is good enough markedly to improve the carcass when the Oxford ram is used in cross-breeding and up-grading.

Oxfords are fully as hardy as any of the dark-faced breeds and the ewes continue to breed until they reach a ripe old age. Although they are large sheep and quite capable of handling heavy forage crops, they are also able to do fairly well on the feed furnished to the average farm flock in the eastern and central parts of the United States. This ability, together with their superior shearing qualities, makes them desirable as a farmer's sheep (Fig. 89).

On account of their heavy yield of milk and strongly developed maternal instinct, Oxford ewes are splendid mothers. Twins are frequent and the lambs are large, weighing about ten pounds at birth. Singles frequently weigh more. The lambs grow rapidly but they do not attain weight quite so rapidly as the Hampshire.

Fig. 89.—Lambs bred by the University of Illinois; sired by Oxford-Down ram in Fig. 152 and out of Western ewes in Fig. 148. These lambs, born in March, made rapid growth and were pronounced prime for the market before July 1st.

Both in the United States and Germany, Oxford rams have proved satisfactory for crossing on Merino and Merino-grade ewes. Especially is this true when the female offspring are to be retained as breeding stock for, in addition to the mutton qualities imparted, a beautiful fleece of desirable weight is obtained.

**Distribution.**—At present the breed is well distributed over Great Britain, the United States, and Canada, and flocks are to be found in nearly or quite all of the leading sheep countries. The American Oxford Down Sheep Record Association was organized in 1884 and the Oxford Down Sheep Breeders' Association of England in 1888. Both associations issue a pedigree volume.

## QUESTIONS

1. Compare the histories of the Southdown, Shropshire, Hampshire and Oxford and determine in which the origin of the breed seems to be most clearly known.
2. In what respects are Oxfords most different from Hampshires?
3. Do Oxfords resemble Cotswolds?
4. Can you think of any reason why it would be better to make a breed by crossing the Hampshire and the Cotswold than by crossing the Hampshire and the Romney Marsh?
5. How far is the native home of the Southdown from that of the Oxford?
6. Aside from the first cross between Cotswolds and Hampshires how was breeding conducted to develop the Oxford?

# CHAPTER XIV

## THE SUFFOLK

**History.**—The native home of the Suffolk is northeast of London, England, in the counties of Suffolk, Cambridge, and Essex. In this region there existed at the beginning of the nineteenth century and before, a horned breed known as the Norfolk. It was a hardy, active sheep and produced mutton of superior grain and flavor. Between 1800 and 1850 the Southdown was extensively used in the old Norfolk flocks for the purpose of improving form and fattening properties. By the middle of the century the resulting Southdown-Norfolks were widely known as "Black-faces," and in 1859, at the annual meeting of the Suffolk Agricultural Association, they were given their present name, "Suffolk" (Figs. 90 and 91).

**Description.**—Suffolks are little if any larger than Shropshires, mature rams weighing about 250 pounds and ewes 165 pounds. They are hornless and the head, ears, and legs are black and free from wool covering. Their ears are long and their faces are long and distinctly Roman. In conformation they tend to ranginess, but when well-finished they are plump and well-developed in the parts most valuable for meat. The wool is short and similar to the Hampshire in quality. As one would surmise from the fact that it does not extend over the head and frequently not as far as the knees and hocks, it often fails to cover the under side of the body. Although reports of nine pounds per fleece have been made, it is doubtful whether pure-bred flocks will average more than seven (Fig. 92).

**Properties.**—The Suffolk is very highly regarded for the quality of its mutton. It has no superior for a large proportion of lean and the grain is fine and firm. It has more than held its own with other breeds at the great Smithfield fat stock show in London in both the live and carcass classes.

Returns made annually since 1887 by owners of registered Suffolk flocks show that on the average 100 ewes will raise 133 lambs. The lambs grow rapidly if well grazed and are ready for the English butcher when six months old. At eight to ten months of age they often yield carcasses of eighty to ninety pounds weight.

Fig. 90

Fig. 91

Fig. 90.—Suffolk ram. There is no wool on the head of the Suffolk nor on the legs below the hocks and knees. The hair on face and legs is more nearly black than in any other Down breed.

Fig. 91.—Suffolk ewe. The muzzle showing an "undershot" jaw is not typical.

Hardiness is one of the strong claims made for the Suffolk. They are good at travelling and hence do well where their feed must be gathered from large areas. It is this ability which seems to cause them to be favorably regarded at present in South Africa.

Suffolk rams are now used in some western range flocks and a number of breeders are active in their promotion. Suffolk lambs grow rapidly and it is claimed by some that they possess a high proportion of lean meat.

**Distribution.**—Flocks exist in a number of counties in England, but its native haven is still its chief stronghold. Modest importations have been made to various sheep countries. Suffolks are increasing in North America but are not so numerous as some other medium-wooled breeds. The Suffolk Sheep Society of England was organized in 1886. Its volumes, published annually, contain valuable data concerning the breed. An association was formed in the United States at Des Moines, Iowa, but up to 1935 it had published no flock book.

Fig. 92.—Suffolk ewes, property of Wm. T. Paul, England. Note the uniformity in markings and the thick, firm legs of mutton.

## QUESTIONS

1. Where was the Suffolk developed?
2. Compare the Suffolk with the Hampshire.
3. How does the Suffolk rank in the quality of its mutton and wool?

## CHAPTER XV

# THE DORSET HORN

**History.**—*The Old Stock.*—The native home of the Dorset Horn is in the counties of Dorset and Somerset in south central England. In soil and climate these counties are similar to those adjoining them on the east in which the Hampshires were developed. No accounts are given to show exactly how the Dorset Horn was made, but as nearly as is known it was developed entirely by selection from a native stock bearing a close resemblance to, but not identical with the old Wiltshire that was so prominent as one of the progenitors of the Hampshire. Descriptions of this parent stock refer to its horns, fine wool, and also to the color of the lips and nostrils which in the main were black but occasionally were flesh-colored. The flesh color of nostrils and lips characteristic of the modern Dorset Horn seems to have prevailed first in Somerset, where the sheep were somewhat larger and more rangy than those in Dorset.

**Development of the Modern Dorset Horn.**—During the first half of the nineteenth century Leicesters, Southdowns, Merinos, and still other breeds were crossed on the old Dorset Horn stock. For a time the Southdown became very popular and it seemed as though the native sheep in their purity of breeding would disappear. About 1850, however, the tide began to turn in their favor, evidently because a few breeders in West Dorset had been steadily improving them by selecting toward the type desired without losing any of the fecundity and hardiness characteristic of the old stock. By thickening the shoulders the form was greatly improved and through selecting for flesh-colored nostrils and lips and for horns that curled around by the side of the face without rising above the head or inclining backwards, a uniform, distinctive and pleasing type was secured.

Richard Seymour, living in southwest Dorset, near Bridport, a little city close by the coast of the English Channel, was the first notable improver of Dorset Horns. Between 1830 and 1840 he increased size and improved symmetry to such an extent that his flock was the best to be found. A group of twenty or more followed his example and made further improvement along the same lines, and it was largely through the sale of stock from their flocks that the improved type became prevalent in the county (Fig. 93).

**Description.**—*Form and Size.*—The Dorset Horn is really a Down breed, but strikingly unlike the other prominent Down breeds because of its horns and its all-white color. The body is long, the bone and head features are strong and the whole make-up is more suggestive of ruggedness than of quality. The face is inclined to be long, and the muzzle is thicker than in the other

FIG. 93.—The Dorset Horn ram has massive horns which give his head a most masculine appearance.

Down breeds. High, open shoulders with a noticeable drop behind them and a rump deficient on either side of the spine are not of infrequent occurrence. Before the day of their improvement, Stevenson said of the Dorset that the ewes were much more complete in form than the wethers or rams, an observation which applies to a certain extent to the modern type. Dorset Horns are large, mature rams weighing approximately 275 pounds and ewes 180 to 200 pounds.

*Wool.*—A tuft of compact wool covers the forehead, and there is wool on the cheeks, but none on the face. On the legs the wool extends to the knees and hocks, and sometimes from the hocks to the pasterns. The growth on the belly is short and thin, and bare bellies are not uncommon. In twelve months the wool attains about two and one-half inches in length. It is of good commercial quality, but since flocks do not average as much if any more than seven pounds per head, the fleeces weigh less than farmers think a large sheep ought to shear (Fig. 94).

**Fig. 94.—The Dorset Horn ewe has horns, but they are much more refined than those of the ram.**

*Markings and Skin.*—The face and legs of the Dorset Horn are white. The lips and nostrils are free from dark pigment, and the same is true of the hoofs. In rams the horns come from the crown of the head on a straight line from each other and well apart. They are long and thick, and curve backward and around spirally, "coming as close to the face as may be without cutting," while those of ewes are much smaller and curve slightly backward, then outward, down and in, the tips being about level with the eyes. Males, unsexed when they are only a few weeks old, develop horns of about the same size and shape as those of ewes.

In presenting a standard of excellence for the breed, the Dorset Horn Sheep Breeders' Association, of England, names the following as being objectionable: "Spots on the skin, fleece, or markings on the horns, coarse hair on legs, tendency of horns to grow back" (Fig. 95).

Fig. 95.—Dorset Horn flock of James Flower (deceased), England.

**Properties.**—The Dorset Horn does not rank as high in quality of mutton as the dark-faced Down breeds, but the lambs are favor-

Fig. 96.—Dorset Horn lambs grow rapidly.

ably regarded as a meat product, and they grow so rapidly that they early develop to marketable weight.

Dorset Horns are considered hardy, and on either pasture or forage crops they are good feeders. They have abundant capacity for feed, and in order to look well, must be fed rather liberally. Especially is this true when the ewes have lambs at side, because they yield too much milk for their food requirements to be ignored.

Modern Dorset Horns are famous for their habit of breeding earlier than any other of the improved mutton breeds. They have a comparatively large number of twins and it is possible to get two crops of lambs from them within twelve months. This habit was peculiar to the old stock and was made use of during the first part of the nineteenth century in the production of what was then known as house lambs. Being disposed to breed early and to grow their lambs rapidly, the ewes are unsurpassed as producers of lambs for special seasons. When they are bred to Southdown rams the lambs are the very best to be had for marketing when young to an exclusive out-of-season trade. The Dorset Horn-Delaine Merino Cross is said to produce a capital farm flock ewe, the fleece being heavier than that of pure Dorset Horn and the breeding and milking powers almost as well developed (Fig. 96).

**Distribution.**—Chiefly on account of their light shearing qualities, Dorset Horns have not become widely distributed. In England there are not many flocks outside the native home of the breed Of the other countries, the United States and Canada probably lead in the number of flocks. Probably seventy-five per cent of the flocks of Dorset Horn sheep are in the northeastern part of the United States. The Dorset Horn Sheep Breeders' Association, of England, published its first flock book in 1892. In 1891 the Dorset Horn Sheep Breeders of America organized, but a disagreement among the members in 1897 resulted in a second and presumably rival organization known as the Continental Dorset Club.

## QUESTIONS

1. Where was the Dorset Horn developed?
2. Is it a lowland, upland, or mountain breed?
3. State the desirable and undesirable characteristics of the old stock from which the Dorset Horn came.
4. Under what conditions would you consider the Dorset Horn one of the best breeds to raise?
5. Would you consider Dorset Horns better able to defend themselves against dogs than Southdowns?
6. Which would grade higher on the open market, Dorset Horns or Southdowns?

## CHAPTER XVI

# THE CHEVIOT

**History.**—The Cheviot is a native of the Cheviot Hills, which form about 30 miles of the border country between England and Scotland. These hills rise gradually from an elevation of 1600 feet in the west to a little over 2600 feet in the east. Their flanks are scored by deep narrow glens that run in every direction and on the numerous smooth declivities, short nutritious grass furnishes pasture upon which sheep feed and thrive in spite of storms and rough weather (Fig. 97).

No authentic account can be given of the origin of the Cheviot. Like all of the native sheep from which the modern English breeds have descended, they come from a stock that was ungainly and deficient in mutton form. Wrightson says: "The monks of the Middle Ages bred Cheviots around the monasteries, and to the churchmen of Teviotdale are we indebted for the first improvement of the breed." Crosses were made with the Leicester, Black-faced Highland, and probably the Merino, but the most significant improvement was brought about through careful selection after 1854, in which year John Robson, a great improver of Cheviots, made use of rams from Lincolnshire.

After 1800 Cheviots gained rapidly in popularity in the border country and they practically drove their rivals, the Black-Faced Highlands from all the farms in southern Scotland except in the more mountainous districts of Ayrshire and Lanarckshire. After 1860, however, the tide turned back to the Black Faces in those districts where conditions were a little too rigorous, even for the Cheviots (Fig. 98).

**Description.**—The Cheviot possesses the characteristics requisite of a hill or mountain breed. Its high shoulders necessary in hill climbing, trim build, alert carriage, and active movements indicate that it is well adapted to its rugged native home. The face profile is Roman; the eyes are very bright and prominent and the ears are short and erect. In the typical Cheviot the face and head bones are rather prominent and very suggestive of quality. The legs are

Fig. 97.

Fig 98.

Fig. 97.—Cheviot ram. The clean-cut head, pure white face and short alert ears are typical.

Fig. 98.—Cheviot ewe. A consistent prizewinner. Owned by Alvin Helms, Belleville Ill.

neat and trim, and free from wool below the knees and hocks. Mature rams in breeding condition weigh about 175 pounds and ewes from 135 to 150 pounds.

*Wool.*—The Cheviot has no wool on the head and ears nor on the legs below the hocks and knees, but the body is well covered. The wool is pure white, about four inches long when of twelve months' growth and contains very little yolk. Fleeces weigh from six to eight pounds.

Fig. 99.—Cheviots on the way to market.

*Markings and Skin.*—The head and the ears are covered with short, hard white hair free from a reddish tinge. Distinct black spots often appear on the ears and occasionally on the face, and the nostrils, lips, and hoofs are black. The skin is a deep rich pink. The ewes are hornless, but not all of the rams (Fig. 99).

**Properties.**—Hardiness is the leading property of Cheviots. Although a hill breed, they do surprisingly well on the level lands of the Corn Belt in the United States. They are distinctly a grazing breed, and they fatten quicker on the grass than in the feed lot. In regions where the grass is more luxuriant than in their native home they are inclined to become larger and coarser than the border country Cheviot.

Either Cheviot mutton or lamb is of excellent quality, being firm and free from an undue amount of fat. Because of their lighter weight at maturity, Cheviots have an advantage as mutton in the American markets (Fig. 100).

Cheviot ewes are prolific and, although somewhat nervous, are excellent mothers. The lambs are so vigorous that they seldom chill and die when born out of doors in stormy weather. They grow at a fairly rapid rate, but they do not attain weight and finish as fast as some of the Down breeds.

In England and Scotland, aged Cheviot ewes are taken from the hills to the lowlands, where feed is more abundant and here they are bred to Border Leicester or Lincoln rams. The resulting half-breds are very popular, both as a lamb-mutton product and also as a breeding ewe to be bred to rams of the same breed as the sire; or half-bred ewes may be bred to half-bred rams. The half-bred is appreciated to such extent that a class is made for it at the annual show of the Highland Agricultural Society of Scotland. Oxford rams are also favorably regarded for crossing on Cheviot ewes brought out of the hills to the lowland country.

Fig. 100.—Cheviot lamb bred by the University of Illinois. The alert pose is typical.

Cheviots have not been used extensively for cross-breeding in America, although some use has been made of them on the western range both in the United States and Canada. One serious drawback to putting them on the open range is their disinclination to stay in a comparatively compact band while feeding.

**Distribution.**—Few Cheviots are to be found outside of England, Scotland, and North America. In the border country there are many large flocks. In North America there is a sprinkling of flocks in Quebec and Ontario, Canada, and in the east and middle western states. The Cheviot Society of Great Britain was organized in 1891 and the American Cheviot Sheep Society in 1900.

The latter is an amalgamation of the American Cheviot Sheep Breeders' Association, organized in 1891, and the National Cheviot Society, organized 1894.

## QUESTIONS

1. How far is the native home of the Southdown from that of the Cheviot?
2. What breed lives higher up in the Scotch Mountains than the Cheviot? What breed in the valleys below the home of the Cheviot?
3. How is the Cheviot different in conformation from the other mutton breeds studied thus far?
4. Contrast the Dorset Horn and the Cheviot in markings and skin.
5. How does the Cheviot rank in hardiness?

## CHAPTER XVII

# THE LEICESTER

**Two Types of Leicester.**—There are two types of Leicester, the English or Improved Leicester and the Border Leicester. In England, Scotland, and New Zealand, the Border Leicester is regarded as a breed distinct from the English Leicester, but in the United States and Canada no such distinction has been made. In fact, American breeders have mingled the two types, and in so doing some breeders think a better sheep has been secured than either the English or Border Leicester (Fig. 101).

**The English Leicester.—History.**—About 1760, Robert Bakewell, who lived in central England near Loughborough in the county of Leicestershire, began improving the old Leicester sheep. They were large, coarse, ill-formed, slow maturing animals with long coarse wool and flesh of poor quality. Nothing is known concerning their origin, but probably they were gradually evolved into a type considered suitable for a rather fertile country. By the middle of the eighteenth century conditions surrounding agriculture had changed to such extent that the old sheep were not sufficiently profitable. No one was more fully aware of their faults than Bakewell, and hence his objects in improvement were well-defined and definite. He wanted earlier maturity, more propensity to fatten, more carcass in proportion to the live weight, and better quality of flesh. These objects necessarily involved improvement in body conformation and general quality. In addition, Bakewell linked utility of form with beauty of form, and unhesitatingly sought for a more beautiful sheep than the old type.

**Bakewell's Method.**—For a man of his time and occupation, Bakewell travelled extensively in search of specimens which he believed would breed toward the type of sheep he wished to secure. Just how far away he went for some of the animals he used is not definitely known, but very likely most of his selections were made in his home community and in nearby counties. He was a keen observer of animals and skillful in mating them so as to make progress toward the type he desired. So far as is known he was the first animal breeder to make deliberate use of in-and-in breeding. Instead of selling rams he let them for a season. This gave him an opportunity to call in and use those whose progeny favorably impressed him. In his hands the old Leicester sheep was changed to a broad-backed, thick-fleshed, easy-feeding, early-maturing breed with much less waste in dressing and more quality in their mutton. But in getting these things it is said that he lost some of the con-

Fig. 101.—English Leicester ram. First prize R.A.S.E., 1904, bred by E. F. Jordon, England. The English Leicester has a small tuft of wool on the forehead. The long wool lies in ringlets or "pirls." (From "Farm Livestock in Great Britain," by Wallace).

stitution, prolificacy, milking qualities, and heavy shearing qualities characteristic of the old sort.

Because of his achievements in improving sheep, Long Horn cattle, and other stock, Bakewell became a noted person, and visitors from various parts of England and Continental Europe came to his place to see his flocks and herds. He was genial and charming as a host, but evidently he was not fond of telling how he got his results, for little is known of the various steps taken in changing the old sheep into the New Leicester breed. What he accomplished, however, was plainly evident and enough of the principles and methods he followed became known to have a "beneficial effect upon all the different breeds of domestic animals."

**Description.**—The English Leicester is a white-faced breed with a very wide, deep, rectangular-like body and a short, thick neck which does not carry the head much above the shoulders. The general form of the face is wedge-shaped; the nose is slightly narrow and Roman; the ears, which extend about straight out from the head, are well-proportioned and in size harmonize with the size of the

FIG. 102.—Border Leicester ram. The Border Leicester has no wool on the head, and depth of body in proportion to its length and width is not as great as in the English Leicester.

head. Mature rams in breeding condition weigh from 225 to 250 pounds; ewes from 175 to 200 pounds.

*The wool* of the English Leicester forms a tuft on the forehead and extends below to the knees and hocks. It terminates in "short twisted curles" which give a striking and pleasing external appearance to the fleece.

*Markings and Skin.*—With the exception of an occasional black speck, the face, ears, and legs are covered with short, bluish-white hair, but the hoofs and the bare skin on the nose are black. The body skin is pink or cherry in color. Both sexes are hornless (Fig. 102).

**The Border Leicester.—History.**—The Border Leicester was developed by the Cully brothers, who lived near Wooler, in the eastern part of the border country between England and Scotland. In their community there was a popular long-wooled breed known as the Teeswater, from which they selected ewes and mated them with Bakewell rams. They continued to use Leicester rams until they established a flock of Leicesters of a type which has become known as the Border Leicester.

**Description.**—According to Wrightson, the Border Leicester is "larger and longer than the English Leicester, and the belly is not quite so full in outline, being carried rather the more lightly" and adding to the appearance of legginess. But the most noticeable differences between the two are to be seen in the head, which in the Border Leicester is free from wool, clear-white, bold and carried high. The nose is aquiline, the muzzle large, the nostrils wide, and the ears erect. As a whole the Border Leicester is of bolder and more stylish appearance than the English Leicester.

**Properties of Leicesters.**—None but capable, painstaking sheepmen should attempt to keep Leicesters, for they are not adapted to shifting for themselves over rough ground without an abundance of feed and without protection from the rougher elements of the weather. They are lacking in fecundity, although under good care one hundred per cent lamb crops can be raised and the lambs grow rapidly.

Mutton from pure-bred Leicesters tends to be coarse, lacking in flavor and too fat. It is best when procured from lambs six to eight months old, for then the fat is not so excessive nor the joints or cuts so large.

For the purpose of producing fat lambs Leicesters cross well with Merinos. The lambs grow much faster and develop more external fat than the pure Merino. This cross was first tried in France and from it was developed the Dishley Merino, a hardy sheep with desirable mutton properties. This same cross has since been frequently made in North America, South America, Australia, and New Zealand for the purpose of producing lambs for market. In some regions Leicesters are crossed with the Down mutton breeds, the result being growthy, easy-feeding lambs, good enough in quality of flesh to give satisfaction as a mutton product.

In North England and South Scotland the Border Leicester-Cheviot cross is favorably regarded for producing a hardy and prolific ewe flock for poorer soils. These sheep are so much in favor that classes are provided for them at the annual Highland Show in Scotland. Either half-blood or pure Leicester rams mated with the ewes produce lambs that are very popular on the British markets (Fig. 103).

**Distribution.**—Leicester sheep have been sent to all of the im-

Fig. 103.—Border Leicester ewe. The Border Leicester carries its head higher than does the English Leicester.

portant sheep countries. At the beginning of the nineteenth century they were widely distributed in England, but breeders found it better to modify the local breeds rather than to maintain Leicesters. In many instances they did not take kindly to conditions and it was found that their mutton was lacking quality.

At the present time pure-bred flocks are not numerous in any country. In North America they are perhaps more prominent in Ontario, Canada, than elsewhere.

In Bakewell's time the Dishley Society was organized for the purpose of assisting in establishing the new Leicester breed. It adopted some almost iron-clad rules and was very influential for many years. At the present time there is a Leicester Sheep Breeders' Society in England and the American Leicester Sheep Breeders' Association was established in 1888.

## QUESTIONS

1. When did Bakewell live?
2. In what ways did Bakewell improve the old Leicester? What did he lose in getting this improvement?
3. What is known of Bakewell's methods?
4. Compare the English Leicester with the Border Leicester.
5. Compare the making of the Southdown with the making of the Leicester.
6. Compare the mutton of the Leicester with that of the Suffolk.

## CHAPTER XVIII

# THE COTSWOLD

**History.**—The native home of the Cotswold is in the Cotswold Hills of Gloucester, where the land, though not fertile, is rich in lime and grows a short nutritious grass.

As nearly as can be determined the Cotswold Hills formed one of the first seats of sheep husbandry in England, and it seems that long-wooled sheep have been kept there since the occupation of the country by the Romans. According to tradition, the sheep gave the name to the hills, for the name Cotswold is supposed to be derived from two words, "cote," meaning a shelter for small animals, and "wold," referring to a wild, open country. The Cotswold sheep were noted for their long wool, which was in demand both at home and abroad. In general appearance they resembled the old Leicesters, but they were somewhat superior to them in quality of wool (Fig. 104).

The closing years of the eighteenth and the first quarter of the nineteenth century formed the period of transition from the old to the modern Cotswold. Improved Leicesters were used by a number of leading breeders, who in addition to introducing this blood, practiced careful selection, having in view the improvement of the form and quality of the breed without diminishing size or materially reducing the weight of fleece. Marked improvement was secured and the Cotswold took its place beside the Leicester as an improved breed. A practice which undoubtedly contributed to the excellence and popularity of the Cotswold was the holding of annual ram sales on the farms of the breeders. These events stimulated healthy rivalry and furnished opportunities for fruitful studies of breeding (Fig. 105).

**Description.**—The Cotswold is a large, upstanding, up headed sheep which resembles the English Leicester, but it is more stylish, being about on a par with the Border Leicester in this respect. Its head is rather long and the head features are fine in outline. The nose is more nearly straight than that of the Leicester and the ears are longer, more flexible, and inclined rather upward, while the Leicester's ears extend almost straight out from the head.

Fig. 104.

Fig. 105.

Fig. 104.—Prize-winning Cotswold ram. Imported by Frank Harding, Waukesha, Wisconsin. The Cotswold is upstanding, high headed and grows a heavy tuft of wool on the forehead.

Fig. 105.—Prize-winning Cotswold ewe. Imported by Frank Harding, Waukesha, Wisconsin. Sometimes the face and frequently the legs of the Cotswold are not pure white.

It is somewhat larger than the Leicester, mature rams in breeding condition weighing 275 to 300 pounds, and ewes from 180 to 225 pounds. Highly fitted show specimens frequently attain such enormous weights as 400 pounds and possibly more.

*The wool* on the forehead is much longer than on the English Leicester, and in show specimens it is never shorn off and hence falls down over the face in long, flowing locks, thus making the head very attractive. The wool lies at the surface of the fleece in large open curls; it covers the body well and not infrequently

Fig. 106.—Yearling Cotswold rams in their native hills on the farm of Robert Garne, England.

extends as short, downy wool below the knees and hocks. It is perhaps somewhat coarser than the wool of the Leicester, but it is lustrous and sells well as a long, coarse wool. The Cotswold is a heavier shearer than the Leicester. In twelve months the wool attains a length of from ten to fourteen inches, and unwashed fleeces weigh from ten to fourteen pounds. According to Wrightson, fleeces from the best English flocks average nine and one-third pounds, but presumably this weight refers to washed wool (Fig. 106).

*Markings and Skin.*—The hair on the face is either white or white with light gray specks, and frequently the cheeks and the regions around the eyes are bluish-white. The hair on the legs is either white or white and mixed with light gray. The lips and nostrils are black as in the Leicester, and so is the skin next to the eye. The body skin is a deep, rich pink, approaching red in color.

**Properties.**—From its size and nature of fleece, one would judge the Cotswold to be a lowland breed, but it is necessary to keep in mind that it is a hill breed. In its native home and in similar regions it is regarded as unusually hardy for a large, open-wooled breed. It is better adapted to comparatively light stocking on short pastures than to heavy stocking on a luxuriant plant growth. When exposed to heavy rains its wool parts along the spine and allows the water to reach the skin, thus causing colds and catarrhal troubles. On this account Cotswolds, although once common, have

Fig. 107.—Cotswold lambs on ranch of J. R. Allen, Draper, Utah. The Cotswold ram is popular in the West for crossing with Rambouillet ewes. The offspring carry heavy fleeces of high commercial value and their wool withstands range conditions well.

almost disappeared from the farms in eastern and central United States.

Like the Leicester, the Cotswold yields mutton of secondary quality. It is often too fat, and the muscle fibers are long and coarse.

Cotswold ewes are fairly prolific, and since they yield a large quantity of milk and are strongly developed in maternal instinct, they are excellent mothers. The lambs are fairly strong at birth and grow at a fair rate, but as a rule they do not become plump and firm at an early age. If placed on a fattening ration late in the autumn they make excellent gains at comparatively low cost.

When Cotswolds are mated with Merinos the offspring are large, hardy, and favorably regarded as producers of both mutton and wool. In western United States, Cotswold blood has been introduced into many pure Merino flocks for the purpose of improving the mutton properties without sacrificing much, if any, in the value of the wool product. About 1860 to 1870 Cotswold rams were used rather extensively in England for crossing with the Down breeds, but this custom has practically died out (Fig. 107).

**Distribution.**—The Cotswold is known in all of the important sheep countries, but its distribution is less general than it was fifty or more years ago. In England it is to be found chiefly in its native hills, whereas a half century ago, there were many flocks in outside regions. In the United States and Canada there is a sprinkling of flocks. Breeders in Utah have demonstrated by the superior sheep they have bred that the Rocky Mountain Region affords locations second to none for the production of high-class Cotswolds.

The Cotswold Sheep Society of England was organized in 1892, and the American Cotswold Sheep Association in 1878.

## QUESTIONS

1. How far from the Cotswold Hills is Loughborough, where Bakewell lived?
2. Give reasons for the disappearance of Cotswold flocks in the Middle West of the United States.
3. How would you distinguish a Cotswold from an English Leicester; a Border Leicester?
4. Would pure or high-grade Cotswolds be suitable for producing early market lambs?

## CHAPTER XIX

## THE LINCOLN

**History.**—The native home of the Lincoln is in the low country on the east coast of England in Lincolnshire. Long before the day of the improved Lincoln the rich pastures on the Lincoln fens were the feeding grounds of long-wooled sheep reputed for their great weight of fleece. They were white-faced sheep, coarse, ungainly, and bred for wool with practically no attention given to their mutton qualities. They were large consumers of feed and matured slowly, but nevertheless, they were popular with Lincolnshire farmers and when the practice of using English Leicester rams was begun there was bitter opposition on the part of a number of breeders. But without losing much in weight of fleece, the offspring from the Leicester sire matured earlier and possessed better mutton form than the pure Lincoln, and as a result the use of Leicester rams continued until the improved Lincoln was finally evolved (Fig. 108).

**Description.**—There is a strong general resemblance between the Lincoln and the Leicester, but the Lincoln has greater size, more robust appearance, firmer flesh, and more wool. The head of the Lincoln is longer, the face broader, the profile of the face fuller and bolder, and the ears larger and thicker than in the Leicester. The Lincoln lacks the quality of the Leicester, but makes up for it in substance. From brisket to twist the carcass is thick and heavy, and in these respects it is not surpassed by any breed. Large development in the leg of mutton is especially emphasized. Mature rams in breeding condition weigh about 300 pounds, ewes 250 pounds, but highly fitted specimens greatly exceed these weights. The wool covers the body and forms a tuft on the forehead, but it does not extend over the top of the head just above the eyes. On the legs it extends to the knees and hocks.

The Lincoln leads the mutton breeds for length and weight of wool. On the average, the length of staple representing one year's growth is about twelve inches, and sheep producing less than eight-inch staple are considered unworthy of registration by the National Lincoln Sheep Breeders' Association. The wool is rather coarse, but very strong and highly lustrous. Sheep in well-kept pure-bred flocks should average fifteen pounds in weight of fleece.

With the exception of the hoofs and skin at the lips and nostrils, the markings of the Lincoln are white. Sometimes a little dark

Fig. 108.—Lincoln ram, champion at English Royal Show. The Lincoln is the largest of the long wool breeds.

Fig. 109.—Lincoln ewes, champions at English Royal Show, 1913. The Lincoln grows a tuft of wool on the forehead which is larger than that grown by the English Leicester and smaller than that grown by the Cotswold. The long, heavy growth of wool is typical of the breed.

color is seen on the ears and legs. The skin is a very healthy pink, approaching a cherry red, in color. Both rams and ewes are hornless (Fig. 109).

**Properties.**—Lincolns are noted for great size and for weight of fleece. Being a heavy feeder it is not adapted to scanty pastures and hence it is not a cosmopolitan breed. In quality of mutton it is not of first rank, but the ewes are first-class mothers.

**Distribution.**—In England the Lincoln is confined mainly to its native home and nearby counties where there are many prosperous breeders. During the past twenty years it has been in strong demand in the Argentine for crossing on Merinos, and English breeders have carried on prosperous export trade with that country. They have also exported considerable numbers to New Zealand and Australia.

On the fertile pastures in the Argentine, the Lincoln-Merino cross makes a large growth and develops the high finish essential for the foreign frozen mutton trade. The wool is heavy, long, strong and lustrous, but not so desirable in fineness and softness as the Australian and New Zealand wools. In New Zealand, the Lincoln has been used in developing the new breed known as the Corriedale, a sheep derived from crosses between English long-wool breeds and Merinos. It was also used in developing the Columbia by the U. S. Department of Agriculture. Lincoln rams and ewes were brought to this country from New Zealand in 1928.

Lincoln flocks are not numerous in the United States and Canada, but they can be grown into good specimens in many parts of these countries. In Ontario some grand sheep have been produced and they can be developed to a high state of perfection in the Coast Region of Oregon. Lincolns have been used to advantage in the range flocks in western United States, where, because of the wool and mutton to be secured, still greater use should be made of them, particularly in those regions in which feed is fairly abundant.

Breeders in England organized the Lincoln Long-wool Sheep Breeders' Association in 1892, and the National Lincoln Sheep Breeders' Association came into existence in 1891.

## QUESTIONS

1. How does the improved Lincoln differ from the old Lincoln?
2. What of the value of the Lincoln for crossing purposes?
3. Where do Lincoln breeders in England find a market for their sheep?
4. For what are Lincolns noted?
5. What sections in the United States suit pure-bred Lincolns?

## CHAPTER XX

## THE ROMNEY MARSH

**History.**—The native home of the Romney Marsh or Kent[1] sheep is in southeastern England in Kent on the alluvial plain known as Romney Marsh. This plain, nearly on a level with the sea and protected from it by strong walls, has an alluvial clay soil with occasional outcroppings of sand or gravel. It is flat and every few rods there are open ditches almost full of water, which are quite as effective as fences for keeping the sheep confined to definite areas. The climate is moist and in winter, cold, damp winds sweep over the marsh and make it an uninviting place in which to live. In summer the fine, rich pastures which are never turned by the plow, will carry as many as twelve two-hundred-pound wethers to the acre, and even with this heavy stocking it is sometimes necessary to put a few bullocks in with the sheep to graze down the grass that is beginning to grow long, for utilizing it to advantage depends on keeping it grazed close (Fig. 110).

Sheep have been kept on the Marsh for several centuries. The old type, similar in many respects to the old Lincoln, but perhaps even worse in its shape, was a coarse, loose-jointed, big-bellied sheep, yielding long, coarse wool. Improvement was brought about by the use of Leicester rams and careful selection, but it is claimed that the modern Romney Marsh does not carry as much of the Leicester blood as the improved Cotswold and Lincoln breeds. It was found that the introduction of Leicester blood beyond a certain point produced sheep too tender in constitution to withstand the hardships attending poor feed on the bleak, unsheltered winter pastures. Through the use of Leicesters, a more compact, earlier maturing type was secured, and the fleece was improved in fineness and felting properties, but reduced somewhat in weight. Romney Marsh breeders have shown a great deal of enterprise during the past half century in still further improving their breed (Fig. 111).

**Description.**—The Romney Marsh is a large, rugged, rather low-set sheep noted for its constitution and strength of bone. The

[1] The American Romney Breeders' Association has adopted the word Romney instead of Romney Marsh.

forehead is very broad and the head features as a whole indicate the stamina characteristic of the breed. With the exception of black hoofs and dark nostrils and lips, the markings are white and there is no wool on the face or on the legs below the knees and hocks. As a rule, there is a tuft of wool on the forehead. As compared with the Cotswold and Lincoln the wool is not so long nor as lustrous, but it is thicker on the skin and finer, and the weight of fleece about equals that of the Cotswold.

**Fig. 110.**—Romney Marsh ram owned by Robert Kenward, England. The deep body, full brisket and heavy bone are typical of the breed.

**Properties.**—Hardiness has always been an outstanding property of Romney Marsh sheep. The old practice of making them get all of their feed from the marsh pastures through all seasons is still in vogue, and none but hardy sheep can subsist on these pastures in winter, for the feed is poor and the exposure to the cold, damp wind is a drain on vitality. No breed is better suited to low pastures, and it has proven itself adaptable to higher, more rolling regions than its native marsh.

It is said that foot rot and liver fluke (liver rot) seldom affect Romney Marsh sheep and they are regarded as being highly resistant to the diseases commonly affecting sheep. Since they graze and lie singly, they do not taint their pastures to as great extent as do sheep that are more gregarious in instinct.

The Romney Marsh is superior as a grazing sheep. Big wethers, grazing on the Marsh, attain prime condition without the use of grain.

In quality of mutton, the Romney leads the coarse-wool breeds and crosses between it and Southdowns or Hampshires are said to produce mutton of superior quality.

Romney breeders have aimed at a strong lamb to each ewe rather than toward a large percentage of twins. The ewes are good mothers and suckle well.

FIG. 111.—Romney Marsh rams. For a large breed the Romney Marsh is low set.

**Distribution.**—During the last twenty years the Romney has become much appreciated in the Argentine, New Zealand, and Australia. Breeders in the north island of New Zealand lay claim to having developed a more useful type than the English Romney, but this is stoutly denied by the English breeders. As yet Romneys are not to be found in the United States and Canada in large numbers, but they have been introduced to these countries and it has been found that they do exceedingly well in the low costal region of Oregon and on the ranges of Washington. Undoubtedly there are many other districts in the United States where they will do equally well.

Some attempts have been made in this country to develop new breeds by crossing the Romney and Rambouillet. The success of these ventures is still problematical as the type has not been fixed nor the adaptability of the sheep widely determined.

The Kent or Romney Marsh Sheep Breeders' Association of England was formed in 1895. The American Romney Breeders' Association was formed in 1911.

## QUESTIONS

1. How far is Kent from Lincolnshire?
2. Compare the properties of the Romney Marsh with those of the Leicester.
3. Compare the native home of the Cotswold with that of the Romney Marsh.
4. At the present time where are the breeding grounds of the Romney Marsh?
5. What of the Romney Marsh in North America?

## CHAPTER XXI

# BRITISH BREEDS NOT WIDELY DISTRIBUTED IN THE UNITED STATES

### THE SCOTCH BLACKFACE HIGHLAND

**History.**—The Scotch Blackface Highland, or the Blackface as breeders frequently call it, is a mountain breed, native to the Highlands of Scotland. Its origin cannot be definitely traced, and as for the methods used in improving it, Usher says: "The probability is that they were allowed for ages to pick up a precarious subsistence as best they could, and multiply and replenish the earth according to their own natural instincts. No doubt it (improvement) was brought about gradually by men of intelligence and judgment, in careful selection . . . but as Blackfaced flocks occupied wide tracts of country where fencing was unknown, the benefits of such selection were often, in a measure, lost by the tups (rams) being put to them indiscriminately" (Fig. 112).

**Description.**—The Blackface is a wild, active, small sheep with black or mottled face and legs. In case of mottled markings, the spots should be quite distinct, thus leaving the face and legs free from tinges of gray. There should be no wool on the head or on the legs below the knees and hocks. The wool is coarse, wavy, and loose, and when of twelve months' growth, hangs down almost to the ground. Ewe fleeces weigh from four to five pounds, and two-year-old wether fleeces as much as seven pounds. The make-up of the Blackface suggests its adaptability to the difficulties it must encounter in its mountain home. The body is short and muscular with the shoulders high and "formed for freedom of action." The nose is broad and prominent; the eyes are bold and flashing; in rams, the horns are large, taking one or more spiral turns, according to age; in ewes, they are small, flattened and curved, but not spirally formed. The tail is short, reaching only to the hocks, and it is customary among breeders to leave it undocked.

**Properties.**—The Blackface is the hardiest of the mountain breeds and it thrives best on pastures which require much travelling to obtain food. Hence, it is better adapted to the high mountain pastures, yielding moss, heather, and a little grass, than to the succulent green pastures of lower altitudes. When Blackfaces are taken to shelter for fattening, however, they do exceedingly well.

Blackface mutton is famous for its superior flavor and quality, and crosses with either Cheviot or Border Leicester are said to yield mutton almost or quite as good as that of the pure Blackface (Fig. 113).

**Distribution.**—Outside of their native home few Blackfaces are to be found. Their mission seems to be to occupy high altitudes presenting conditions too severe for other breeds. Years ago the

Fig. 112.—Blackfaced Highland ram. The long coarse wool is typical. Often there are areas of white hair on the face.

Cheviot threatened to drive them out of the Scottish mountains, for they were preferred to the Blackfaces where soil and climate were at all suited to their production; but continuous cold, stormy weather in 1859–60 and 1860–61 killed vegetation to such extent that the Cheviots died in great numbers, while the losses in Blackface flocks were comparatively small.

## THE LONK

The Lonk is a native of the wet, hilly districts of North England. It resembles the Scotch Blackface, but it is larger, and more upstanding, and its wool is finer and heavier. It is a very hardy breed and its mutton is of very high quality (Fig. 114).

Fig. 113.—Blackfaced Highlands in their native home. These small sheep travel over rough, rugged places with ease.

Fig. 114.

Fig. 115.

Fig. 114.—Lonk ram. The Lonk resembles the Blackfaced Highland but is larger
Fig. 115.—Herdwick ram. The Herdwick is small and has coarse wool.

### THE HERDWICK

The Herdwick is a small hardy mountain breed that is little known outside of its native region in North Lincolnshire, Cumberland, and Westmoorland. The face is either light gray or white, and often the wool on the belly is gray, and an all gray fleece is not considered objectionable. The wool is coarse and in old sheep inclined to be kempy. The rams have horns, but the ewes are hornless (Fig. 115).

**Fig. 116.—Exmoor ram. The Exmoor bears some resemblance to the Dorset Horn.**

Herdwick mutton ranks very high in quality. Ewes drafted from the pure-bred flocks are often taken to lower altitudes, and mated with Leicester and Wensleydale rams for the purpose of producing fat lambs.

### THE EXMOOR

The Exmoor is a native of the hills of West Somerset and North Devon. It resembles the Dorset Horn somewhat, but it is smaller and the skin at the muzzle is black.

It is a hardy breed and one of the best to place on poor natural pastures. The ewes are good mothers, and after raising three crops of lambs in the hills they are sent down to the low country to raise market lambs (Fig. 116).

### THE WELSH MOUNTAIN

The Welsh Mountain is a very old breed native to the highest hills of Wales. It is a small hardy sheep with white or tan markings and fine, dense wool which is not altogether free from kemp. In conformation, it is a rather long, narrow sheep, and light in the fore quarters. The ewes are hornless, but the rams have strong curved horns. The mutton is of such quality as to rank with Southdowns and Blackfaced Highlands.

In disposition the Welsh Mountain is wild and restless, and hard to keep within fenced enclosures. The ewes are good mothers and they are taken to lower ground in large numbers to raise fat lambs (Fig. 117).

### THE RYELAND

The Ryeland originated in Herfordshire, early in the nineteenth century, from crossing Leicesters on a small white-faced polled breed that produced about two pounds of exceedingly fine wool. The Leicester cross improved the size of body and weight of fleece without materially reducing the quality of mutton, fineness of wool, and hardiness, characteristic of the old breed. In conformation, the Ryeland resembles the earlier type Shropshire so much, that it has been spoken of as the white-faced Shropshire. Its lambs grow rapidly and Ryeland rams are known to be good sires of lambs intended for market.

Ryeland flocks are found mainly in Herfordshire. At one time they were largely replaced by Down breeds, but now seem to have regained their old-time popularity. In 1928 a number of these sheep were imported to Kentucky (Fig. 118).

### THE DORSET DOWN

The Dorset Down originated in Dorsetshire from original stocks that closely resembled the parent stock of the Hampshire. In fact the Dorset Down is a modified Hampshire which Dorsetshire farmers have found suitable to their conditions. It is smaller than the Hampshire and more refined in head and bone. The face, ears, and legs are lighter in color, being a grayish-brown, rather than a deep brown, bordering on black.

Dorset Downs are adapted to grazing either on pastures or on

Fig. 117.

Fig. 118.

Fig. 117.—Welsh Mountain ram.
Fig. 118.—Ryeland ram. Except for its white face and legs the Ryeland resembles the earlier type Shropshire.

forage crops where the hurdling system is in vogue. Their mutton is said to be of excellent quality.

Wallace states that they shear about five pounds,[1] but he very likely refers to washed wool (Fig. 119).

### THE KERRY HILL (WALES)

The Kerry Hill is a breed that has been developed in Wales since 1840, from a stock that was more or less of a mountain type. In general appearance it looks like a grade Down sheep, because its face, legs, and ears are speckled black and white. Its fleece resembles that of the Shropshire, but it is not so good in quality. Horns in either sex are objectionable, but sometimes they appear in rams (Fig. 120).

In size, the Kerry Hill about equals the Shropshire. It is hardy and produces a superior quality of mutton. The ewes are excellent mothers and in grazing districts, they are sought after as producers of fat lambs.

### THE WENSLEYDALE

The Wensleydale sheep was made by crossing English Leicesters on native sheep in Yorkshire. It is a large, long, upstanding, firm-fleshed sheep, growing long wool which is very lustrous and which separates into distinct wavy locks or staples. The skin on the face, ears, and legs of the Wensleydale has a decidedly bluish tinge, and frequently this shade of color extends all over its body.

For a long-wool breed, the mutton of the Wensleydale is of good quality. It is an active, hardy breed, but a little slow in maturing (Fig. 121).

### THE DEVON LONG WOOL

The Devon Long Wool is a very large, coarse-wool breed of sheep that is kept in large numbers in Devon and Somerset. It was made by crossing English Leicesters and possibly Lincolns on two old native breeds, the "Southern Notts," and "Bampton Notts." These were large, coarse sheep that produced long, heavy fleeces.

---

[1] Wallace, "British Breeds of Live Stock," 1913.

Fig. 119.—Dorset-Down ram. The Dorset-Down resembles the Hampshire, but is smaller and more refined in general features.

Fig. 120.—The Kerry Hill Ram.

Fig. 121.

Fig. 122.

Fig. 121.—Wensleydale ram.
Fig. 122.—Devon long wool ram.

Fig. 123.

Fig. 124.

Fig. 123.—South Devon ram.
Fig. 124.—Dartmoor ram.

The South Devon, which resembles the Devon Long Wool, is a breed that is kept in Cornwall and South Devon. It is said to be robust in constitution and adapted to either grazing or feeding on forage crops between hurdles.

The Devon Long Wool, the South Devon and also the Dartmoor resemble the Lincoln in many respects (Figs. 122, 123, and 124).

## QUESTIONS

1. Which breeds mentioned in this chapter are mountain breeds? Hill breeds? Lowland breeds?
2. Which breeds resemble the Down breeds? The Long wool breeds?
3. How are mountain breeds different from Hill and Lowland breeds?

## CHAPTER XXII

# THE CORRIEDALE

**History.**—The Corriedale is regarded as a new breed, having been developed in New Zealand since 1880. Prior to this time most of the sheep in New Zealand were pure Merinos, but when it became possible to ship frozen carcasses to London, New Zealand sheepmen realized the need of producing sheep of better mutton quality. Accordingly, rams of the various English mutton breeds were placed with the Merino flocks. It was found that the crosses between the long-wool mutton breeds and the Merino produced the kind of sheep best suited to New Zealand conditions. These half-breeds grew rapidly upon the luxuriant pastures, yielded a heavy fleece of valuable wool, and developed a carcass of high finish and quality. No known breed of sheep seemed so well adapted to certain New Zealand conditions as they, and so a number of breeders set about to fix a type similar to these cross-bred sheep. Lincoln rams and some Leicesters, but to a lesser extent than Lincoln, were crossed upon Merino ewes and after close culling toward the type desired, the hybrids (half-breds) were mated together. In each generation close culling was practiced, and as a rule each breeder limited his selections of breeding stock to his own flock. That this procedure in breeding has brought gratifying results is indicated by the fact that it is now claimed that the Corriedale shows no more variation in type than exists in many of the older breeds (Fig. 125).

**Description.**—In all essential characteristics the Corriedale is a blend between the fine-wool and coarse-wool types from which it came. In mutton conformation and disposition to fatten it is superior to the Merino, but not equal to the Lincoln or Leicester. Its wool being of medium quality, strong, even in structure, comparatively light in yolk, and three inches or more in length, fulfills the requirements of the wools bringing the highest price on the markets. The fleeces average from ten to twelve pounds in weight.

The face, ears, and legs of the Corriedale are white. Both sexes are hornless, but there is a tendency for horns to appear in the rams (Figs. 126 and 127).

Fig. 125.—Corriedale ram bred by King Bros. Co., Laramie, Wyoming. This ram, champion at the Pacific International, 1935, and the Denver Stock Show, 1936, is an outstanding example of the modern Corriedale.

Fig. 126.—Corriedale stud rams. Property of Leonard White, New Zealand.

**Properties.**—Corriedale mutton is better than that from any of its parent breeds. It is thicker and fatter than Merino mutton and free from the coarseness and excessive fatness characteristic of the mutton produced by Lincolns and Leicesters. On the great Smithfield market, London, Corriedale lamb carcasses are known as Canterbury lambs. As a rule, they show prime finish and quality.

Fig. 127.—Corriedale ewe, champion at Christ Church, New Zealand.

It is said of Corriedale ewes that they are prolific, and that 120 per cent lamb crops are not uncommon. It is also claimed for Corriedales that they are adaptable to different climates, as is shown by their ability to thrive on mountains 6000 to 7000 feet above sea level, and in arid tropics of Queensland, Australia. At the United States Sheep Experiment Station in Idaho 1184 Corriedale lambs averaged 69 pounds at weaning time, as compared with 71 pounds for Rambouillet and 77 pounds for Columbia lambs. The percentage of Corriedale lambs suitable for slaughter exceeded that of either of the other breeds and compared favorably with lambs sired by black-faced mutton breeds. The first flock book was published in New Zealand in 1911. The American Corriedale Association was organized in 1916.

## CHAPTER XXIII

# THE COLUMBIA

**History.**—The Columbia is still in its formative stage of development as definite efforts to produce a sheep of this type were not begun until 1912. The task of directing its establishment was undertaken by the United States Department of Agriculture. The early work was done at Laramie, Wyoming, but in 1917 the sheep were transferred to the range-sheep experiment station at Dubois, Idaho. In the original mating Rambouillet ewes were bred to Lincoln, Leicester, Cotswold, and Romney-Marsh rams. When the lambs produced by these crosses came to breeding age they were carefully inspected. Since the Lincoln-Rambouillet cross proved to be most satisfactory the others were discontinued. The lambs resulting from this mating were carefully culled in accordance with the type that it was desired to produce and were then mated together without the further introduction of the blood of either of the parent stocks. As this process continues through succeeding generations the tendency to extreme variation is reduced and a type may be fixed that will eventually be of great service to many parts of the range country. Owing to the great differences between the two breeds entering into the make-up of the Columbia it is obvious that the development of a well-defined type that will be regularly produced is a matter requiring some years.

**Description.**—While at this time it cannot be said that the character of the breed is completely determined, the most acceptable representatives do show satisfactory size under range conditions (Fig. 127a). Mature rams in breeding flesh weigh from 225 to 275 pounds and mature ewes about 150 pounds. They are somewhat larger than the Corriedale and are of more robust build which is evidenced partly by the heavier bone of the foreleg and a little more coarseness of head features. They may be said to resemble the Corriedale in white color of face and in freedom from extreme wool covering below the eyes, knees, and hocks. The fleece is relatively long, attaining a length of about four inches in a twelve-month period, with an average weight of eleven pounds under range conditions. The amount of grease in the fleece is comparatively small yet the wool shows very desirable commercial qualities. It is usually of quarter-blood or low quarter-blood in quality.

**Properties.**—Columbia lambs grow rapidly but are not equal in their fleshing qualities to the lambs of the more highly devel-

Fig. 127a.—Yearling Columbia Rams bred by the U. S. Dept. of Agr. Sold for $145.00 each as range rams at the national ram sale, Salt Lake City, Utah.

oped mutton breeds. The ewes are good milkers and under good conditions produce well over a 100 per cent lamb crop.

**Distribution.**—Few of these sheep are to be found except in the range states, principally of the northwest. Some years ago they were given a limited trial in Illinois where they proved satisfactory except for the variation which occurred in type.

There is no organization of breeders promoting these sheep.

## CHAPTER XXIV

# THE AMERICAN TUNIS

**History.**—In the Arizona Experiment Station Bulletin 69 Professor F. W. Wilson gives the following account of the American Tunis:

"The history of Tunis sheep in America dates from 1799, when General William Eaton, U. S. Consul at Tunis, bought ten head of the fat-tailed sheep of that country from the Bey of Tunis and sent them to America on the man-of-war *Sophia*. Only one pair, Carmelli and Salena, survived the voyage. They were placed on the farm of Judge Richard Peters, of Belmont, near Philadelphia, and lived to a ripe old age, when both were killed by dogs. Selena raised her last lamb in her sixteenth year.

"Judge Peters offered the free use of his rams to breeders, and was so well patronized that, in a short time, flocks had found their way to Georgia, the Carolinas, and Virginia. During the Civil War the breed was exterminated with the exception of the sheep held by Col. Maynard R. Spigler, of Columbia, South Carolina. The present Tunis blood in America has been preserved through this flock of Colonel Spigler, who bred them for over fifty years. Several other importations of Tunis sheep have been made; namely, in 1806, by Commodore Barron, of the U. S. Navy, to Virginia and the District of Columbia; later, a ram and a ewe by President Jefferson, and, in 1825, thirteen head to New York, one pair of which was sent to General Rensselaer, of Albany.

"In 1894, J. A. Guilliams, through correspondence with Colonel Washington Watts, of Laurens, South Carolina, learned of the flock of pure-blood Tunis sheep on the plantation of Colonel Spigler. He bought ten head and shipped them to Putnam County, Indiana. They were exhibited at the fair at Crawfordsville, Indiana, where they attracted much attention. Their quaint conformation and lack of wool, however, gave them an unfavorable introduction. Nevertheless, Charles Roundtree, near Crawfordsville, Indiana, who is now the largest breeder of Tunis sheep in America, purchased additional animals from the Spigler flock, and with several other farmers became interested in the breed. He conceived the plan of

Fig. 128.

Fig. 129.

Fig. 128.—American Tunis ram. The hair on the face and legs of the Tunis is usually reddish brown.

Fig. 129.—American Tunis ewe. The long pendulous ears are typical of the breed.

improving the breed by introducing outside blood, and for this purpose selected two Southdown ewes. The Roundtree type contains one-sixteenth Southdown blood, and is a marked improvement over the original Tunis breed" (Fig. 128).

**Description.**—As suggested in the above account, Tunis breeders are attempting to breed a sheep that approximates the ideal mutton type in conformation. In most specimens, however, the neck is rather long, the chest lacks somewhat in width, and the legs tend

Fig. 130.—American Tunis ewe and her lamb. Note the tendency toward excessive fatty development at the dock of the lamb, which is more or less characteristic of the breed.

to be close together at the knees and hocks. With the exception of the long, pendulous ears, the head features indicate quality. In rams the face profile is slightly Roman, while in ewes it is almost straight. Mature rams in breeding condition weigh between 150 and 175 pounds; ewes about 125 pounds. As a whole, the breed is hornless, but stubs of horns occasionally appear in the males. The color of the hair on the face, ears, and legs varies from a reddish brown to white and not infrequently a wide bar of white hair extends from the nose to the forehead while the remainder of the face is brown (Fig. 129).

The Tunis has a long, combing wool which is to be criticised for coarseness. As a rule it is white, but in every flock there is to be found a number of gray fleeces. At birth the lambs are either spotted or a reddish brown. Judge Richard Peters, writing of the Tunis in 1810, said that the lambs were white, red, tawny, bluish, and black and that all except the black lambs grew to be white in general color of fleece, though most commonly they were colored in spots, and around the cheeks and shoulders either tawny or black wool appeared. The fleeces average from eight to ten pounds in weight.

**Properties.**—Hardiness, prolificacy, early maturity, and good quality of mutton are the properties which Tunis breeders emphasize as characteristic of their sheep. Professor Wilson also shows that the Tunis sheep more than any other breed except the Merino remain in a compact band while feeding on the range. In their North African home, the Tunis breeds twice a year, and American breeders maintain that this property has been retained. The lambs are strong at birth and the ewes are good nurses; hence, the Tunis ewe has, to a certain extent, met with favor in America as a producer of winter lambs (Fig. 130).

**Distribution.**—The breed has not become numerous although there are flocks to be found in several states. An association known as The American Tunis Sheep Breeders' Association was organized in Indiana in 1896.

## QUESTIONS

1. Locate the country of Tunis.
2. Give the favorable qualities of the Tunis as advocated by Tunis breeders.
3. Criticise the Tunis.

## CHAPTER XXV

# BREEDS OF THE WOOL TYPE

ALL of the existing wool breeds have descended from the Merinos of Spain, hence wool sheep and Merino sheep are practically synonymous terms. Outside of Spain, distinct types have been developed in Germany, France, Australia, and North America.

**Origin of Merinos.**—There is no definite information as to just how the Merino came into existence, but it is thought that it was developed from sheep imported into Spain from Italy and Northern Africa centuries ago. There were two great groups of Merinos in Spain, the Estantes, or stationary flocks, and the Transhumantes, or travelling flocks. The latter, owned by the nobility and the clergy, outnumbered the former four to one and were considered the more important. They were maintained in very large flocks numbering into the thousands, and they were handled by shepherds who herded them over a range of two or three hundred miles, so that they obtained their living almost entirely by grazing. The owners of these flocks did not make a practice of going to outside sources for their breeding stock; hence each flock possessed a type peculiarly its own. Yet all of them were maintained for the distinct purpose of producing fine wool.

**Merinos in Various Countries.**—When other countries took up Merinos they drew from various flocks in Spain, and in many cases Spanish types were commingled to breed the kind of sheep most desired. In Saxony, Germany, close attention was given to fineness of fleece, the result being the Saxony Merino which possessed wool finer than any produced by the Spanish flocks. In France attention was given to size and form in the hope of producing both mutton and fine wool; the result was the Rambouillet, now famous as a large mutton-type Merino. In Australia three types were developed: one comparatively small and growing very fine wool impregnated with much yolk or oil; another a large, robust sheep having coarser and longer wool and much less yolk; and the third a type midway between the two already mentioned. In North America emphasis was first placed upon weight, length and fineness of fleece, the result being the American Merino, a rather small sheep with great folds or wrinkles on the neck and body, and dense fine wool heavily impregnated with yolk. Another evolution was the American Delaine, with a smooth mutton-like body and long, fine wool for worsteds.

## THE AMERICAN MERINO

**History.—Importations.**—Merino sheep were brought to the United States as early as 1793, but they did not begin to get a substantial footing in this country until commercial difficulties arose with England and France in 1807. In that year the Embargo Act was passed and wool soon rose to one dollar per pound. This started a boom for Merinos which resulted in the importation of 6000 to 8000 head in 1809, 1810, and 1811. Before the close of the War of 1812, wool sold for two and one-half dollars per pound. During the period, 1808–1813, it was no unusual thing for imported Merino rams to sell for a thousand dollars each and ewes sometimes sold for as much. Then came the Peace of Ghent (1815) which reopened commerce and practically ruined the infant manufactures of the United States. The decline in value of raw wool was so violent that before the close of the year 1815, pure-bred Merino sheep sold for one dollar per head. According to Randall, wool did not materially rally in price for nine succeeding years, and during that period most of the full-blood flocks of the country were broken up or adulterated in blood.

**Stephen Atwood.**—During those dark and discouraging years one man, however, held on faithfully to his Merinos and pursued a definite policy in breeding. This was Stephen Atwood, of Woodbury, Connecticut. For foundation stock, Mr. Atwood purchased a six-year-old ewe in 1813 and five ewe lambs in 1810. These females were descendants of the very choice sheep imported by Colonel David Humphreys, of Derby, Connecticut, in 1802. All of Atwood's breeding rams were also descendants of Humphrey's stock and when he could no longer find pure Humphrey's blood in other flocks, he resorted to his own for sires. He was a progressive breeder, producing better and better sheep as years advanced, but his great contribution to the evolution of the American Merino lay in the fact that he preserved a pure strain of Spanish Merinos through a dark period when all but a very few either crossed their Spanish sheep with Saxony Merinos or in various ways permitted their flocks to degenerate.

**Edwin Hammond,**[1] of Middlebury, Vermont, a customer of Atwood for the first time in 1844, is regarded as having done more than any other one breeder in developing the American Merino. Randall said of him that he effected quite as much of an improvement in the American Merino as Mr. Bakewell effected among the long-wool sheep of England. Using Atwood sheep, he wrought great improvement in both form and fleece in a comparatively short time. He purchased "Old Black" in 1849, a sheep described as being "long, tall, flat-ribbed, rather long in the neck and head, strong-boned, a little roach-backed, deep chested, and moderately wrinkled; his wool was about an inch and a half long, of medium thickness, extremely yolky, and dark colored externally; face a little bare and not much wool on shanks. He weighed about one hundred and thirty-five pounds and cut about fourteen pounds of wool unwashed." Contrast with "Old Black" the ram "Sweepstakes" bred by Hammond in 1856 and regarded by many as one of the best he produced. "Sweepstakes" weighed about one hundred and forty pounds and was almost perfect in form, being defective in no essential particular. His head and belly were admirably covered and he was strongly wooled to the feet. In full fleece, his wool was two and one-half inches long, fine and extremely even, and he yielded a year's growth weighing twenty-seven pounds.

**Popularity of the Hammond Sheep.**—Prominent breeders began to be attracted by Mr. Hammond's sheep about 1850. In a few years they were eagerly sought by both home and foreign breeders. On several occasions he could have sold his breeding rams for as much as $2500 each. So many visitors came to his place that his hospitable home is reported to have resembled a prosperous hotel. Through the hundreds of people who inspected his flock and the many sheep he distributed far and wide, the distinctive type he bred came to be pretty generally known and was regarded as better suited to American conditions than the old Spanish type.

As suggested elsewhere in this chapter, Mr. Hammond's sheep were different from their Spanish ancestors, both in form and fleece. They were thicker, shorter in neck and legs, stronger in bone, and somewhat heavier. They were more nearly perfect in wool covering and much superior in length, density, fineness, and weight of fleece.

---

[1] Associated with Edwin Hammond was his brother William, who acted as shepherd and manager.

Their greater weight of fleece was due not only to increased density and length of wool, but also to the development of larger and more wrinkles or folds in the skin, thus giving a greater surface upon which to grow wool.

**Other Pioneer Breeders.**—Although the prominent part Hammond had in developing the American Merino is generally acknowledged, it is perhaps too sweeping to say that it originated solely from his work. For, during his time and shortly after, there were a number of capable breeders who deserve mention as belonging in the pioneer ranks. Not all of them can be mentioned here, but important ones include the names of Charles Rich, of Shoreham, Vermont, and his sons, John T. and Charles, and also his grandsons, J. T. and Virtulan; Tyler Stickney, also of Shoreham, and William R. Sanford, of Orwell, Vermont. All these stand out prominently in the history of the American Merino. For years Vermont was a Mecca for Merino breeders in search of stud stock, but there were many splendid flocks further west in New York, Pennsylvania, Ohio, Michigan, and a few in Illinois and Wisconsin. In fact, in order to be just to New York, Ohio, and Michigan, they should be mentioned with Vermont as the regions in which the American Merino attained its highest degree of perfection (Fig. 131).

**Description.**—A single description will not fit the American Merino of to-day, or of any other time for that matter. This is true because breeders vary type somewhat with respect to form of body, wrinkles or folds in the skin and properties of fleece. Hammond kept three strains of blood, the representatives of which were said to be easily distinguishable because of differences in external characters. In the best of flocks three types are usually to be found. These have come to be known as the A, B, and C types. Since they come from the same parent stock, they are very much alike in many respects. The rams, as a rule, have heavy, spirally-turned horns and the ewes are hornless. The hair on face, ears, and legs is white, fine and silky, although reddish-brown spots sometimes appear around the muzzle and eyes, and on the ears; the lips, nostrils, and skin are deep pink and the hoofs are white. The wool completely covers the body and extends well over the face and legs, and although it varies with each type in length, density, fineness, and amount of yolk or oil, it has a marked resemblance in all three types. The wool is very fine and uniform in structure, as is indicated by the evenness with which the waves or crimps are carried along the whole length of the fibers; and there is an unusual degree of uniformity of fineness of fibers throughout the fleece. In the best specimens there are no kempy fibers, that is, coarse, hair-like fibers and bluish-white, structureless, tender fibers that will not take the vegetable dyes used in coloring wool. Because the yolk is liquid and comparatively free from coloring matter, the wool is a rich, creamy white. This is not true, however, of the external appearance of the fleece, because the yolk, upon coming to the

FIG. 131.—A-type Merinos bred by S. M. Cleaver, Delaware, Ohio. Although these sheep are covered with folds and wrinkles they are thick and compact, showing that extreme development in wool need not be wholly divorced from mutton qualities.

outer end of the wool fibers, hardens and darkens into a dark gray or brownish-black.

**The A-Type.**—Extreme development of folds on neck and body is the outstanding characteristic of the A-type Merino. Because of its great surface of skin, dense wool, and large percentage of yolk, it yields a very high percentage of unscoured wool to weight of body. In twelve months the wool attains a length of about one and one-half inches. Rams will shear from 25 to 30 pounds of grease wool (wool just as it comes from the sheep's back) and ewes from 15 to 20 pounds, but exceptional specimens have yielded considerably more than the weights mentioned here. The shrinkage of the wool in the process of scouring is often as much as 75 per cent.

The description already given of the conformation of the wool

Fig. 132.

Fig. 133.

Fig. 132.—A-type ram. The A-type Merino is distinguished by the folds and wrinkles extending over the entire body.
Fig. 133.—A-type Merino ewe.

Fig. 134.—B-type Merino ram. The B-type has heavy folds on the neck and few wrinkles on the body.

**Fig. 135.—B-type Merino ewe in field condition**

type in Chapter VI fits the A-type Merino fairly well. Mention should be made, however, of its deep body and comparatively short legs. Mature rams in full fleece weigh from 130 to 160 pounds and ewes from 90 to 125 pounds (Figs. 132 and 133).

**The B-Type.**—As compared with the A-type, the B-type carries more mutton and fewer folds or wrinkles. Three to four large folds are to be found on the neck, fairly prominent ones appear at the flanks and around the dock, and a goodly number of small ones on the thighs and sides of the body. As a group, the representatives of the B-type are somewhat fuller in the thighs, wider and higher sprung in the ribs, and perhaps slightly thicker through the shoulders than those of the A-type. Mature rams weigh from 140 to 170 pounds and ewes from 100 to 125 pounds.

In most respects the wool of the B-type is similar to that of the A-type, but the fibers tend to be a little longer and there is slightly less yolk, which, together with the fact that the surface of the skin is relatively less, makes the percentage of fleece to body weight less than in the A-type. The average run of stud rams will shear close to 25 pounds and the ewes about 16 pounds (Figs. 134 and 135).

**The C-Type or Delaine.**—The body of the C-type is free from folds and only two or three small ones appear on the neck. It is considered objectionable if the neck folds are at all prominent on top of the neck. As compared with the B-type American Merino, the C-type is more desirable as a mutton animal not only because its pelt is smooth, but also because its body is wider, the thighs better filled, and the flesh thicker. Most C-type strains are somewhat larger than the A-type sheep. Rams range from 150 to 200 pounds in weight, and ewes from 100 to 150 pounds. The rams are both horned and hornless, as the owners of the various strains are not agreed on the matter of horns in males. All of the ewes are hornless.

The wool of the C-type is at least three inches long when of twelve months' growth. All things considered, it is the best grease wool, *i.e.,* wool just as it comes from the sheep's back, produced in America, being fine, strong, soft, and of lighter shrinkage than other fine wools. To be typical the fleece should be carried evenly with respect to length and fineness over all parts of the body and it should extend well over the face and legs. Rams shear from 15 to 25 pounds of unwashed wool and ewes from 10 to 15 pounds (Figs. 136 and 137).

FIG. 136.—C-type Merino ram. With the exception of slight folds and wrinkles on the neck the C-type is smooth.

FIG. 137.—C-type Merino ewe

**Properties.**—Hardiness is an outstanding property of all three types of the American Merino. The lambs are somewhat tender at first, but after they are a few days old they are hardy and no breed in America is equal to the Merino for withstanding indifferent care and at the same time yielding fairly good returns. Its dense, oily coat is a good protection against rain and fluctuations of temperature; therefore, it can stand outdoor exposure under conditions wholly unsuited to a number of the mutton breeds. The Merino also fares pretty well when forced to subsist on a scanty supply of feed. Fine-wool breeders have observed that when their sheep are given just a little more feed than is necessary for maintenance, they produce finer wool than when they are liberally fed. Between 1820 and 1830, when the Merino breeders of Saxony received great prices for their exceedingly fine wool, they resorted to light feeding in order further to increase the fineness of fleece. And so accustomed were the old Merino breeders in the United States to light feeding that they vigorously contended that liberal feeding would have a pronounced effect toward reducing the vitality of the flock.

The twinning habit has not been bred into the Merinos, hence their prolificacy is not marked, nor are their milking properties any too well developed. At birth the lambs weigh about eight pounds. They do not mature rapidly, but apparently their longevity is compensation for their slow rate of growth. Sometimes the ewes are not bred until they are well past two years old, but many a Merino ewe is sound and in her prime as a breeder when eight years old. Because of their slow rate of growth they do not yield their heaviest weight of wool until about the third fleece, while in the mutton breeds the first fleece is as heavy as any other.

**Distribution.**—At the present time, Ohio, Vermont, and New York are the strongholds of the pure-bred flocks of American Merinos. Because of the demand for mutton they are not as popular as they used to be, the A-type particularly, but there is fair demand for them in the regions in which they are produced and in a few places in the West. Prior to the outbreak of the European war in 1914 annual exportations of these sheep were made to South Africa. Some were exported since the war.

The Merino breeders of the United States deserve the compliment of having developed consummate skill in sheep breeding, but they have never been closely and efficiently organized. Such men as Atwood, the Hammonds and the Riches, were extremely individualistic and, therefore, poorly adapted to promoting a breed organization. The strength of their personalities showed not only in the sheep they bred, but also in the manner in which the American Merino was developed and promoted. There came to be known the Rich Merinos, the Hammond Merinos and many others, taking, as a rule, the name of the man who developed them, and each individual's sheep possessed certain peculiarities which made possible their existence as a separate family or strain. Then state organizations came into existence under various names, some of which suggested an attempt to gather all of the breeders of the country under the same banner, but if such was the hope it was never realized. What more could have been accomplished had breeders efficiently organized themselves in a national society is, in part, a matter of conjecture, but had such action taken place, surely some of the conservatism, which resulted in clinging blindly and doggedly to certain types long after their appropriate day, would not have developed. In the writer's opinion this conservatism has been responsible to a degree for the passing of the Merino from many sections. Had the type been modified to more nearly suit conditions it would have stayed longer and much to the advantage of the sheep industry of the country.

## QUESTIONS

1. Indicate the formative period of the American Merino.
2. What circumstances led up to the first wave of popularity for Merinos in the United States?
3. Contrast the work of Atwood and Hammond.
4. Compare the A-, B-, and C-types of American Merinos and indicate the conditions under which each would be most popular.
5. Compare the prolificacy of the American Merino with that of the Shropshire.
6. Compare the milking functions of Dorset Horns with American Merinos.
7. Suggest a breed that is more efficiently promoted than the American Merino.
8. What breed seems to you as most unlike the American Merino in rate of growth?

## CHAPTER XXVI

# THE DELAINE MERINO

**History.**—The Delaine Merino is a pure Merino descended from the same original stock as the American Merino, but distinguished from it by its smooth body and its long, fine wool, which attains a length of three inches or more in twelve months. Breeders developed the smooth bodies in order to get a sheep suitable for mutton, and they bred for long, fine wool with a view to getting a product suitable for making worsteds, a type of cloth requiring wool long enough to be combed out so that the fibers are arranged parallel to each other.

There are several types of Delaine Merino to which various names have been given. These types have been supported by different societies, but they are very similar and really should be considered, not as separate breeds, but as strains of the same breed. Some of the original importations of Merinos were bred to maintain a smooth body and a neck with a light fold, which were characteristic of the sheep as they were bred in Spain. A notable example was the flock of Counsel Jarvis, but the owners of flocks of this sort did not aim consistently at increasing the length of fleece or at improving the mutton conformation.

The breeding which resulted in the development of the real Delaine Merino occurred in eastern Ohio and western Pennsylvania. About 1809, W. R. Dickinson, of Steubenville, Ohio, got possession of some of the sheep that Humphrey imported in 1802. He maintained these in their purity until 1830, when he disposed of his flock. At the time the flock was dispersed, Adam Hildebrand, formerly in the employ of Dickinson, bought a few of the ewes, and James McDowell, who also had been in the employ of Dickinson and was then working for Hildebrand, received as a part of his remuneration two of the best ewe lambs and the second best ram lamb in the last crop bred by Dickinson. These lambs were sired by a large, fine ram known as Bolivar, and it is said that they were the foundation from which the Dickinson Delaine descended.

Over in Pennsylvania, the foundation stock was an importation made in 1820 by R. W. Mead. The sheep first came into the hands of Alexander Reed, and their descendants were furnished to a half dozen or more breeders, who developed important flocks, but the final steps in developing the real Delaine type in the Pennsylvania flocks consisted in using two rams, one being Spanish Black Top, a ram bred by C. J. Beal, of West Virginia, and used in a flock belonging to the sons of Ebeneezer McClellan, and the other a Spanish ram named Victor, bred by J. M. Miller and used by R. H. Russel and J. C. McNary. Just what is meant by the term Spanish and Black Top as descriptive of the breeding of these rams is difficult to explain, but it seems that Victor and the Beal ram more nearly resembled the American Merino in folds and properties of fleece than the smooth ewes upon which they were bred. In fact many Delaine breeders, after years of experience, have advocated the use of rams bordering on the American Merino type, when the ewe flock begins to slip backward in weight of fleece. They observe that such a cross greatly improves weight of fleece without having a material adverse effect on the length of wool and the mutton properties of the carcass. In Volume 2 of the Standard Delaine Register this statement is made: "It is with great difficulty that covering and density can be kept up in the absence of all folds." And there appears another statement to the effect that breeding a ram of the class B Merino on ewes free from folds has been most satisfactory and encouraged by Standard Delaine breeders.

Both the Black Top Spanish Merino and the Improved Black Top Merino are smooth Merinos of the Delaine type and should be regarded as belonging in the Delaine group. Their distinctive character is their very dark exterior due to a rather abundant clear, flowing yolk that becomes very dark in color when it hardens on the surface of the fleece. These sheep were first selected out from their lighter colored flock mates because they seemed more hardy. As separate strains they are unusually well developed in mutton properties, for they carry even, solid backs and well-filled thighs.

**Description.**—The description of the C-type American Merino coincides with that of the Delaine.

**Properties and Distribution.**—In producing the Delaine Merino, breeders have sought to produce a useful farmers' sheep. Therefore, they are more prolific, heavier milkers, and more reliable mothers than the American Merinos. Also the lambs are stronger at birth and hence more easily raised.

It is doubtful whether a better breed than the Delaine could be found for certain sections in Ohio, Pennsylvania and West Virginia, and farmers who own them in these regions will do well by going slow in deciding to replace them with some other breed. Delaines have been very popular in various regions of the West, one especially being the interior of Oregon, which served as a breeding ground from which sheepmen of Washington, Idaho, and Montana drew heavily.

At the present time it is impossible to make a sharp distinction between the C-type American Merino and the Delaine in either appearance or breeding.

In 1906 there was organized The American and Delaine Merino Record Association. This association which has its headquarters in Ohio resulted from the amalgamation of several smaller societies and is now the leading organization promoting the Merino sheep.

## QUESTIONS

1. What characteristics distinguish the Delaine from the A-type American Merino?
2. What characteristics in the Delaine were of especial importance to farmers?

## CHAPTER XXVII

# THE RAMBOUILLET

**History.**—The Rambouillet, a pure descendant of the Spanish Merino, originated in France. In 1785, Louis XVI, being impressed by the importance of wool and wool manufactures in the industrial growth of his country, asked the King of Spain, as a personal favor, for "permission to import from the celebrated Spanish flocks a flock of sheep with the highest quality of fine wool." His request was granted, and in October, 1786, 318 ewes and 41 rams, representing the best that M. Gilbert, the French agent, could find, were quartered in their new home on the government farm at Rambouillet, near Paris. Henceforth, these sheep were to take the name of this farm, which was formerly the property of the Marquis de Rambouillet, the famous Savant of the time of Louis the XIV, but taken over by the government during the French Revolution and ever since maintained for experimental purposes.

With the possible exception of the Leicesters, no other well-established breed of sheep has been developed with as definite a purpose in view, and beyond any question the progress of any other breed has not been so faithfully recorded as that of the Rambouillet in its original home. From 1786 to the present time the carefully kept records of the French flock have been preserved without a break. It is only by taking into consideration the various changes in directors, periods of discouragement and depression, and especially the recklessness and confusion of the Napoleonic wars, that one can realize what it has meant to keep these records.

The purpose uppermost in the minds of those who directed the making of the Rambouillet was to produce a fairly large, robust sheep yielding a fine fleece of good weight and a carcass of desirable mutton. In other words, they aimed at a dual-purpose sheep. In certain periods the emphasis seemed to be laid somewhat more strongly on the fleece than on the carcass, and in others the emphasis seemed to be reversed, but the net result has been a sheep suitable for both wool and mutton. It is doubtful, however, whether the carcass was ever developed quite so much for mutton in the government flock as it was in some of the privately owned flocks first of France and later of Germany.

Most of the privately owned flocks of France were founded on stock bred at Rambouillet, and probably all of them secured animals from that source. These were either sold or distributed as gifts for the purpose of encouraging the keeping of improved sheep. During the rule of Napoleon, and immediately afterwards, a great many Spanish Merinos were driven into France and blood from this

FIG. 138.—Rambouillet ram, B-type; a prize-winner bred by F. S. King Bros. Co., Laramie, Wyoming. The heavy folds on the neck and the wrinkles on the body back of the forelegs, on the thighs and at the dock indicate that this sheep is a B-type.

source may have been commingled with that received from the government farm.

The Germans got their foundation stock from the privately owned flocks of France, but they called it Rambouillet just as the French breeders had done.

**Importations to the United States.**—Rambouillets were brought to the United States in 1840, but at that time the American

Merino was coming to the front and the French sheep did not get a favorable reception in the East. When California began to be a place of importance, shortly after the gold craze of 1849, these French sheep were gathered up and sent to the Pacific coast, where they served as the foundation stock of the California French Merinos.

Although a few breeders in Ohio and Michigan bred Rambouillets in a rather quiet way, it remained for a German, Baron Von Homeyer, to introduce the Rambouillet as such to the United States

Fig. 139.—Rambouillet ram, C-type. Bred by University of Illinois, sold at auction, Salt Lake City, August, 1917, for $675. This sheep shows no wrinkles on the body and his conformation indicates the mutton qualities characteristic of the C-type.

and to attract the attention of the sheep breeders of this country toward them. This he did at the Columbian Exposition in Chicago in 1893 through W. G. Markham, of Avon, New York, who acted as his American agent. Baron Von Homeyer's sheep were so exceptional in size and shape that people gazed on them in wonder. To the breeders of American Merinos they seemed an almost impossible creation out of Merino blood. But they were what was wanted, for the wool market was depressed and the demand for mutton was rapidly growing, and just as soon as the country began to recover from the financial panic following 1893 these sheep attained a popularity that has never waned (Figs. 138 and 139).

**Description.**—Compared with other fine-wool breeds, the Rambouillet is a big sheep, somewhat upstanding, strong in bone, and distinctly robust in appearance. It bears evidence of mutton characteristics in thickness of body and fullness of thighs. The sheep with smooth bodies show more mutton than those tending toward numerous folds in the skin; in fact, many of the smooth Rambouillets have almost as good backs as some of the prominent mutton breeds. Mature rams in full fleece, and in good breeding condition weigh from 225 to 250 pounds, and ewes from 140 to 170 pounds. Show specimens usually exceed these upper limits in weight, and it is not uncommon for pregnant flock ewes to tip the beam at close to 200 pounds. Most of the rams have large spirally-turned horns, but the ewes are hornless.

In twelve months Rambouillet rams grow from 15 to 25 pounds of wool, and ewes from 10 to 18 pounds, but exceptional individuals often greatly exceed the upper limits given. The length of fleece varies from one and one-half inches to three or even more. The wool of the average Rambouillet is not as fine nor is it as even in structure throughout the fleece as that of the American and Delaine Merino. It is also more often open to criticism in color on account of the deposition of gummy yellow yolk.

Most Rambouillet breeders emphasize great extension of wool over face and legs, a matter which has been carried too far for practical purposes. Many specimens being completely covered with wool over the head and face are blind, and a blind sheep in a flock or band is a nuisance because it is crazy. Extreme covering over the legs collects mud and snow and hence is an inconvenience. It is time for Rambouillet breeders to revise their notions a little on head and leg covering.

The color of hair on face, ears, and legs of the Rambouillet is white, and the hoofs are also white. Either deep or light brown spots sometimes appear on the lips, ears, and around the eyes, and occasionally there are stripes of black in the hoofs. These small areas of dark pigment in either the hair or hoofs do not amount to disqualifications, but they are tolerated rather than desired. Soft, silky-like hair is regarded favorably, but, taken as a whole, the Rambouillet does not grow hair on face and legs as fine as does the American Merino (Figs. 140 and 141).

**Type.**—No standard of excellence has ever been constructed for the Rambouillet and, with respect to folds in the skin, the breed

FIG. 140.—Rambouillet ewe, B-type, bred by the University of Illinois. This ewe is what may be termed a light B-type. Note the heavy folds on the neck and the fold dropping from the underline.

FIG. 141.—Rambouillet ewe, C-type. Note the smooth mutton-like body.

varies almost as much in type as the American Merino. Certain breeders favor very strong folds on the neck and also a few on the body at such places as the dock, upper thighs, and fore and rear flanks. Such sheep when shorn may show many small wrinkles (called pin wrinkles) on the body. These heavily folded Rambouillets carry comparatively dense and oily fleeces and the wool tends to be shorter than in the smoother types. On the outer surface of the large neck folds, the wool is often so coarse that it is more like hair than wool. This kind of growth has been encouraged by a few breeders because they consider it indicative of a robust constitution, but it is a bad fault that should be discouraged, for it reduces the value of the fleece.

Fig. 142.—Rambouillet ewes bred by University of Illinois. The strong, rugged features of the head are characteristic of the breed.

Certain other breeders do not favor the type showing folds on the body and still others go so far as to object to pronounced wrinkles on the neck. As a rule, the smooth or plain Rambouillets are the more popular in the West because, with their better shape and lighter pelts, they sell for more as mutton and professional shearers object to shearing the wrinkled kind. In Ohio, New York, and Michigan, where sheep with heavy folds and wrinkles have been kept for a hundred years and where there was export demand for heavy fleeced sheep before the outbreak of the war, Rambouillets carrying wrinkles and folds are favorably regarded. (See Chapter XLII, also.)

Many breeders think they cannot produce heavy fleeces by using smooth rams. An inspection of flocks throughout the country would probably show that all but a small percentage of the ewes are comparatively smooth over their bodies and there would not be a large percentage with large wrinkles or folds on the neck. In other words, breeders differ with respect to types, mainly on the make-up of breeding rams used in stud flocks, some being willing to sacrifice considerably in mutton for the sake of extreme fleece qualities, while others insist upon a well balanced sheep as regards wool and mutton (Fig. 142).

The Ohio State Fair management has provided two classes for Rambouillets known as Class B and Class C. Class B includes the

Fig. 143.—Rambouillet lambs bred by Purdue University, LaFayette, Indiana. Note the small wrinkles on the body which disappear as the wool grows longer.

sheep having the more extreme development in fleece as indicated by wrinkles on the body, density and extension of wool over the body and the amount of yolk in the wool, while Class C includes the smooth sheep carrying only a few light folds on the neck and no wrinkles on the body (Fig. 143).

**Properties.**—Rambouillet mutton does not rank so high as that of the leading mutton breeds, but when well finished it is good mutton, good enough to satisfy an educated and discriminating palate.

Of the fine wool breeds, all of which are hardy, none are more so than the Rambouillet. Being large, strongly muscled, and capable of a long stride, they are able to travel far and to handle various kinds of forage. The ewes are fairly prolific, and the number of lambs, born to the number of ewes bred, ranges from 125 to 150 per cent. They are also good in maternal instinct and fair in yield of milk. At birth the lambs are strong and large, averaging about 10 pounds. If well fed they grow rapidly, and few if any of the mutton breeds produce lambs that increase in weight more rapidly after they are four or five months old.

Rambouillets, like the other fine-wool breeds, stay close together when on the open range, and of course this trait helps to make them popular in the West. But at present they are more popular in our

Fig. 144.—Rambouillet ram, Big Chief, bred by F. S. King Bros. Company, Laramie, Wyoming, and sold at auction, Salt Lake City, August, 1917, for $1300. This elephantine specimen of the breed weighed 375 pounds and walked with ease, showing that he was in no wise fatted to overdone condition.

range regions than the other fine-wool breeds, due doubtless to their superior size, greater prolificacy, and mutton qualities equal to the Delaine and C-type American Merino. When crossed with rams of the mutton breeds, the ewes produce excellent market lambs (Fig. 144).

**Distribution.**—Rambouillets are still kept in considerable numbers in France and Germany. Of both the older and newer countries the United States is their stronghold, but they have attained prominence in the Argentine, and South Africa has made some use of them. During the last few years many rams and ewes have been sold for exportation to Russia, Japan, Manchuria, Chili, Peru, and other countries. The American Rambouillet Sheep Breeders' Association is the most prominent organization promoting this breed of sheep. At the close of 1936 more than 350,000 sheep had been recorded by this society since it was organized forty years before.

## QUESTIONS

1. How was the Rambouillet breed developed?
2. When and why did the Rambouillet become popular in the United States?
3. In what respects do the Rambouillets differ from the American Merino?
4. In what parts of the United States are Rambouillets most popular?

## CHAPTER XXVIII

# THE KARAKUL (A FUR-BEARING BREED)[1]

**History.**—The Karakul [2] comes from the province of Bokhara. Its history is not definitely known, but it is thought that the foundation stock was the Arabi, whose blood has been combined with that of the Black Danadar to produce the sheep in the vicinity from which the Karakul derives its name. It is said that owners of sheep in Bokhara do not follow systematic methods of breeding and that on this account the Karakul can be regarded as a breed only in a general sense (Fig. 145).

**Description.**—The conformation of the Karakul clearly indicates that it has not been bred for mutton production because the top of the body is too narrow and too uneven to permit of a large quantity of meat in the regions of the valuable cuts. As a rule the leg is lacking in fullness, the rump is steep, the loin high, and the back depressed just behind the shoulders. It is characteristic for a triangular mass of fat weighing five or six pounds to develop at the upper part of the tail, and hang down toward the hocks. Because of this characteristic, the Karakul is known as a broadtail breed.

The wool of the mature sheep is very coarse and wiry, and it is brown in color. When the lambs are born, they have tightly curled, glossy black coats; and in order to get good fur they should be slaughtered before they are five days old, for if they are allowed to live longer their coats rapidly deteriorate as a fur product.

**Properties.**—In the United States Karakuls have been found to be hardy, vigorous and long-lived and adapted to arid or semi-arid conditions, although there are some flocks in humid regions. The ewes are good mothers and their lambs are large at birth and grow rapidly. Because of its coarseness and lack of uniform color, Karakul wool generally sells as carpet wool. There is usually some discrimination against high-grade or pure-

[1] See account of Karakul in U. S. D. A. Farmers' Bulletin 1632 and Texas Bulletin 405.

[2] The word Karakul is derived from Kara Kul, the name of a village in the eastern part of Bokhara.

bred Karakuls when sold for mutton. In the main, the industry has not yet been developed to a sound commercial basis in this country.

**Distribution.**—Several countries have recently become interested in the Karakul on account of the value of the skins of the young lambs. Large numbers have not been brought into the United States because of the long distance from Bokhara, and other difficulties incident to getting sheep out of that country.

Fig. 145.—Karakul ram. The great gaudy rump consists of a mass of fatty tissue.

About sixty-seven head have been imported and at present the number of pure-breds cannot be large. The pure-bred rams have been crossed with the well-known breeds of sheep, such as the Merino, Cheviot, Lincoln, Leicester, and Cotswold. The best results for fur bearing have been obtained by crossing with the long-wool breeds producing luster wools, and the poorest with the Merino cross. Just how valuable the crosses and grades are as breeding animals has not yet been definitely determined. It seems, however, that half or three-quarter blood rams, when crossed upon ewes containing no Karakul blood, are of little or no value as sires of fur-bearing lambs.

**Types of Lamb Fur.**—The fur taken from young lambs is known as Persian, Astrakhan, Broadtail, Krimmer, etc., and with the exception of Krimmer, which is supplied chiefly from the Crimean peninsula, it is obtained in large part from the Karakul, of Bokhara. Since they have the best defined, most uniform, and tightest curl, the Persians are of greatest value.

Fig. 146.—Karakul ewe and lamb. The wool of the mature sheep is coarse and wiry, but the lamb has a soft, glossy, black coat which can be made into valuable fur if the animal is slaughtered when it is only a few days old.

The Astrakhans have less luster or gloss, longer hair, and a more open curl than the Persians. The Broadtail skins, which are usually from lambs prematurely born, are soft, pliable, and light in weight, with shorter hair than the Persian, and instead of being tightly curled have a very attractive wavy pattern. The Krimmer is a gray fur, while the other types are black. Caracul is an open, lustrous type.

Lambskins vary greatly in value, according to quality. At the annual summer fair at Nijni Novgorod, in Russia, where practically all of the Bokhara skins are sold, the average wholesale value of skins in 1913 was $6.25. By the time they reach New York, the best dyed skins sell in small lots at from $12 to $20, while the inferior ones may sell for no more than $3. At the New York Auction Company's 1928 spring sale, fine character skins brought $4.00 to $6.00 and those of good character $2.25 to $2.75. It is reported that in 1927 fur traders in the United States handled over 4,580,000 Karakul pelts.

After careful work with Karakuls the Texas Station believes that one of the chief problems to be solved in placing Karakul sheep production on a sound commercial basis is improvement in breeding to reduce the variation in types of skins produced in a flock and assure a high proportion of similar lustrous, beautiful skins. Another difficulty is the development of a marketing system which will give the seller of small lots of skins access to the markets, but the Texas investigators conclude: "One would be quite optimistic to expect the time to come when the man with fewer than 100 skins will get nearly as much for his skins as the same kind of skins will bring in bales of 500 and more. From a purely business standpoint these sheep do not seem to offer as much profit as other breeds in regions where other breeds will thrive."

## QUESTIONS

1. In what particulars is the Karakul different from any other breed of sheep you have studied?
2. Where is the native home of the Karakul? What of its climate?
3. When should the Karakul be slaughtered to yield good fur?
4. What crosses have been made between the Karakul and other breeds with a view to producing fur?
5. What do you think of the Karakul as a mutton sheep?

# PART IV
## THE MANAGEMENT OF THE FLOCK

## CHAPTER XXIX

# ESTABLISHING THE COMMERCIAL FARM FLOCK

**Methods of Establishing the Farm Flock.**—There are two methods of establishing the farm flock. One is to begin with a few ewes and through increase of progeny gradually build up in numbers until the flock is of suitable size. The other method consists in beginning with as many ewes as the farm should maintain in the system of farming being followed.

For the beginner with sheep, the first method is the better, particularly if he has had little experience with other classes of livestock, because in the small flock the performance of individuals can be studied, while in a large one observations have to be limited largely to the performance of the flock as a whole. When the flock is small the owner can easily become familiar with the characteristics of the best and the worst ewes. He fixes in mind the kinds that produce the largest, fattest lambs and yield the heaviest fleeces. He also takes note of the kind that remain rugged through a long period of profitable production. Then, too, he becomes so familiar with each of his sheep that he develops the power to detect slight disorders in his flock, and this power is a fundamental qualification of the successful shepherd.

But not all of the advantage lies with the man who begins with the small flock. He who buys a flock of the size he thinks suitable for his farm has assurance of keeping his land stocked more nearly up to its capacity than can he who adds to his flock slowly.

He also has an advantage in that he can make more economical use of his labor and can market to better advantage. The man with the small flock often is embarrassed in attempting to find an outlet for the few lambs he has for sale, while the owner of a large flock may have enough lambs to justify shipping to a central market.

Whether the beginner starts with a few or with all he should ever have, really depends on whether or not he counts on permanently staying in the sheep business. If his plans are temporary and his intentions more or less speculative, he had better begin fully equipped. But if he aims at permanence he would do well to begin modestly in order to educate himself through observing the performance of particular individuals. Should he begin with only a few he should plan ultimately to have a flock of sufficient size to make it well worth his while to give it adequate care. When the flock is very small, the temptation to neglect it for larger interests is strong when labor is costly or scarce. The well-established flock should contain at least thirty-five ewes if it is to be given adequate care without excessive labor cost per head. Indeed, some studies have shown very little difference in labor requirement, except at lambing time, whether the flock numbers 35 or 100 breeding ewes.

**Where Ewes for the Farm Flock May Be Secured.**—There are two main sources from which to draw ewes for the farm flock.

Fig. 147.—Fancy selected native breeding ewes, showing uniformity in breeding. (Illinois Station Bulletin 129.)

First, they may be secured locally in almost every part of the country where farm flocks are kept. Second, they may be purchased during the summer and early autumn months on the large livestock markets where both native and western ewes are sold as foundation stock for farm flocks (Figs. 147 and 148).

**Selecting Ewes for the Farm Flock.**—One of the first considerations in selecting ewes for the breeding flock is uniformity. They should be as nearly alike as possible in breeding and size, because uniformity in these particulars is necessary if a uniform lot of lambs is to be secured. When the owner has a uniformly good lot of lambs he can market all of them at the same time and such lots always meet with ready demand on the market. Should the ewes be very unlike in breeding their lambs are almost sure to lack in uniformity, even though they are all by the same sire. Then, too, the wool from ewes lacking in uniformity of breeding is likely to vary so much in quality that it can not be disposed of to the best advantage.

Second, ewes selected for the farm flock should be well grown and thrifty. If they look as though they have been well cared for and have had a chance to become fully developed, the owner has

FIG. 148.—Choice Western breeding ewes suitable for producing prime market lambs when mated with pure bred rams of proper mutton type. See lambs from these ewes in frontispiece and in Figs. 75, 85 and 89.

reason to feel that their inherited maternal powers will function to full extent. Sometimes stunted ewes are good producers of lambs, but more often they are not. It is seldom advisable to start with unthrifty females for the reason that they are usually infested with internal parasites, such as stomach worms, lung worms, and tapeworms. Unthrifty ewes may do exceedingly well when placed where sheep have not been grazed for years, in which case their purchase seems to be a bargain, but they are likely to infest the pastures with the result that before the owner is aware of it he is beset with parasitic troubles (Fig. 149).

Third, breeding ewes should be not only well grown and thrifty, but they should also bear evidence of strong constitution. They should be active in their movements and alert to strange sights and sounds. They should carry their heads well up; their chests should be wide and their bosoms full; their legs should be fairly short, wide apart and placed so that they support the body well. Their whole contour should suggest style, compactness, capacity, and vitality. Without hardihood and productive power, breeding ewes are of little use to their owners, and these properties are not present to the fullest extent in ewes having weak constitutions.

Fig. 149.—Old thin ewes past their day of usefulness for breeding purposes. As a rule such ewes do not have good teeth nor sufficient vitality for growing either lambs or wool. (Illinois Station Bulletin 129.)

Fourth, ewes selected for raising market lambs should possess good mutton form. If they are undesirable in form their lambs, even though sired by a ram that is ideal in form, may reach market finish and weight too slowly, or they may not be sufficiently good in form ever to develop into a choice or prime market product.

Fifth, ewes intended for the farm flock should have dense, compact fleeces. Wool, being a non-conductor of heat, tends to lessen the effect of sudden changes in temperature on the body and the structure of the wool fiber is such that to a certain extent it holds water and foreign substances away from the skin. Therefore, sheep that are clothed in dense, compact fleeces extending over all parts of the body are much better prepared to withstand the hardships brought about by changes in weather than are those bearing scant, open fleeces. It should also be remembered that even though wool may be comparatively low in price, it brings in some revenue and helps somewhat toward making the flock profitable. The best types of wool are those that grade from "one-fourth blood," "three-eighths blood" or "half blood" combing. These wools range from $2\frac{1}{2}$ to 4 inches in length, and in fineness they correspond to the wool produced by the Down breeds. Ewes are at their best for wool when 2 or 3 years of age, later fleeces being lighter, with a marked decline coming at 7 or 8 years.

Sixth, the flock mothers should be of quiet disposition. This statement is in no sense a contradiction to what was said in discussing the constitution of breeding ewes. We are here distinguishing between the ewe possessing sense and the one devoid of sense. Reject the fools; they are always upsetting something, most often the shepherd's temper.

Seventh, breeding ewes should be sound and in their prime. Their teeth should be in good condition, that is, they should be intact and not worn down short. Their udders should be soft and pliable, the teats intact and free from hard cores. Very fat individuals should be rejected, for they are either non-breeders or so filled with internal fat that their lambs are likely to be small and weak. It is not safe to buy ewes that are lame or addicted to coughing. As a rule, ewe lambs should not be selected for breeding, as they are too young to be sufficiently developed at lambing time. Hence, they are likely to have trouble in lambing and to be deficient in maternal instinct.

Eighth, the purchaser of breeding females should know his needs and select accordingly. If he is in a neighborhood of good lamb raisers he would do well to buy ewes that will produce lambs about like those of his neighbors. By so doing, he will be in position to coöperate with them in the disposal of his lamb crop. If he has a great deal of heavy, coarse feed to dispose of he can handle large ewes to advantage. If he has hilly, extensive range with sparse vegetation, smaller and more active ewes are what he should select. If he wishes to engage in a specialized business, such as winter lambs, the selecting of his ewes is a problem requiring care.

**Selecting Ewes After the Flock is Established.**—There may be two reasons for selecting breeding ewes after the flock has been established: (1) to increase the size of the flock, (2) to replace poor individuals. Reject:

1. Ewes not bringing lambs regularly.
2. Ewes habitually bringing late lambs.
3. Ewes failing in general condition.

In case the owner replaces ewes "culled out" or adds to his flock with ewes of his raising, he has an opportunity to take advantage of several important factors in selecting ewe lambs for the breeding flock:

1. Select early maturing ewe lambs of approved type. By so doing he will accomplish something toward building up a flock which will produce early maturing lambs. This is a matter of no little importance, for the lambs which grow into a marketable product in a short time are likely to be the most profitable.

2. The ewe lambs should be from heavy milking dams. This will be accomplished if early maturing lambs are selected because they are usually well fed on mother's milk. The breeder should know whether or not the dams of the ewe lambs he proposes to reserve for breeders are desirable milkers.

3. The ewe lambs reserved for the breeding flock should be nearly of the same age, and preferably from the first, rather than from the last of the lamb crop. By all means, the very late-born ewe lambs should not be retained, for there is a tendency for them to breed late and they oftentimes fail to develop into large, thrifty ewes. Those of nearly the same age may be expected to breed at about the same time and hence contribute toward a crop of lambs that is uniform with respect to age. Young ewes are not sufficiently mature to place with the ram until after they are one year old.

4. The ewe lambs selected should be those that were born as twins if it is hoped to develop a flock showing marked prolificacy. Although lambs born as twins will not often grow as rapidly as single lambs, they do reach the same mature weight and the profitableness of farm flock husbandry hinges upon the raising and marketing of a large percentage of good-type lambs per ewe. The ewe which produces a pair of twin lambs that grow fast has shown her milking ability in a most convincing way and affords a good basis for selection on performance. As a rule the ewe increases in prolificacy until the fifth or sixth year, with a marked decline after the eighth year.

**Selecting the Ram for the Farm Flock.**—The ram should be pure bred and of correct market or mutton type. It has already been conceded that the ewes of the farm flock are likely to be grades which, if true, make it imperative that the ram be a pure-bred. If the ewes should be pure-bred, it would be ridiculous,

Fig. 150.

Fig. 151.

Fig. 150.—Pure-bred Shropshire ram suitable for siring market lambs; sire of lambs in Fig. 75.

Fig. 151.—Pure-bred Southdown ram, sire of lambs shown in frontispiece.

of course, to advocate the use of a grade ram. A pure-bred ram should be used in the grade flock as he carries a greater concentration of good blood than a grade ram. When bred to grade

Fig. 152—Pure-bred Hampshire ram suitable for siring market lambs; sire of lambs in Fig. 85.

Fig. 153.—Pure-bred Oxford-Down ram; sire of lambs in Fig. 89.

ewes his get have a tendency to resemble him in greater degree than they resemble their dams (Figs. 150–153) while such is not likely to be true of the get of the grade sire.

Since lambs sired by a pure-bred ram will so often resemble him, it is necessary, indeed, that he be of desirable market or mutton type. He should be wide and deep for his length. He should be symmetrical, that is, evenly developed. Well sprung ribs, wide loin, well-filled thighs, a wide, full twist, and a deep, even covering of firm flesh are all points of mutton excellence which should be sought. He should be active and vigorous in order to sire lambs

Fig. 154.—Common rams with shallow bodies and narrow chests. Mixed in breeding. The kind that should never be used for breeding purposes.

full of life and vigor, the kind of lambs that will have the advantage in the race toward market perfection. Indications of activity and vigor are bold, brisk, direct movements, stylish carriage, wide-open, bright eyes, wide nose and well-expanded nostrils, deep chest, and well-extended brisket.

As in the case of ewes selected for the flock the ram should be well grown, though it is not necessary that he be an unusually large representative of his breed. In fact, it is safer to select a ram of medium size, since the over-large animal is in many cases coarse, and this coarseness, if transmitted, will reduce the value of the lamb crop when it reaches the market (Fig. 154).

If the owner intends to reserve ewe lambs for breeding purposes, he should select a ram with a compact fleece of good length, quality, and weight, but if he plans to sell the whole lamb crop he can afford to disregard fleece qualities. He can also afford to ignore breed type in the ram to considerable extent. It would not be advisable to select an individual so badly "off type" that he does not show to what breed he belongs. There is often an opportunity, however, to buy a ram of excellent conformation but deficient in some of the "fancy" points of the breed and such an animal would no doubt beget first-class offspring for market purposes. If the ewe lambs are saved for breeding purposes it is desirable that the successive rams be of the same breed so that a uniform flock may be secured.

FIG. 155.—Range Hampshire rams. These rams are pure-breds, uniform in type and thrifty and hence are highly satisfactory for range or any other breeding for market purposes.

It is well to select the ewes before choosing the ram to mate with them. If they are inclined to excessive length of neck and legs, particular emphasis should be placed on short legs and neck in the ram. Whatever the general defect in the ewe flock, an attempt should be made through the ram to correct this fault in the offspring. But in so doing, it is not advisable to use a ram with any pronounced defect merely because he happens to be strong where the ewes are weak. Remember that the lambs may inherit the defects of both parents, hence the necessity of using a sire well developed in all his parts.

**Selecting Ewes for Range Flocks.**—In selecting ewes for range flocks about the same rules apply as in the selection for the farm flock. If the range flocks are to be handled by herders on unenclosed land it is necessary that the sheep have enough Merino blood to preserve their herding instinct and to prevent their fleeces from becoming too open and dry. Their feet should be sound and strong. They must be able to withstand rather hard conditions. The rangeman never selects old ewes. Since it is impossible for the rangeman to select large numbers by very careful individual inspection he bases his choice on general appearance, size, and shearing qualities. Ewes larger than the average size of the flock are, as a rule, the best lamb producers and likewise yield heavy fleeces. The fleece weights obtained at shearing time, length of staple, shrinkage, and grade of wool are used in culling ewes for wool production.

Fig. 156.—Range rams, Rambouillets, on a ranch in Wyoming.

**Selecting Rams for Range Flocks.**—As a rule rams are subjected to very hard service on the range, and unless they are acclimated to range conditions, they are likely to be of little use. All those qualifications which are indispensable in the rams for farm flocks must also be possessed by the ram selected for the range flock, with special emphasis placed upon activity and hardiness (Figs. 155 and 156).

## QUESTIONS

1. What are the methods of establishing farm flocks?
2. Discuss the advantages and disadvantages of each method.
3. Where would you secure ewes to establish a farm flock?
4. Name the features to consider in selecting the ewes. Discuss each.
5. After the flock is once established need the owner practice selection?
6. What are the advantages of raising your own ewe lambs?
7. Discuss the selection of the ram.
8. Why pay attention to the character of the ram's fleece?

## CHAPTER XXX

# THE BREEDING SEASON

**Condition of the Ewes.**—To be in proper condition at mating time, ewes should be gaining rather than losing in weight. When they are thriving instead of "standing still" or "going back" in condition, they are more likely to come in heat and the whole flock will breed within three or four weeks. The lambs come at the time desired, are the same age, and develop uniformly. Ewes supplied with healthy blood, gaining in weight likely secrete more reproductive cells (ova). English investigators believe that it is necessary to have a high state of nutritional activity each breeding season if ewes are to produce a large percentage of lambs. An increase of over 18 per cent is reported by American investigators for ewes given extra feed and bred at their first and more productive "heat" period (Fig. 157). It is certainly true that a ewe thriving at mating time gives the developing fœtus a good start to become a lusty, vigorous offspring at birth.

**How to Condition the Ewes.**—As the time for breeding approaches, ewes that have raised lambs are often in thin condition, but since the breeding season usually comes at a time when the days and nights are becoming cooler, all healthy ewes are disposed to take on flesh if sufficient feed is available. Hence, about ten days before the ram is to be turned with them, it is advisable to begin giving them extra feed by turning them into more luxuriant pasture than they have had, or by giving them a light grain ration of about one-half pound per head daily in addition to their usual pasture.

Pumpkins broken and scattered over the pasture serve as a supplement to it, and when fed in this way furnish a means for "flushing," as this practice of stimulating the ewes with extra feed is called. Fresh growths of rape can also be utilized to advantage. In England, white mustard seed is frequently mixed in the feed for the purpose of inducing the ewes to come in heat, and there are also other stimulants, but natural feeds should be tried before these more or less artificial measures are employed.

Very succulent grazing, such as green second-growth clover, even though it be of rampant growth, is not very satisfactory for ewes at breeding time. They do not improve in condition on such feed to any great extent and they often come in heat several times before getting in lamb. As regards other green growths, however, there is no other way of flushing which is more efficient or as convenient as turning the ewes in on a fairly luxurient pasture of bluegrass, timothy, or mixed grasses.

Sometimes good producing ewes are inclined to be overfat. They should be kept on very scant grazing for some time before the breeding season, and then, about the time the breeding season begins, placed on good feed.

Fig. 157.—These ewes being thrifty and gaining in flesh are in proper condition for mating.

**Feeding the Ewes Just after Mating.**—Mansell, a prominent English authority, advocates keeping ewes on a rather scant ration for several days after they are mated with the rams. He thinks that continuing them on abundant and stimulating feed causes them to recur in heat two or three times and thus the time of becoming pregnant is delayed.

**Preparing the Ewes for Mating.**—If the owner wishes to keep an accurate breeding record, he should place numbered metal tags in the ears of the ewes and on their sides he should stamp numbers corresponding with those on the tags with either wood or iron stencils. Then by turning the ram in with the ewes for an hour or so each day the owner can manage to keep a record of the service (Fig. 158).

It is always well to clip the wool close around the docks of the ewes; it prevents them from befouling themselves and removes obstacles for the ram in serving. In case ewes are very fat and gaudy at the rump, the wool should also be clipped close on the top of the rump (Fig. 159).

**Condition of the Ram.**—The ram should be active, vigorous and in medium flesh during the breeding season. To do effective service, he should be strong in his pasterns and well supported by his hind legs (Fig. 160).

Fig. 158. Fig. 159.

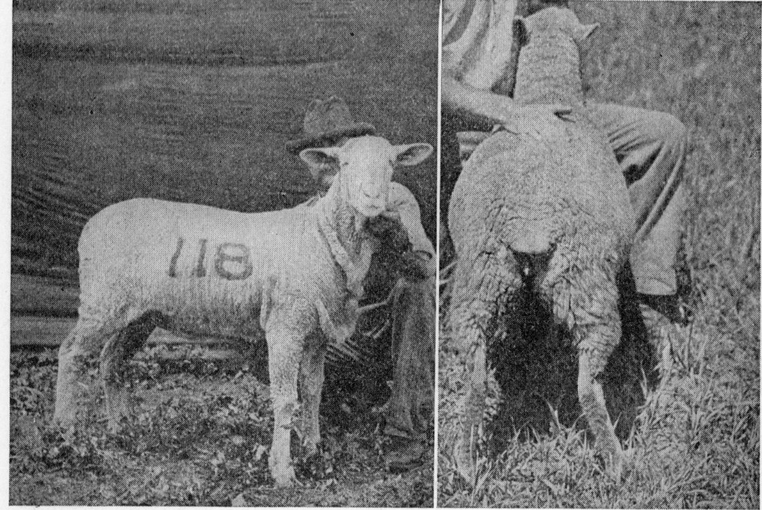


Fig. 158.—It is easy to record the date of breeding of a ewe with stencil mark on her side.

Fig. 159.—A ewe thus trimmed around the dock is properly prepared for mating with the ram.

**Feed and Exercise.**—In many flocks the ram is turned in with the ewes and allowed to go without any special attention. Such a method seems careless and inadvisable; nevertheless, it possesses some merit. Usually an active, vigorous ram is of nervous temperament and if he is removed from the flock for a part of each day he spends the time in worrying. Sometimes he may even refuse to eat while away from the flock, and he reduces in condition faster than if he were allowed to remain with the ewes. With such a ram it would be better to allow him to remain with the ewes most of the time, taking him away just long enough each day to have a feed of grain. Should the ram be of quiet disposition and not disposed to fret when taken from the flock, it is advisable to keep him by himself for about half the time, or with wethers or perhaps with two or three ewes in a lot where he will take a moderate amount of exercise.

It is not always possible to have the ram in good condition in the breeding season. He may be old or lame, or for unknown reasons thin in flesh. He may be fit for some service, but in order to have

FIG. 160.—A vigorous, active ram in proper condition for breeding season.

him sire a considerable number of lambs his energies must be conserved. He should be allowed with the flock for only an hour or two each day and should have a liberal supply of choice green feed.

Whether or not the ram is allowed to run with the flock in breeding season practically all of the time he should be given grain, the amount to depend on his size. If he be of medium size, he should eat at least one pound per day of some such mixture as three parts oats and one part wheat bran by weight. These feeds are excellent for a ram at service, as the bran acts as a mild laxative and the oats are invigorating. In case the ram is in thin flesh, it may be well to add corn and linseed oil meal to the grain part of his ration, making a mixture of corn, five; oats, ten; bran, three; and oil meal, two parts by weight.

**Preparing for Mating.**—As a rule the ram will copulate with greater ease if the wool on his belly is clipped short for several inches in front of the penis. Fat, clumsy rams should be shorn close all over the body, as they are more active and less subject to overheating after the fleece is removed. In England what is known as a "teaser" is employed if the breeding ram is so fat and heavy on his feet that circulating through the flock in search of ewes "in heat" tires him. The "teaser," a light, active ram with an apron tied in front of his penis so that he cannot effect copulation, is allowed to circulate through the flock in order to locate the ewes "in heat." By removing and placing them in a small pen or lot with the breeding ram his strength is conserved and he can breed many more ewes than would otherwise be possible (Fig. 161).

Fig. 161.—Preparing the ram for better breeding service by shearing the wool from his belly.

By smearing a paint, non-injurious to the wool, between the fore legs of the ram each day, a paint mark will be left on all the ewes he serves. This aids in keeping records. Every 16 days English breeders change the color of the paint. Then it is possible to discover which ewes recur in heat. For this purpose mix enough red or other ochre or lampblack with lubricating oil to make a thick paste. (Fig. 162.)

The number of ewes a ram will serve in a season depends on his age and vigor, and to a certain extent upon his breeding. Western sheepmen claim that a ram of any of the English mutton breeds will serve more ewes than a Merino of similar age and state of thrift.

The method of handling the ram also has an influence on the number he will serve. If he is allowed with the flock a short time each day his energy will be conserved to such an extent that he will get more ewes in lamb than if he were allowed with them all the time.

FIG. 162.—Smearing paint on ram in order to mark ewes when mating.

The above statement may not hold for a very nervous ram. A vigorous ram from one to four years of age is sufficient for 35 to 50 ewes if allowed to run with them all the time; if allowed with them for a short time each day he is sufficient for 50 to 75 ewes.

## QUESTIONS

1. Discuss the necessity of having the ewes in a gaining condition in breeding season.
2. How would you condition the ewes?
3. What is the advantage of keeping the ewes on rather scant rations for a few days directly after they are mated?
4. Outline a good method of keeping records on the ewes at mating time.
5. Discuss the condition of the ram at breeding time.
6. When is it advisable to turn the ram in with the ewes at breeding time and let him go without any special attention? When is it not advisable?
7. Would you give the ram grain during the breeding season? Why?
8. What is a "teaser"?
9. Is it possible to have the ram mark the ewes at the time of service?
10. How many ewes will a ram serve in one season?
11. Upon what factor may this depend?

## CHAPTER XXXI

## CARE OF EWES DURING PREGNANCY

**Condition.**—Ewes should not be given a fattening ration during the period of pregnancy, but they should be put in rather high condition, for the following reasons: First, they are more likely to give birth to strong, vigorous lambs, and to have the amount of milk necessary to make their offspring grow rapidly. Second, being well-fed, and having an adequate supply of milk, they are less likely to disown their lambs than are thin, improperly nourished ewes. Third, when the lambs are born, the ewes should have a considerable reserve of fat to assist in carrying them through the suckling period, for this is a time when the demands on them are so great that they usually fail to maintain their weight even though they are liberally fed. So important is this matter of proper condition at lambing time that in case a number of ewes are in very thin condition at the close of the breeding season they should be taken out to themselves and given an extra amount of feed (Fig. 163).

**Feed in Fields.**—On most farms, particularly in the corn belt of the United States, there are pastures, oat or wheat stubble, and corn stalks to be utilized in the fall of the year. It is the best policy to make use of the stubble and stalks as early as possible before they have deteriorated in feeding value through exposure to rains and frosts. Bluegrass and timothy pastures and even old clover fields can be left for use until late autumn and early winter in case the stubble and stalks furnish an abundance of food. In fact, pastures in the corn belt can be grazed with sheep most of the time during all of the winter months, but they should not be injured by over-pasturing and, unless they constitute a large acreage for the number of sheep kept, they should not be depended upon as the only source of feed during that time.

If the amount of pasture is limited, some succulent autumn and winter feed may be obtained by sowing rye late in August or early in September at the rate of one bushel per acre. In the northern states, however, rye as a winter pasture should not be regarded as a feed of considerable sustaining and fattening power, but it furnishes some succulence, and grazing gives ewes the exercise they need.

**Harvested Feeds.**—Ordinarily it is best to begin feeding pregnant ewes grain or hay or both not later than January first, and often it is advisable to begin a month earlier than this. In fact, it is impossible to set a definite time for beginning to use harvested feeds, and the owner must be guided solely by the supply of feed in the fields and the condition of his flock. Unless the ewes are in thin flesh the amount of grain fed should not be more than five-tenths to seven-tenths pound per head per day to individuals weighing

FIG. 163.—Ewes in proper condition for lambing. These ewes are in rather high condition with respect to flesh and fat and being so will have enough milk for their lambs.

140 to 175 pounds. Whole oats are always considered good feed for sheep, but other grains and concentrated feed products can be used. Corn alone is not considered by many of the best shepherds as a good grain feed for breeding sheep because they think that it is too heating. The writer, however, believes corn has been too harshly criticised by many shepherds, for it is a good feed when used with discretion. If it is mixed with oats or with several concentrates palatable to sheep, it can form a useful part of the ration. Breeding sheep will do fairly well on a moderate amount of grain composed entirely of corn, provided good leguminous hay is fed.

Economy and efficiency are what the owner must think of when compounding rations. Such feeds as linseed oil meal and bran are usually costly and hence, when placed in the ration, add to the cost of maintaining the flock. If the flock can be kept in good condition with less expensive feeds than oil meal and bran it would be better not to use them. In most cases, it is possible to keep pregnant ewes in desirable condition by feeding oats, corn, and some leguminous roughage, as clover, alfalfa hay, soybean or cowpea hay. Indeed, it is often unnecessary to feed any grain when these roughages are available. Too much dependence must not be placed on poorer grade roughages that are low in protein and mineral content. Pregnant ewes that were fed on a mixed grain ration with timothy hay and oat straw failed to produce as strong lambs or to suckle them as well as ewes given the same grains but supplied with legume roughages. Many cases show that ewes fed only legume roughages during pregnancy produced stronger lambs than ewes fed non-legume roughages with additional grain.

**Silage.**[1]—Of late years the question has been frequently asked: "Is corn silage a good feed for pregnant ewes?" Indeed, it is a good feed, provided certain precautions are observed in making it and feeding it. It should be made when the grains on the ears of corn are passing out of the dough stage and beginning to harden. In the process of making it the corn plant should be cut very fine and distributed evenly in the silo so that there will be a minimum of moldy silage. In feeding it care should be taken not to give the sheep any that is moldy or frozen. The usual recommendations are to feed limited amounts of silage and never use it as the only roughage. However, tests at the Illinois Station involving many ewes over a five-year period furnish the basis for saying that there need be no fear in using silage as the sole roughage throughout pregnancy. The use of small amounts of protein supplement and ground limestone or bone meal to correct the protein and mineral deficiencies of silage resulted in a ration fully equal to alfalfa, soybean, clover, or lespedeza hays. In fact, throughout all the trials, ewes fed daily about six pounds of silage, one-fifth pound of soybean oil meal and one-half ounce of limestone or bone meal excelled ewes fed about three and one-quarter pounds of legume hays in gain in weight, in thriftiness and in cleanliness of wool. Lambs of the ewes fed silage were at birth fully equal in vigor and size to those of other groups.

Silage is regarded as a cheap feed and because of its succulent nature should be given favorable consideration as at least

---

[1] See Chapter XXXIX for further discussion on silage and roots.

a part of the ration of pregnant ewes. For a very small flock it is difficult to feed silage fast enough to prevent spoilage, but owners of farm flocks usually have other classes of livestock and this difficulty will not often arise.

**Roots.**—In England, Canada, and northern United States, roots are an important sheep feed. Swedish turnips and mangels are the kinds most commonly used. For pregnant ewes the turnips are preferable; however, mangels are fed to ewes at the Illinois Station from October till April or May with good results. The chemical analysis of roots shows them to be comparatively low in feed nutrients. It has been well said that there is something in roots good for sheep, not listed as nutrients. The presence of certain vitamines and minerals meet the needs of pregnant ewes and young lambs during the season when green pastures are lacking. In the corn belt region of the United States and in other regions having about the same weather with respect to summer temperature, much of the growing season is too hot for Swedish turnips. Instead of growing firm and solid they become hollow and worthless. Mangels, however, can be grown successfully in the corn belt and in other regions of similar climate, but the yields are not as large as in regions farther north. Moreover, they, and turnips as well, require a great deal of hand labor, which is very scarce on American farms. Hence in corn-growing regions silage largely takes the place of roots. But if the flock is small and if no other classes of livestock that consume silage are kept it will pay to seed an acre or two to mangels, by starting in very early spring.

Silage and roots are similar in that each furnishes succulence, the importance of which has long been emphasized by many of the most successful sheepmen, and, like silage, roots must be fed with care if good results are to follow. In regions where large root crops are grown there is a temptation to save the hay and grain and to feed roots to excess, which, if yielded to, often results in abnormal losses of both ewes and lambs at lambing time. Wrightson in his "Sheep, Breeds, and Management" advises against feeding more than twelve pounds of roots per head daily to pregnant ewes, and evidently Wrightson refers to sheep of great feeding capacity. Most American sheepmen would not feed more than three or four pounds per head daily. For winter use, mangels and other roots should be stored in a well ventilated root cellar. If they are harvested when dry and stored without bruising they keep well. Most roots are sliced or pulped before they are given to sheep.

**Water.**—Plenty of good drinking water is very necessary to the health and thrift of pregnant ewes. In coldest weather ewes receiving nothing but dry feed will drink from two to four quarts per head daily. Avoid snow and ice water when water of proper drinking temperature can be had.

**Salt and Minerals.**—Salt is a necessity for the health of sheep of all kinds and especially for bred ewes. When it is kept before them in some suitable form at all times they are assured of an adequate supply. With a liberal supply of legume roughages, particularly those grown on soils containing an abundance of lime and phosphorous, there is usually no need to supply additional minerals unless cases of goiter develop. Under such circumstances one ounce of sodium iodide, thoroughly mixed with a barrel of salt, has been recommended.

**Exercise.**—Daily exercise is good for pregnant ewes because it stimulates the circulation of blood and assists in keeping the digestive organs in good condition. It does ewes the most good when they take it upon their own initiative, but if they are not inclined to exercise, which is often the case toward the close of the pregnant period, they will be benefited some by being driven from fifteen to thirty minutes each day at a moderate pace; but some ewes become so heavy and clumsy that they ought not to go more than a few steps at a time. A good way to induce ewes to take exercise is to scatter their dry roughage as corn stover over the ground for a considerable distance. Hayracks may be distributed over a well-drained and well-bedded open lot. In moving from one rack to another the ewes get about all the exercise they need. The feed lot may be some distance from where the ewes sleep. Give them a little feed in this lot each day. They go to and from this lot of their own accord. Corn stover set up in the form of a huge stack in a lot serves as a strong objective for the ewes.

All violent exercise should be avoided, particularly after their pregnant condition becomes apparent. Few things can be more disastrous to the prospective lamb crop than to have the ewes chased by dogs. The effects of violent exercise are abortion and defective lambs. It is a mistake to allow pregnant ewes to walk through deep stiff mud. In so doing there is danger of straining to such an event that abortion may result. The same thing may occur if ewes are made to jump over obstacles or if they are allowed to crowd through narrow doors (Fig. 164.)

**Shelter.**—It is necessary to protect pregnant ewes from the cold rains of autumn and winter. Many people make the mistake of not housing their ewes until they have become wet, when practically all of the damage has been done. As soon as it begins to rain they should be driven to shelter and kept there until the storm is over. Snow, unless very wet and heavy, does little harm to ewes because

Fig. 164.—Ewes advanced in pregnancy should travel at a leisurely gait.

they shake off that which collects on their backs. As a rule, they like to bed down in a deep, dry snow, and generally they may do so without injurious results.

The barn or shed provided for ewes should be well ventilated but free from strong draughts that blow directly on them. The floor should be dry, and the surrounding lots should be well drained.

During the pregnant period there should be no particular effort to make the shelter warm, as the chief danger with respect to temperature lies in making it too warm (Fig. 165).

**The Ram.**—As to what should be done with the ram after breeding season depends upon his disposition and behavior toward the ewes. If he becomes "bossy" and butts and crowds them about he should be removed and placed in a separate pen. In case the owner prefers not to have very late born lambs in his flock it will

Fig. 165.—A good barn for pregnant ewes—note the wide doors.

be necessary, of course, to take the ram from the flock after the breeding season is considered closed unless it is certain that all of the ewes are with lamb.

**Rations for Pregnant Ewes.**—The foregoing discussion leads to the conclusion that it is possible to use a wide variety of feeds and a great many different combinations of them in deciding upon rations for pregnant ewes. It seems from a review of many experimental feeding trials and from observation of many flocks in various sections of the country that the flockmasters who use ample amounts of home-grown feeds of good quality and who are careful to see that these feeds provide fairly generous quantities of protein and mineral need have little concern regarding the outcome of the approaching lambing season.

The amounts to supply are dependent to a large degree upon the kinds of feed used and the size of the ewes. It would seem advisable to provide sufficient quantities to enable ewes to gain from at least 15 to 30 pounds per head between breeding and lambing times, provided, of course, they were in proper condition when mating occurred. Ewes will lose much of this gain when they drop their lambs, and those ewes which are good milk producers will have lost all of it in a short time. For economical maintenance roughages or roughages and pastures must be the basis of the winter ration. During the period when grain is fed the cost of the ration is likely to be unnecessarily great if the grain is fed in a high proportion to roughage. One pound of grain to three pounds of dry roughage is a sufficiently high proportion for use during the last month or two of pregnancy. Indeed, a ratio of one pound of grain to five or six pounds of dry roughage is very often ample.

The following tabulations indicate the amounts of feeds to be supplied to pregnant ewes under various conditions. The amounts are given in pounds and refer to the daily feed per ewe, which is divided between morning and evening feedings. In all cases the quantities indicated are based on ewes weighing approximately 125 to 150 pounds.

*Ration No. 1*

| | |
|---|---|
| Alfalfa hay | 3.5 |

Ample for the entire pregnancy period. Improved through the use of .5 pound of oats or corn or both mixed equal amounts by weight during last month or two before lambing. Clover, lespedeza, or soybean hays may be substituted for alfalfa.

*Ration No. 2*

| | |
|---|---|
| Alfalfa or other legume hays | 2.0 |
| Corn silage | 3.0 |
| Grain as in No. 1 | .5 |

*Ration No. 3*

| | |
|---|---|
| Alfalfa or other legume hays | 2.0 |
| Oat straw, corn fodder | 1.0-2.0 |
| Grain as in No. 1 | .5 |

*Ration No. 4*

| | |
|---|---|
| Alfalfa or other legume hays | 2.0 |
| Sheaf oats | 1.0-2.0 |

*Ration No. 5*

| | |
|---|---|
| Corn silage | 7.0 |
| Supplement,* fed on silage | .25 |
| Oats as in No. 1 | .5 |

*Ration No. 6*

| | |
|---|---|
| Alfalfa or other legume hays | 2.0 |
| Bluegrass, wheat, rye or other pasture | |

*Ration No. 7*

| | |
|---|---|
| Non-legume hays | 2.5 |
| Supplement as in No. 5 | .25 |
| Grain | .5 |

In many cases the grain portion of the ration may be improved by using a mixture of feeds. The following are some mixtures suggested by various experiment station workers:

*Mixture A*

| | |
|---|---|
| Oats | 50 lbs. |
| Corn | 30 " |
| Bran | 20 " |
| Linseed oil meal | 10 " |

*Mixture B*

| | |
|---|---|
| Oats | 50 lbs. |
| Corn | 25 " |
| Bran | 25 " |

*Mixture C*

| | |
|---|---|
| Oats | 80 lbs. |
| Bran | 20 " |
| Linseed oil meal | 10 " |

*Mixture D*

| | |
|---|---|
| Corn | 50 lbs. |
| Oats | 20 " |
| Bran | 20 " |
| Linseed oil meal | 10 " |

Except for old ewes having poor teeth the grinding of grains is unnecessary. Cutting or grinding roughages does not improve their nutritive value, although the percentage refused may be lessened. Compared with careful feeding of long hay the feeding of ground or cut hay is seldom economical.

* A supplement for use with corn silage or non-legume roughages may be made as follows:

400 pounds soybean oil meal
50 " ground limestone
50 " salt

Linseed oil meal or cottonseed meal may be substituted for the soybean oil meal.

## QUESTIONS

1. What pasture crops can be utilized to good advantage by pregnant ewes in the fall?
2. Of what value is rye as a late fall and winter pasture crop for pregnant ewes?
3. Is it advisable to feed the ewes grain during the period of pregnancy?
4. How should the owner be guided with regard to feeding harvested feeds to pregnant ewes?
5. What is the average grain requirement for a pregnant ewe for one day?
6. Discuss the value of corn as a feed for pregnant ewes.
7. What precautions should be taken in making and feeding silage?
8. Why are roots important as a sheep feed?
9. Outline a method whereby the ewes will receive plenty of exercise during the period of pregnancy.
10. When is shelter necessary for sheep?
11. Under what circumstances should the ram be removed from the flock as soon as the breeding season is over?

## CHAPTER XXXII

## THE LAMBING PERIOD

**Preparation for Lambing.—Quarters.**—Lambing is usually conducted under shelter and more space is needed for the flock at this period than at any other time of the year. It should be broken up into smaller divisions and ewes should be taken from the flock and penned with their offspring. Under such circumstances every nook and corner of the barn is occupied.

If lambs are born in cold weather warm quarters are a necessity. The young lamb is most in need of a warm place immediately after it is born, because it is wet and, not having had a fill of its mother's milk, is more susceptible to the cold than at any other time. When the weather is cold, the ewes almost due to lamb should be placed in the warmest part of the barn and watched very closely. If it is very cold it is well to place a comparatively large number together so that the heat from their bodies will furnish enough warmth for new-born lambs.

The barn, as a whole, may be too open for lambing in cold weather. But it should be possible to make a section into a warm room by partitioning off that part which is most protected from the cold winds, and by closing up the cracks and crevices that admit the cold. Such a room will be warm enough unless the weather should be extremely cold, in which case boards can be nailed about four inches from the walls of the room and straw stuffed in between them and the walls. In the attempt to make the room warm provision for ventilation should not be overlooked (Fig. 166).

**Lambing Pens.**[1]—The lambing pen is a necessary part of the equipment for early lambing. Before or soon after a ewe has lambed she should be placed in a pen about four feet square and having no openings large enough to allow the lamb to escape. In this small pen the ewe and her lamb become acquainted and accustomed to each other much more quickly than they do when they are with the flock, for upon first getting to its feet the lamb is without its "bear-

---

[1] For construction of lambing pens see chapter on "Buildings and Equipment."

ings" and is inclined to wander wherever its legs will take it. It is such an awkward little thing that the ewe has difficulty in getting it to nurse and in protecting it. It is likely to be bunted over or trampled by other ewes, or it may creep under a trough or through an opening and become chilled. Should the ewe have two lambs they may wander apart so that she cannot give adequate attention to either. Under these circumstances she tends to abandon one and give her undivided attention to the other, the result being that the shepherd has a disclaimed lamb to deal with. Thus it is apparent that the small enclosure, known as the lambing pen, is effective because it keeps mother and offspring together. It is effective also

FIG. 166.—An open-shed type of shelter with lambing apartment for cold weather. (From Kentucky Agricultural College.)

because it directs the attention of the shepherd to the ewe and her lamb, should anything be wrong with them, more quickly than if they were with the whole flock or a portion of it. And if they need his special attention he can care for them more easily when they are in the lambing pen (Fig. 167).

How long the ewe and her lamb should be left in the lambing pen depends on the readiness with which they become accustomed to each other and on the strength of the lamb. As a rule they can be placed with the other ewes and lambs when the lamb is three or four days old.

**Supplies.**—There are a few drugs and appliances which should be secured before the lambing season starts. The more important drugs are carbolic acid or liquid sheep dip, to be used as a deodorant and disinfectant; epsom salts, castor oil, and raw linseed oil, to be used as physic; olive oil (sweet oil), to form the body of useful lotions; fluid extract of belladonna for dilation of parts; sweet spirits of nitre for urinary troubles; tincture of iron, gentian and ginger, to be used as a tonic; soap to be used in making an enema for animals suffering from constipation; vaseline to use on the hand if it is necessary to give the ewe assistance in lambing; a mixture of lead acetate, zinc sulfate and boric acid to be used on inflamed udders; and tincture of iodine, to be used on umbilical cords and swollen udders.

Fig. 167.—A lambing pen showing an arrangement for converting it into a lamb creep. When used as lambing pen, the larger opening is closed with the wide board.

The following appliances (Figs. 168, 169) are important: Rubber nipples, a glass graduate sufficiently small that a nipple can be slipped over it, small necked bottles, a small and a large syringe, a funnel, three or four feet of half-inch rubber tubing, a sheep pelt with a good lot of wool on it, a large jug, and facilities for heating water. The small graduate is useful in case the lamb will not nurse from the teat or if the ewe has very little milk. By milking into the graduate and adjusting the nipple the lamb can be given a little milk without delay. This cannot be done so easily with a bottle, but in case a rather large amount of milk is to be fed the bottle is preferable. The large syringe is needed in case the ewe should need injections or "flushing out," as are also the funnel and rubber tubing.

FIG. 168.

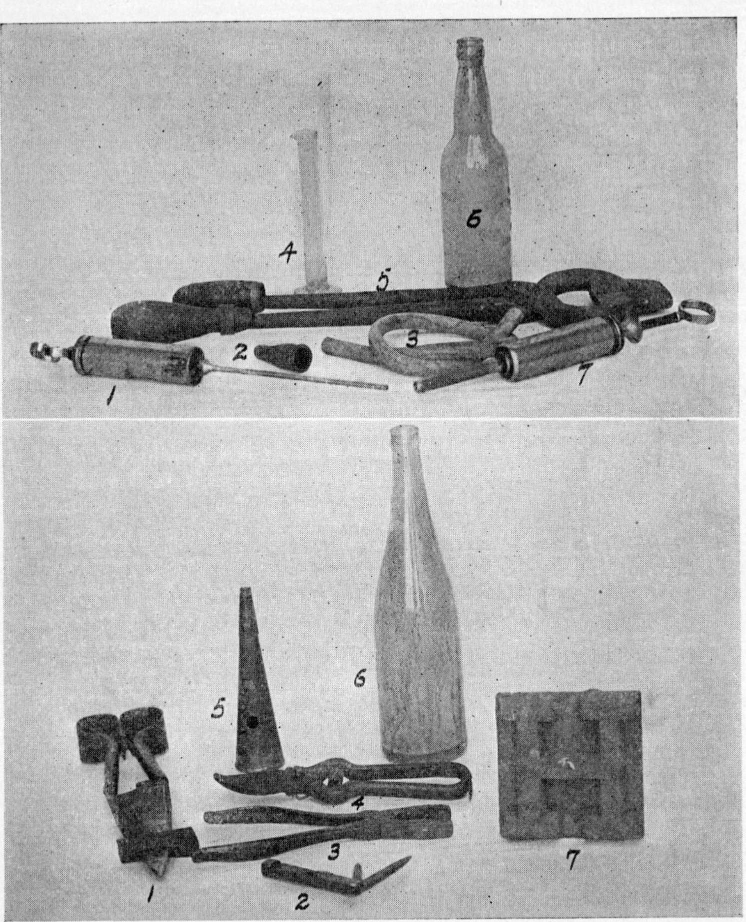


FIG. 169.

FIG. 168.—Appliances for lambing. 1, syringe with long small nozzle—suitable for treating lambs or grown sheep with injections; 2, swan-bill nipple; 3, rubber piping; 4, small glass graduate over which a nipple may be placed; 5, a type of docking iron; 6, drenching or nursing bottle; 7, syringe with large nozzle—suitable for drenching or giving injections to grown sheep.

FIG. 169.—Appliances useful around the sheep barn at nearly all times in the year. 1, sheep shears; 2, knife for trimming feet; 3, punch for making holes in ears, or for notching ears; 4, pruning shears—suitable for trimming feet; 5, drenching horn—type used in Australia; 6, drenching or nursing bottle; 7, wooden stencil for painting letters or figures on body of sheep.

The small syringe is useful should the lamb be constipated and need injections of soapy water. Warm water, the sheep pelt, and the jug are brought into service in reviving a chilled lamb.

**The Shepherd.**—No matter how good the equipment may be, the preparation for lambing is poor if the flock is without a good caretaker. He needs to be a man who knows how to take ewes through the lambing period and he must be willing to stay on the job both day and night. It is no time to leave home when the lambs are coming. For this reason alone it is advisable to have the lambs come early if the shepherd must help in the fields when the cropping season begins.

Fig. 170.—The good shepherd has the confidence of his flock.

The right kind of a shepherd has the confidence of his flock; he knows when lambing is to begin; he sees to it that there are no openings in the barn walls close to the ground that are large enough to let a young lamb creep through; and he keeps his flock where pigs can not get to it, for he knows what a dainty morsel a young lamb is for a pig (Fig. 170).

**Caring for the Ewe.—Before Parturition.**—During the last days of pregnancy the ewe should be where she can be quiet and contented. She should have plenty of room so that all jamming and crowding can be avoided. Her ration should consist mainly of clean, palatable roughage, such as clover hay. A little grain and succulent feed will do her no harm, but it is dangerous to be generous as to quantity of grain, as some who have neglected their ewes are inclined to do, because milk fever may develop after parturition. When the ewe is very woolly about the udder she should be sheared in order to allow the lamb to get to the teats. A new-born lamb will suck a lock of wool almost as readily as it will the teat, and thus lead the shepherd to believe it is getting its feed. But an experienced shepherd cannot be fooled in this way, and it may not be necessary to shear the udder until after the lamb has come. It is not advisable to shear off a large amount of wool because the udder may be injured from exposure to cold.

**Care During Parturition.**—It is easy to tell when the time for giving birth to the lamb has arrived. The ewe becomes uneasy and paces about or turns around a great deal. She is very likely to paw at the bedding with her fore feet and if she is possessed of a great deal of mother instinct, she looks about and bleats for her lamb. In advance of any of these indications, however, the physical appearance of the ewe often shows that the time of parturition is very near, for she is usually abnormally sunken in front of the hips and on the rump at either side of the spine.

When the ewe is of the right conformation, vigorous, and in good condition as a result of proper care, she seldom has difficulty in lambing unless the lamb is not in proper position for birth. During the first stages of labor she should not be disturbed, but she should be helped if she labors hard and shows little progress after the normal lapse of time. Or if she quits laboring for a longer period than the normal intermission between the recurrence of labor pains an examination should be made to see whether the lamb is alive and in normal position. If it is in normal position the fore feet are coming first and the nose is placed down snug on the fore legs. Occasionally the head is back over the shoulders, or one leg is back, or the body is doubled up with the back coming first. If possible the shepherd should insert his hand, push the lamb back and get it into normal position. Before this is done the shepherd should take proper precautions to guard against the infection of either the ewe or himself by trimming his nails close and bathing his hand and arm in disinfectant. He should also grease them with vaseline to make the entrance easier. It is usually easier to introduce the hand if the head of the ewe is lower than her rump. In case the pressure of her labor is too great to permit the introduction of the hand it is advisable to elevate her rear parts high enough to cause the lamb to fall back into the womb. If this takes place it will then be comparatively easy to introduce the hand. After the lamb is placed in normal position birth will probably be effected without further difficulty. If it is found that the breech is coming first it may not be necessary to put the lamb in normal position, as it is often possible to safely deliver it when it is in this position by getting hold of the hind legs and pulling steadily outward and downward toward the udder (Fig. 171).

Frequently ewes have trouble in lambing because the lamb is too large to pass through the parts. If the attendant can get the fore legs and head delivered it is usually comparatively easy to complete the birth, although there are cases where the shoulders are so large that it is hard to get them through. One of the best ways to assist in the delivery of the head is to pull steadily on the fore legs and press in on the vulva just back of the lamb's head. Professor Kleinheinz,[2] of the University of Wisconsin, says that he has found it to be of assistance to smear raw linseed oil in the outer part of the vagina just above the lamb's head. This makes the interior of the vagina more slippery and serves to dilate it further. After

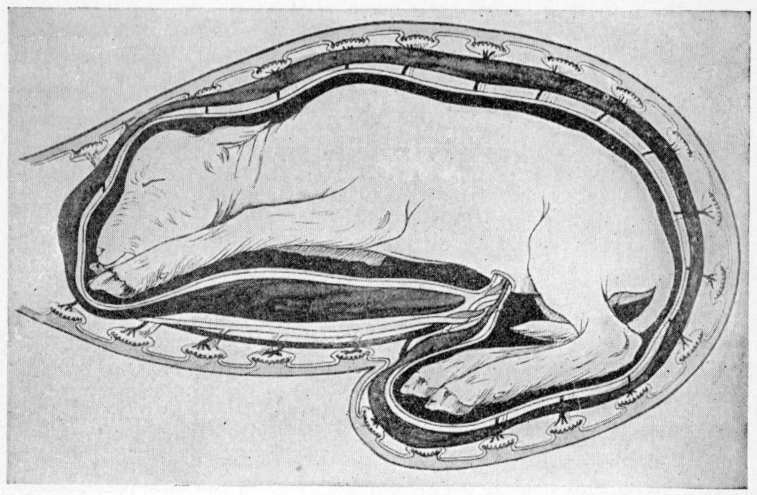

Fig. 171.—Proper position of lamb in the uterus of the ewe for normal birth.

the head and feet are delivered, the shepherd should pull on the fore legs outward and down toward the ewe's udder in order to deliver the shoulders. After the shoulders come through, the birth of the lamb is practically completed.

There are instruments for dismembering the fœtus in case either the ewe or the lamb is so abnormally developed that delivery cannot be effected in any other manner. This is a last resort and since the life of the ewe is the whole consideration great care should be taken to avoid such injury to the womb as will cause her death. Just before starting to operate the instruments should be sterilized and

[2] See "Sheep Management and Breeds of Sheep," by Kleinheinz.

the hands of the operator thoroughly disinfected with a two per cent solution of carbolic acid or some other good disinfectant.

Every shepherd should realize the importance of skill in delivering the lamb. In pure-bred flocks, particularly where it is nearly always advisable to retain good breeding ewes long after they have begun to decline in vigor, the ability to know when things are not going right in lambing and the further ability to make them right are invaluable. Some are blessed more than others with the natural ability of knowing what to do and how to do it, but it requires much practice on the part of any one to develop the skill necessary to deal successfully with the various emergencies that arise. Diagrams and written descriptions will give some assistance, of course, but the skill is developed by actually handling cases.

**After Parturition.**—For several days after the lamb is born the shepherd should keep the ewe under close observation. He should see to it that she casts the placenta (after birth); that her bowels and udder are in good condition; that she is not exposed to cold draughts, and that she is properly provided with drink and sound, easily digested feed.

**Feed.**—When the ewe is in good condition it is well to feed grain sparingly or not at all for the first three or four days after the lamb is born, but if she is in thin condition and has very little milk it may be advisable to begin giving her grain when the lamb is only a few hours old. Sometimes the ewe has no appetite, in which case she should be offered the most palatable and most easily digested feeds such as bran, linseed oil meal, and the very best clover or alfalfa hay. Loss of appetite for a few hours may not be a serious matter, but if the ewe continues to have no desire for feed the shepherd should note whether or not her bowels are in good condition. A good physic with 4 ounces of raw linseed oil or 4 ounces of epsom salts [3] often brings a ewe to her feed in a short time, and a teaspoon each of tincture of gentian and ginger in a half pint of tepid water given three times daily will stimulate her appetite. If she is thin in flesh a teaspoon of tincture of iron added to each dose may assist in building her up so that she can take care of her lamb.

**Water.**—Since she is usually in a feverish condition the ewe is very thirsty just after parturition and, although she should be

---

[3]A quick acting physic is made by mixing 2 ounces of raw linseed or castor oil with 4 ounces of Epsom salts. An injection of soapy water is good in case the ewe is constipated.

allowed to drink, she should not be permitted to take a large "fill" of water. She should not be given very cold water, and if the shepherd has the time one of the best ways to treat her with respect to drink is to give her about a quart of almost tepid water at intervals of about two hours until her thirst is satisfied.

**Caring for the Ewe That Has Had Difficulty in Lambing.**— The ewe that has considerable difficulty in lambing is likely to become very weak and in need of a stimulant. A tablespoonful of aromatic spirits of ammonia or camphor in a small amount of water may be given. If the ewe fails to regain her strength the dose should be repeated after about an hour.

A ewe that has assistance in lambing is likely to be more or less lacerated inwardly, and hence in need of something soothing and healing for the torn places. A good remedy is a wash composed of one-half ounce zinc sulfate and two ounces of tincture of opium in a quart of water. If the ewe is lacerated or if she fails to cast the afterbirth soon after the lamb is born she should be "flushed" once or twice daily with the zinc sulfate and opium wash or with a carefully prepared one per cent solution of carbolic acid or other suitable disinfectant. A disinfectant rather than the zinc sulfate-opium wash is advisable if there is an offensive odor. The flushing, which can be done either with a large syringe or with rubber tubing, should be continued until all odors and unnatural discharges have ceased. In case the tubing is used the part inserted should be coated with vaseline. The other end, in which a small funnel is inserted, should be held well up above the ewe while the solution is being poured into the funnel. Injected washes should be lukewarm.

Occasionally a ewe suffers from eversion of womb after lambing. As a rule this is caused by great difficulty in lambing. For treatment "Shepherd Boy" in "Modern Sheep: Breeds and Management" gives the following directions:

"The operator should have an assistant who lays the ewe on her back and, grasping her hind legs gently, lifts her hind quarters about a foot from the ground. By this method the organs can be readily replaced. The operator should next take a pint of lukewarm water and put into it two teaspoonfuls of sugar and one of pulverized alum and inject the same into the womb twice a day. In stubborn cases a leather band may be placed so as to prevent the womb from coming out." Two stitches across the vulva are effective.

**Udder Troubles.**—After the lamb is born, if the shepherd does not give close attention to the ewe's udder serious disorders may gain considerable headway before they are discovered. The udder may become very much inflamed and so sore that the ewe refuses to allow the lamb to suck. This condition, known as garget, may be brought on by bruises, colds, chills, lying on wet ground, and inability of the lamb to take enough of the milk.

As soon as the trouble is discovered the udder should be thoroughly milked out, and if the swollen part is feverish it should be reduced by the application of hot compacts wet with a solution of a tablespoonful of equal parts of lead acetate, zinc sulfate and boric acid in a quart of water. Keep the compacts in place all the time by placing over the udder an apron which can be held in position by attaching it to a harness fitted to the body of the ewe (Fig. 172).

Fig. 172.—An apron over the udder to keep compact in place.

In case the swollen part is not feverish it can be reduced by rubbing twice a day with tincture of iodine until the swelling begins to subside. Thereafter one application daily is sufficient until the treatment can be discontinued. This treatment is also good for feverish, swollen udders. Since tincture of iodine is rather expensive, it would not be recommended were it not powerful in reducing inflammation. Should pus form, an opening should be made in the udder to permit drainage and the diseased part should be thoroughly disinfected once a day with a one per cent carbolic acid solution or some other effective antiseptic wash. If mortification sets in the discolored portion should be kept painted with iodine.

Whether or not garget is contagious seems to depend on whether it results from bruises and colds or from erysipelas. If due to the latter, the disease may spread very rapidly. Since it is difficult to distinguish one form of garget from the other it is best to isolate all ewes whose udders are affected. It is also well to wash the udders of the other ewes in the flock with disinfectant and to disinfect the pens from which the diseased ewes are removed. Close watch should be kept for fresh outbreaks of the disease.

From instances noted in the lambing fold and from experience with other classes of animals it would seem best to prevent the lamb from sucking the diseased side of the udder, because in the majority of cases the lamb becomes so poisoned from the milk that it either dies or makes very little growth.

A very common trouble with the suckling ewe is sore teats. This condition may arise from either of two causes. One is the chewing or biting of the teats by the lamb and the other results from pock-like sores that appear on the teats and on the udder. Should the soreness arise from the lamb biting the teats it is well to examine its teeth. If they are long and sharp the cure may be effected by filing them off. This is not always successful, however, and it may be better to dispose of the lamb than to allow it to ruin the udder of a good ewe. If the trouble arises from pock-like sores, the best proceeding is to open these sores and wash them with a disinfectant. A solution of liquid sheep dip made up of one part dip to about twenty-five parts water is very good for this purpose and a few applications usually effect a cure. The shepherd should watch every day for sore teats, for it is a trouble which appears suddenly and causes a great deal of loss and annoyance. If the sores become large the udder is almost sure to be injured and not infrequently it is spoiled, thus making the ewe practically worthless for breeding purposes.

Occasionally a ewe fails to give milk through what seems to be a sound teat. Upon close examination it is found that there is a hard core in it. Some authorities state that the insertion of a small, hot rod, such as a knitting needle, will open the teat so that the milk can be drawn. The writer has never tried this remedy, but he knows of persons who have tried it without success. A teat that has had the end cut off rarely functions satisfactorily.

**Caring for the Young Lamb.**—As soon as the lamb is born the mucus should be wiped from its nose and mouth. It is not imperative that the shepherd perform this duty, for it is well known that many a lamb not receiving this attention comes through safely, but occasionally the amount of mucus in the mouth and nostrils is sufficient to cause strangulation. If the ewe is strong and possessed of mother instinct she gets to her feet and devotes her attention to the lamb shortly after it is born. If she is too exhausted to arise the shepherd should place the lamb near her nose. In fact, it is a good practice to pinch off the umbilical cord about four inches from the body and place the lamb at the ewe's nose before she has time to arise, for then she can both rest and give the lamb the attention which is prompted by her mother instinct. As soon as it is apparent that she intends to care for her lamb it is best to go away and leave them for from twenty to thirty minutes. During this interval the

Fig. 173.—The kind that needs no help. His legs are sturdy and strong, his chest is deep and wide and his head carried high bespeaks health and vigor.

ewe removes much of the mucus from the lamb's body, and by so doing she hastens drying and arouses the lamb's instinct for feed (Fig. 173).

**Helping the Lamb to Nurse.**—If the lamb is able to nurse without the assistance of the shepherd, well and good, but often assistance is necessary. Sometimes the ewe, especially with her first lamb, refuses to let it nurse because she is nervous and desires to see it. When this is the case the shepherd is obliged to hold the ewe while the lamb takes its first feed, but if it is strong and an eager feeder the one holding is usually all that is necessary.

Often a strong lamb, eager to feed, but unable to find the teat, can be trained by being helped once or twice. When assisting such a lamb it is best to let the ewe stand rather than to lay her on her side. By backing her into a corner and placing a knee against her brisket to hold her the shepherd has both hands free to guide the lamb to the teat, which should be done by gently pushing the lamb at the tail with one hand and holding obstructions away from the teat with the other.

**Helping a Weak Lamb.**—A strong lamb is up on its feet, bleating and searching for food a few minutes after it is born. A weak lamb (and there are almost sure to be a few) is very slow in getting to its feet; its bleat is feeble and it does not have much desire for food. Often the teat has to be placed in its mouth and some milk squeezed into its throat before its appetite is aroused. Since it cannot stand while it nurses, the shepherd, if he is without a helper, usually has to lay the ewe on her side in order to get the lamb to the teat. But if it can be avoided it is better not to put the ewe on her side, because the lamb will learn to help itself much more quickly if she is left in normal position.

A good fill of mother's milk generally works wonders for a weak lamb. After it has had its feed it should be placed where it will keep warm and can have an undisturbed sleep. In about two hours after the feed is taken it is usually markedly improved in strength. By the time three or four feeds have been taken the weak lamb, possessing an appetite, is about able to get to the teat unassisted.

The weak lamb, unwilling to feed, presents a more serious problem. Usually such a lamb cannot be induced to suck, and enforced feeding must be resorted to. If the shepherd squeezes some of the ewe's milk into a small glass graduate, slips a swan bill nipple over the end, places the nipple in the lamb's mouth and pours the milk down its throat, the lamb will gain some strength and perhaps will develop such a desire for food that subsequent feeding will be easier.

Occasionally lambs are so weak as to appear almost lifeless at birth. A careful shepherd can often save such lambs by quick action. Respiration can best be started by blowing into the lamb's mouth and by gently beating it on the chest. After the breathing becomes normal the procedure is the same as outlined above for weak lambs.

When a lamb is born with a thickened tongue it is impossible to handle it successfully. Although strong, it is drowsy and utterly unable to nurse. It is best to give up a lamb of this sort at once.

**Handling the Chilled Lamb.**—If the lambing occurs when the weather is cold there will probably be some chilled lambs. There is hope for the chilled lamb as long as life is not extinct. One of the best ways to proceed with it if it is badly chilled is to immerse all but its head in water as warm as the elbow can bear. As the water becomes cool hot water should be added to maintain the proper temperature. The purpose of the bath is to start and to invigorate the circulation, hence when the lamb becomes somewhat lively it should be removed. Immediately upon being taken from the water the lamb should be enveloped by a large towel and rubbed briskly until dry. It should then be fed and placed in a warm spot for its sleep.

If the lamb is not so badly chilled as to require the bath it may be revived by wrapping it well and giving it a stimulant, such as a teaspoonful of gin or whiskey in a little warm milk. If it is placed near a heated stove it should be well wrapped in a cloth or a sheep pelt, because the air currents about the stove and direct contact with the heat seem to have a detrimental effect.

Another method of reviving a chilled lamb is to place the lamb in a barrel half filled with bran and containing a good sized jug of warm water, or a barrel half filled with straw kept near the furnace of the house. If a ewe lambs on a cold night the lamb is taken away from her before she sees it and it is put in the barrel where it is kept until morning. Some shepherds who have used this system say they have avoided many cases of chilling in this way and that the ewe seldom refuses to own her lamb when it is returned to her.

One important thing to remember about the chilled lamb is that it should be fed as soon as it has become revived. Another important thing is that it should be kept away from its mother no longer than is absolutely necessary, for there is danger of her refusing to own it if it has been away from her very long (Fig. 174).

**Young Lamb Troubles.—The Disowned Lamb.**—It is very annoying to have a ewe disown her lamb, because it not only brings about trouble, but her desertion of it appeals to one as being unjust. We do not know what makes a ewe refuse to claim her lamb. Many cases have come to notice in which a ewe has taken one of a pair of twins and has refused the other, an action which is scarcely traceable to lack of mother instinct. Again, a ewe may be very good to her lamb for the first two or three days of its life and then turn against it. It is not an uncommon occurrence for young ewes to fail to claim their lambs, this being particularly noticeable in ewes that are only a year old when the lambs are born. Such ewes are not sufficiently mature to have the maternal instinct well developed.

The first duty of the shepherd toward the disowned lamb is to try to make the mother claim it. As soon as the lamb is born it is a

Fig. 174.—A lamb blanket used in the West to avoid chilling. A young lamb thus blanketed can withstand rough weather.

good practice to take some of the mucus from its mouth and nose and smear it over the nose of the ewe as a case of disowning may be avoided in this way. For the first few days the ewe seems to recognize her lamb solely by means of the sense of smell, and smearing her nose with the mucus from the lamb seems to aid her in recognizing it. If she refuses to own her lamb after it is dry she may be induced to take it after some of her milk has been rubbed on the lamb's rump and also on her nose. She turns her head to smell of the lamb when it is placed to the teat, and the odor of the milk being both on her nose and on the lamb frequently serves to establish recognition of her offspring. In case the ewe seems undecided whether or not to claim her lamb, another means for forcing her to take it is to tie a strange dog in a pen next to the one in which she and her lamb are confined. The fear of the natural enemy makes her seek the companionship of her offspring and arouses her latent mother instinct. Use this as a last resort.

Sometimes it is possible to induce a ewe to take her lamb by keeping her and the lamb in the lambing pen and by holding her frequently to allow the lamb to nurse. This plan will work if the ewe's antipathy for her lamb is not marked. After the lamb becomes pretty strong and has learned well the source of its feed it will persistently tease at the mother for the privilege of nursing, which helps to break down her stubbornness and hastens the time when she will claim her lamb.

Sometimes the ewe exhibits great dislike for her lamb, and she does all she can to prevent it from nursing. She bunts it over whenever she has opportunity; she may even savagely trample it under foot. An extended struggle is usually necessary for inducing such a ewe to own her lamb. She should be tied up short so that she has small chance to harm the lamb. As often as the shepherd can get around to her he should force her to allow the lamb to nurse, since in so doing he may make progress in breaking down her stubbornness. It may be necessary to build a device which will not allow her to move the rear of her body from side to side. As a last resort she may lie down to keep her lamb from nursing, in which case something should be placed under her to hold her up. After every scheme has been tried, from the mildest to the most severe, the ewe may still remain unconquered. But if her lamb is strong and plucky it may manage to get along if the shepherd can find time to hold the ewe for it to nurse several times each day.

When it happens that a ewe refuses to own one of a pair of twins the shepherd finds himself in an exasperating situation, especially during the first few days after the lambs are born, because the more the ewe dislikes one lamb the more she seems to like the other. She attempts to give the favored lamb a great deal of nursing, thus exhausting her supply of milk, so that there is nothing for the disowned lamb when the shepherd comes around to give it assistance. But if the unclaimed lamb can be carried through until it has learned to go after food when its mate does the ewe will soon be obliged to allow it to feed. The unclaimed lamb can be given an equal chance with its mate by keeping both lambs in a pen close to the mother where she can see them. Then when the shepherd comes around he can put both lambs with her and see to it that the chances of each for food are equal.

**The Orphan Lamb.**—A lamb may be orphaned through the death of its mother or because of her inability to suckle it. In caring for it the shepherd's first thought is to find a foster mother and it may be that some ewe has lost her lamb about the time the orphan was born. If so, the dead lamb should be skinned and its pelt kept on the orphan for a few days. The scent from the pelt will cause the ewe to think the orphan is her own lamb. Should it happen that the ewe lost her own lamb some time before a certain lamb became an orphan she may be induced to become its foster

Fig. 175.—Wearing a dead lamb's skin to induce the mother of the dead lamb to believe that her offspring is still living.

mother by some of the methods already outlined for making the ewe claim her lamb. Another plan is to rub sassafras oil or kerosene on the lamb and also on the ewe's face and nose. Every shepherd should endeavor to keep a lamb with each ewe that is able to raise one. Should there be no orphans at the time a ewe loses her lamb it is advisable to place with her one of a pair of twins belonging to some ewe that is unable to suckle two lambs well (Fig. 175).

If there is no chance to place the orphan with a foster mother it will have to be fed by hand on cow's milk. Several authorities state that to prepare cow's milk for lambs it should be diluted with an equal amount of water, but since the analysis of ewe's milk shows it to be as rich in sugar and richer in fat, protein, and minerals than cow's milk this practice is entirely unnecessary.[4]

| | Water Per ct. | Mineral matter Per ct. | Protein Per ct. | Sugar Per ct. | Fat Per ct. |
|---|---|---|---|---|---|
| Ewe's milk......... | 80.8 | 0.9 | 6.5 | 4.9 | 6.9 |
| Cow's milk......... | 87.2 | 0.7 | 3.5 | 4.9 | 3.7 |

For the first week the orphan should have some ewe's milk. A good way to get it is to take the lamb to ewes whose lambs are not yet old enough to take all of the milk. The orphan should be fed milk often, but it should not be given a large amount at one time until it is two or three weeks old. On the first day of its life an ounce (two tablespoonfuls) is a liberal feeding, and it is safer to feed only half that amount. But it should be fed at least every two hours. It is most convenient to feed the milk from a bottle to which is attached a medium sized nipple of the "swan bill" type. The bottle should be kept thoroughly clean and the milk should be fresh and at natural temperature; that is, at approximately 100 degrees Fahrenheit. In order to maintain this temperature the bottle containing the milk should be kept in a vessel partly filled with water heated to 100 degrees Fahrenheit or slightly above. After the lamb is two or three weeks old it is not necessary to feed it more than three times a day (Fig. 176).

Sometimes a ewe has two lambs and only enough milk for one. In such a case, it is usually possible to bring the lambs along nicely by supplementing her supply with cow's milk. At first they may be reluctant to nurse from the bottle, but by persistent encouragement they soon take to the additional feed eagerly. As they learn to eat grain and hay the milk feeding can be gradually diminished and finally discontinued (Fig. 177).

**Ailments and Diseases of Young Lambs.**—*Pinning.*—What is known as "pinning" is the collection of feces at the anus so that evacuation cannot be accomplished. The first feces voided are almost as sticky as glue and hence often cling to the wool and skin of the tail. When this happens the anus is "plugged" and the lamb, unless attended to, may pine away and die. All the treatment that is necessary is to scrape the collection away with a stick or cob and wash with warm water.

---

[4] Composition of ewe's and cow's milk (from "Feeds and Feeding," by Henry and Morrison).

*Constipation.*—Young lambs may be constipated. The symptoms are straining and distress in the attempt to pass feces. Usually this trouble is relieved by injections of warm, soapy water. If this treatment fails, a half to a tablespoonful of milk of magnesia (magnesium hydroxide) or a teaspoonful of castor oil may effect a cure.

*White Scours.*—White scours are caused by digestive disorders in the stomach, which usually result from mistakes in feeding the

Fig. 176.—Happy orphans.

ewes. If they be given clean, wholesome feed and if the nature of their ration is not changed abruptly, white scours do not often occur in the lambs. In fact, nearly all digestive disorders in very young lambs may be due to the feed and physical condition of the ewes. Milk of magnesia, given as in constipation, may be of some help to lambs suffering from white scours.

*Indigestion.*—Sometimes lambs are seized with a violent attack of indigestion. It is marked by great distress and frothing at the mouth. Castor oil (a tablespoonful) is the most efficient remedy the writer has found.

*Sore Eyes.*—Lambs are frequently afflicted with sore eyes. The eyes take on a milky appearance or, in very severe cases, an angry reddish hue. Tears flow profusely. A few drops of silver nitrate solution, known to all druggists as an "eye wash," placed in the eye each day usually relieves the trouble. Argyrol, a preparation

FIG. 177.—A milch goat is useful in lambing time.

often used as a remedy for sore eyes in people, is also a good remedy for sore eyes in lambs. Wing, in "Sheep Farming in America," says that a strong solution of sheep dip is a sure cure for sore eyes. He states that the disease is due to the presence of bacteria which will be destroyed by a thorough bathing with the dip in and all around the eyes. A strong solution of dip applied to the eyes is very painful and hence the other remedies mentioned are to be preferred to using the dip.

Sore eyes are often caused by the eye lashes turning inward against the eyeball. The remedy is to sew the eye open with a needle and silk thread by stitching the loose turned in part of each eyelid to the parts above or below. In a few days the stitch will come out, but in the meantime the eyelid will have thickened so that the lashes will not turn inward. In some cases adhesive tape will hold the eyelid in position as well as the stitching.

*Sore Mouths.*—Scabs and pock-like sores on the lips and nose are also common afflictions of young lambs. Undoubtedly this trouble is traceable to bacteria. Before treatment the scabs should be rubbed off and the sores opened. A thorough application of sheep dip or other mild antiseptic will give some relief. It is now possible to protect lambs against this trouble by vaccination. In flocks where much difficulty is experienced, vaccination will be far more satisfactory than the use of local applications.

*Navel Ill.*—This disease is characterized by swollen knee and hock joints, and it results from infection through the umbilical cord. It can be avoided by disinfecting the cord with tincture of iodine shortly after the lamb is born.

## QUESTIONS

1. Describe a lambing pen and its use.
2. How long should a ewe and lamb be left in the lambing pen?
3. What general supplies and drugs would you have in the medicine chest in the lambing season?
4. Discuss the management of the ewe just before parturition.
5. If it is necessary to help the ewe at the time of parturition how would you proceed?
6. How should a ewe be fed the first few days after lambing?
7. What is garget? Discuss causes and treatment.
8. What are the general causes of sore teats?
9. In case the new born lamb gets chilled how should it be handled?
10. What causes a ewe to disown her lambs? Discuss remedies.
11. How would you handle the orphan lamb?
12. Discuss the feeding of an orphan lamb.
13. Name six common ailments of young lambs.
14. What is pinning?
15. Give remedies for constipation and white scours.
16. How should sore eyes be treated?

## CHAPTER XXXIII

# GROWING THE LAMB

**Importance of Growth.**—In producing lambs for the market an effort should be made to keep them growing rapidly until they attain the weight desired. A lamb that is strong and hearty at birth begins to gain at once if it is properly fed, and it pays to feed it well while it is very young, for at that time the cheapest growth can be secured because the lamb is capable of making its highest rate of gain for the amount of feed it consumes. If there are exceptions to that part of the above statement which pertains to cost of growth, they occur under circumstances when feed is abnormally high while the lamb is young, and unusually cheap when it grows older.

**Methods of Feeding.**—There are two ways of feeding lambs: First, indirectly through the ewes; second, directly by giving them feed such as grain and hay as soon as they are able to take it. Both ways of feeding should be followed if the lambs are to be marketed before they are five months old.

**Feeding the Ewe.**[1]—In order to do her best for her lamb the ewe must have good feed in liberal quantities, because she is not only producing milk, but she is also growing wool and maintaining her own body. If possible her ration should be made up of several feeds rather than of one, because variety stimulates the appetite and assists in keeping the body in good thrift. She should have a ration fairly rich in protein, for sheep's milk is rich in nitrogenous substances and fat. Some succulent feed, such as roots, silage or pasture, should be a part of the ration for the sake of the influence on the amount of milk produced and also for the toning and regulating effect these feeds have on the body. Too often American flock-owners are disposed to overlook the importance of succulence in the rations of nursing ewes. They rely too much on grain and on fields whose plant growth early in the spring is of questionable value; but now that silage is coming into more general use we should be able to compound a better ration with respect to succulence.

On beginning to feed after lambing, the concentrate part of the ewe's ration should be light in nature and small in quantity.

---

[1] A good suckling ewe gives about 3 pounds of milk daily.

Although not indispensable, bran is one of the very best concentrates to begin with. After feeding it for a day or two, oats can be added, and in about a week corn and linseed oil meal can be introduced. Not all of these concentrates are absolutely necessary, and whether or not they are to be used should be determined by their cost and by the nature of the succulent feed and roughages available.

The best roughages are leguminous hays, such as clover, alfalfa, cowpea, and soybean hay. The hay should be sweet and clean, for damaged hay is always likely to lead to digestive troubles, both in the ewes and in the lambs. When plenty of choice leguminous hay is available there is less need for nitrogenous concentrates. Carbonaceous roughages, such as corn stover and straw can be used, but when they are fed the concentrate part of the ration should be rich in protein and if possible these roughages should be used up while the ewes are pregnant.

Just how much suckling ewes should be fed depends on so many variable factors aside from their variation in size and condition, that the owner must make a special study of his flock after the lambs are born. If the lambs are born early, say in February or March, and if the weather is cold, making what is called a backward spring, the demand of the ewes for feed will be heavy. If there is a large percentage of twins, more feed should be given than when such is not the case. In England it is common practice for the ewes with twins to be placed in a separate flock in order to give them more feed than is given to the ewes with but one lamb. This is a practice which could undoubtedly be followed with profit in many American flocks. In the foregoing it is assumed that stored feeds, such as grain, hay, roots, and silage are referred to. If climatic conditions have been favorable for the growth of grass or forage, such as rye, and if there is a considerable area of these growths available, the demand on the stored feeds is much lessened. But too much reliance is often placed on field growths early in the spring before the growing season begins. If the pasture is good when the pasturing season opens it should not be necessary to continue longer to give stored feed to the ewes.

An abrupt change in the rations of suckling ewes may cause digestive disturbances, the effects of which may be transmitted to the lambs through the milk. In spite of the fact that sheep are unequaled among domestic animals in their power of adaptation to grazing it is not always best completely to set them at liberty from the dry lot into pasture, for they may get indigestion from gorging themselves on green feed. This is particularly true of suckling ewes. If they have been confined in the dry lot for several weeks it is best to let them pasture at first for only an hour or two a day.

Variety of feed has often been confused with change of feed. That is, a ration composed of several feeds is advisable, but changing every little while from one feed to another is inadvisable. If possible, before lambing, the ewe should be placed on the kind of ration she is to receive after lambing. If it is a good ration there is no danger of her tiring of it or of failing to thrive on it.

Water and salt are indispensable to all classes of sheep, but their value for suckling ewes should be especially emphasized. When confined in the dry lot they drink large quantities of water, and also when they are in the pasture, if the weather is hot and the grass has become rather dry.

In spite of liberal feeding, ewes are inclined to lose in weight during the first few weeks of the suckling period. No other fact so strongly emphasizes the need of having them in rather high condition when the lambs are born. If such is the case one need not be so much concerned when he observes them losing in condition and the criterion by which one should judge as to whether the ewes are being properly fed is to note whether or not they are growing their lambs well.

**Dry Lot Rations.**—Those rations which prove satisfactory for pregnant ewes during the winter usually prove suitable for suckling ewes if given in larger quantities. This statement pertaining to increased amounts refers especially to the concentrate portion of the ration. In many cases grain fed at the rate of .5 pound daily for some time before lambing should be increased to one pound thereafter until abundant pasture is to be had. Thus, the proportion of grain to roughage is more nearly correct if one pound of grain is fed with each three pounds of roughage than if given in smaller proportion. This may prove inadequate for maximum growth of the lambs if they are not provided with a creep and fed apart from the ewes.

The following rations from various sources have been regarded as satisfactory. The amounts in pounds in terms of "per ewe per day" are suggestive of quantities to be given to ewes weighing 125 to 150 pounds.

*Ration No. 8*

| | |
|---|---|
| Alfalfa or other legume hay | 4.0 |
| Grain | 1.0 |

*Ration No. 9*

| | |
|---|---|
| Alfalfa or other legume hay | 2.0 |
| Corn silage | 4.0 |
| Grain | 1.0 |

*Ration No. 10*

| | |
|---|---|
| Corn silage | 8.0 |
| Supplement (as in Ration No. 5) | .25 |
| Grain | 1.0 |

The grains or grain mixtures listed on page 244 or one of the following may be used:

*Mixture E*

| | |
|---|---|
| Corn | 50 lbs. |
| Cottonseed meal | 10 " |

*Mixture F*

| | |
|---|---|
| Corn | 60 lbs. |
| Bran | 30 " |
| Cottonseed cake | 10 " |

If none of the roughage fed is leguminous, then it is essential that the grain mixture contain liberal amounts of high-protein concentrates and that additional mineral, such as ground limestone or bone meal, be supplied. This mineral may be mixed with the salt and kept before the ewes at all times.

This is a time when the flock is receiving close attention and it is one of the best times to mark ewes for culling. The lambs of some ewes will not thrive or grow rapidly even though the ewes are well fed. This is often due to a lack of milk production by the ewes. When this condition persists in spite of good feeding the ewes should be marked to be culled later on because it is evident that such ewes do not have an inherent tendency to liberal milk production. Without such natural tendencies to produce milk in abundance liberal feeding of the ewes is of little value. Even creep feeding the lambs will not make up for this deficiency.

**Feeding the Lamb.—Quarters.**—Lambs born in cold weather (January, February, and March) should remain in the warm part of the barn until they are at least a week old. After this time they are able to withstand considerable cold, but they should not be exposed in severe weather nor housed where they are not well protected from cold draughts, for they will not make rapid growth when they are uncomfortably cold (Fig. 178).

Aside from food, nothing seems to "tone" lambs and invigorate more than a good sun bath, and in order to permit of every opportunity to have the sunshine, their quarters should be arranged where there is a south exposure (Fig. 179).

Quarters for lambs should be well bedded with straw. Whoever

Fig. 178.—A temporary shelter; well bedded and comfortable for lambs past two weeks old. Shropshire ewes and lambs on the farm of J. C. Andrews, West Point, Indiana.

has observed lambs has learned that they seek a dry place for sleeping; in fact, they often bed down in the soft warm wool on their mother's back.

**Feeding Grain.**—Lambs intended for market should be fed grain as soon as they will eat it, and they will begin to nibble some when from 10 to 16 days of age. At first there is a little advantage in feeding ground grain, but after the lambs are five or six weeks old whole grain is as good or better than the ground grain. Sheep and lambs with good teeth masticate their feed thoroughly. Experiments conducted at the Illinois Experiment Station indicate that western lambs six months old or past will make more gain from whole shelled corn than they will from ground corn.

A good grain mixture for lambs just beginning to eat is ground corn, 2 parts; crushed oats, 2 parts; linseed meal, 1 part; and wheat bran, 1 part. The wheat bran is very essential as it contains mineral matter needed and adds bulk to the ration and aids in developing capacity for feed. The hulls from the oats add bulk. If bran is not to be had, or if it is, clover or alfalfa hay of best quality should be used.

The idea has been advanced that the kinds of grain fed to lambs should be placed in separate compartments allowing choice of feeds. The writer tried this with corn, oats, bran, and linseed cake (pea size). Lambs preferred the linseed meal and did not

Fig. 179.—Enjoying a sun bath.

make enough more gain than lambs that were fed on a grain mixture to justify feeding according to the free-choice system.

It is possible to self-feed growing lambs. Use the above grain mixture and add four parts (by weight) of ground or chaffed alfalfa or clover hay. Lambs thus fed gained four-tenths pound daily until they reached a weight of about 60 pounds. In addition to the milk of the ewes, the lambs ate 1.8 pounds of the mixture for each pound gain in weight.

**Lamb Creeps.**—In order to feed the lambs grain and hay so that they can eat at will, prepare a feeding place for them where their mothers cannot follow. Such a place is called a creep. It should be placed in the most comfortable part of the barn where the lambs would choose to play and sleep. If there is a somewhat sunny place, that is the best spot for the creep.

In construction the creep is very simple.[2] The only point to be taken into consideration is that there are to be openings through which the lambs but not the ewes may pass. Inside the creep there should be troughs for grain and racks for hay. A flat-bottomed trough, nine inches wide, three or four inches deep, with a six-inch

Fig. 180.—A partition in a box rack making it possible to feed little lambs grain in one side and hay in the other.

board supported eight inches above to keep the lambs from placing their feet in the trough proper, is a suitable type. Any device for the hay which will keep the lambs from wasting or befouling it is satisfactory. Combination grain and hay racks may be used, but in most cases it is better to feed grain and hay separately, because in the combination rack the hay becomes mixed with the grain and this seems to make the feeds less palatable (Fig. 180).

**How to Feed the Lambs.**—Cleanliness should be the motto of any sheep feeder, but special emphasis should be placed on this

[2] For details see chapter on buildings and equipment.

motto by the caretaker of young lambs. The troughs and racks should be carefully cleaned every day, and it is a good policy to scrub them with lime-water whenever they become noticeably soiled. The lime seems to make the odor about the troughs pleasant to the lambs. Any surplus feed taken from the troughs and racks can be fed to the ewes, or used for bedding.

When beginning to feed little lambs, only a small amount of grain should be placed in the bottom of the troughs. They are very curious creatures and are inclined to do a great deal of investigating, so that it is not long until some lamb is nibbling at the feed. They are also much given to imitation and on this account often learn to eat through imitating either their mothers or the lamb that first takes to the feed. The writer has induced lambs to start eating grain by quietly offering it to them from his hand. Their curiosity caused them to sniff about the hand with the result that they took to the feed. Scattering a little sugar over the grain may serve to get the lambs started on grain. It is better to give them about the amount of feed they will clean up in a day than to place a large quantity before them to nose over and spoil. The ewes will eat the feed the lambs refuse unless it is mixed with dung, but it is not as palatable as fresh feed.

After lambs learn to eat they increase rapidly in their power to consume feed. Whether or not they should be given all they want depends on the end in view. If they are to be marketed as fat lambs, they should be liberally fed with grain until they are of marketable weight and condition. If all of them are to be marketed, a large part of the grain ration should be carbonaceous in nature, like corn, but if a number of the ewe lambs are to be retained for breeding purposes, not more than half of the grain mixture should be corn, the other half consisting of oats and possibly bran and oil meal.

**Amount of Feed Consumed by Lambs.**—At first the lamb eats only a very little, but by the time it has been nibbling at grain for three or four weeks it will be eating about one-fourth pound daily. If it is confined in the dry lot all the while and is permitted to have about all the grain it wants it will consume about three-fourths of a pound of grain daily in the seventh week after it has begun to eat. When it is on grass or forage it will not eat more than half as much grain as a lamb of the same age confined to the dry lot.

**Green Feed Before Grass Season.**—Rye, old clover, and grass pastured before the beginning of the grazing season are good for both ewes and lambs. Such feeds do not produce much growth, but the exercise the lambs get and the regulating effect of what they consume are beneficial to them. It is doubtful whether ewes with lambs at side should be out in rye and clover fields throughout the day so early in the season, for the ground is very cold and damp. From two to four hours is long enough. If it is possible, however, they should be allowed their own choice between the time spent in the field and in the barn.

**Feeding Lambs on Grass.**—The gain made by lambs on pasture is usually less costly than that secured in dry lot on harvested feeds. Lambs that are kept free of internal parasites may gain as much while grazing good succulent pastures and nursing their mothers as if fed grain in addition. It is not always necessary to creep feed lambs on pastures but there are many instances in which this practice would result in larger gains, less shrinkage in shipping, more attractive lambs and a better meat product. A high, dry place in the field where the flock rests and sleeps is one of the best locations for a creep, as the lambs will eat while their mothers rest.

Lambs upon pasture should have plenty of shade, and if there is no natural shade in the pasture an improvised shed should be built near the creeps. Such a shed can be built at small expense and arranged so that it can be transferred from one pasture to another.

As suggested above, lambs eat a great deal less from the creep after they are turned to grass or forage than they do before that time, and unless the creep is well located they may cease eating grain altogether. The grass is so tender and palatable that they are inclined to forget the grain, and hence it is necessary to exercise care in locating the creep and in keeping the grain fresh and clean. Occasionally it may be a good plan to cease feeding grain through May and the first week in June when the grass is most sweet and tender and then commence again and continue until the lambs are sold.

If the lambs are born late so that the flock is placed on grass by the time they are learning to eat, it is almost impossible to make use of the creep. Sweet, tender grass and the mother's milk seem to satisfy all demands for feed. Since late-born lambs cannot be marketed until autumn or winter, there is really no need to feed grain while they are very young. The writer has found, however, that it is rather difficult to get late-born lambs to eat grain in the late summer and autumn months even though the pastures are very short and dry. In fattening such lambs a plan worth trying is to place them in the dry lot and limit the amount of roughage fed and thus force them to develop an appetite for grain. After this is done it may be possible to give them the run of the fields and still get them to consume enough grain to fatten them.

**Pastures and Forage Crops.**—The standard pasture in nearly all parts of the United States where farm flocks are kept is bluegrass. Sheep relish it and thrive and fatten on it if kept free from the parasites so harmful to them, but being a permanent pasture grass it is difficult to handle so that these parasites will not be present in such numbers as to greatly reduce its value. It is best in the spring and fall and is not an all-season pasture unless there is a very large area available. In midsummer it is too dry, too fibrous, and too unbalanced in nutrients to be an ideal feed for growing lambs or an economical maintenance feed for ewes. Therefore, it is inadvisable to depend on bluegrass alone for carrying the flock through the entire pasturing season. When bluegrass is young and tender, which is in May and the first half of June in the northern states, it is so palatable that lambs abandon almost all other feeds for it, but later they tire of it (Fig. 181).

**Timothy is excellent pasture** in the spring, for it is very palatable and nutritious. When it gets above six inches in height, it becomes too coarse for lambs; when it begins to head it is not a first-class pasture for older sheep. In midsummer it makes so little growth that its feeding value is very low; but should there be sufficient moisture, it makes an ideal fall pasture. Timothy is damaged if kept grazed down very closely by sheep, because the grass blades grow from bulbs which the sheep will eat when the pasture is very short.

**Mixed pastures** are not very common in the United States, but they are prevalent in England. The writer has had limited experience with a pasture composed of blue-grass, timothy, Italian rye-grass, and white clover. It made splendid feed and was capable of carrying a large number of sheep and lambs. The Italian rye-grass coming on very early made this pasture ready for grazing at least two weeks earlier than the regular season for blue-grass and timothy. The rye-grass, being rather coarse, was not so palatable as the other grasses and there was a tendency to graze the blue-grass and timothy too close. By rather heavy stocking, however, it was possible to graze the rye-grass down and then by resting the pasture for two weeks, it was at least as good as average grass. When growing lambs for early summer market, the two weeks of early grazing is important. A mixed pasture that furnishes an abundance of feed is composed of timothy, red clover, alsike clover, sweet clover, and alfalfa. When four pounds of each of these were seeded per acre a very palatable and productive pasture was secured with grazing throughout the season. By including blue-grass or redtop a permanent pasture may be developed, although without these the mixture will last several years.

Sampson[3] suggests a combination of alsike clover, white clover, Canada blue-grass, redtop, and orchard grass for poor soils low in lime content.

Fig. 181.—On the blue-grass.

**Clover and alfalfa** may be classed either as pasture or as forage crops. On account of being so watery while very young they are best in feeding value when above six inches in height. Except for a tendency to cause bloat, both are good feed for sheep and lambs. There is little danger of the lambs bloating, however, so long as they are getting milk. Clover seldom causes severe bloating except when it is very wet. Experience at the Illinois Station indicates that in pasturing alfalfa the sheep should be given a good "fill" of blue-grass or other safe palatable forage and then driven onto the alfalfa. They should then be left on continuously night and day even though there is heavy rain. During six years the losses have been of little consequence. Some reports of farmers support this opinion.

Keeping alfalfa grazed down close will kill it. This, together with its tendency to cause bloat, does not permit many to regard

[3] "Range and Pasture Management."

it as a dependable sheep pasture. In South Dakota few losses were reported during a ten-year period when ewes and lambs were pastured on alfalfa. An acre (yielding about five tons per acre as hay) when used as pasture produced as an average 419 pounds of lamb and at the same time maintained eight ewes during the pasture season. In most regions, however, more good can be secured from it in the form of hay, except in some cases when it is used as a part of a mixed pasture. Under such conditions the danger of bloat seems to be greatly reduced.

**How to Treat Bloated Sheep.**—When sheep are grazing on pasture that will cause bloat, they should be watched closely, for dangerous cases develop very rapidly. Many methods of treatment have been given, but the one which is most likely to be successful is the trocar and canula. These should be inserted three or four inches in front and a little below the hip bone on the left side of the animal. The writer uses the trocar as a last resort because of bad after-effects. It punctures the paunch and it is several weeks before the wound heals. In the meantime, a part of the contents of the paunch may run out into the wool and cause an offensive odor which attracts the flies that cause maggots. Kleinheinze says that freshly drawn cow's milk, given warm, will cure all but the worst cases of bloat. Give a half pint and if the bloating does not begin to go down in a few minutes, another dose should be given. A whole egg crushed and swallowed by the lamb is good. Probably the egg, like the milk, absorbs the gas.

Another method is to put a ¾-inch stick in the mouth like a bridle bit, drawing it close. A heavy string can be used for a head stall to hold it in place. This keeps the mouth open and the jaws working, to expel the gas.

Sometimes the gas can be expelled by pressing in on the sides of the sheep. This should be done, no matter what other method is employed, except in cases where the amount of bloating is so great that pressure may cause suffocation or burst paunch. Horlacher [4] recommends a drench of formalin and water as an effective method of reducing bloat. One-half ounce (one tablespoonful) of formalin in a pint of water is said to give quick relief. The formalin probably checks fermentations.

**Sweet clover** is more like a forage crop than a pasture.

---

4 "Sheep Production."

Fairly extensive use has been made of it in recent years as it makes luxuriant growth and undoubtedly has high carrying power for a short period at least. It is a two-year crop and fits well into common grain rotations. Because of its tendency to grow rank and coarse, one should start pasturing it rather early and a comparatively large number of sheep should be kept on it so that it will not become more than six or eight inches high. From present indications, it would seem that a small area of it would be a splendid asset in dry seasons as in fertile soil it makes a good growth in hot, dry weather. In the corn belt and similar regions, an early spring seeding of sweet clover makes good feed from about the middle of June until late fall. Little lambs and, in fact, old sheep are not fond of sweet clover when first feeding upon it, but they later become accustomed to the taste and eat the leafage and tender stems with relish.

**Rye.**—In the northern states, rye is of most use in the early spring months. If the pasture season opens about the first of May, one can place the sheep on rye about March 25. When it begins to joint it is not palatable; hence, to get the most out of it with ewes and lambs, it must be kept closely grazed. The animals must not be moved to some other green feed with a view of bringing them back to the rye later, for then they will not eat it.

In central Tennessee, rye is used all winter as pasture. It is an important factor in producing the early fat lambs for market.

**Winter oats** furnish good forage in the winter and spring in many parts of the South.

**Rape** is one of the best known forage crops for sheep and lambs, and since it is hardy it is suitable for sowing early in the spring. If sown early it attains sufficient growth to supply feed before the lambs are old enough for market. For this purpose it should be sown just as soon in the spring as it is advisable to work the ground into a good seed bed. Three to four pounds of seed should be sown to the acre and covered lightly by harrowing. Being a luxuriant grower, rape is adapted to a fertile soil and a plentiful supply of moisture. When sown in unfertilized, poor soil it is almost sure to prove a disappointment and a financial loss. Sheep and lambs should not be turned on rape until it has attained a growth of six or eight inches because it produces so much more feed if allowed to develop a great deal of leaf surface. Some care must be exercised in feeding rape in order to avoid bloat, scours, and poisoning. The worst cases of bloat and scours occur when the sheep are allowed to feed on it when it is wet. Frozen rape is very likely to cause death if eaten by sheep that have not been feeding regularly on unfrozen rape for several days or weeks. In getting sheep accustomed to rape, it is best to turn them on it for an hour or two each day after the dew is gone and after the sheep have had a partial fill of hay or grass.

Best results come from rape when it is alternated with something else, such as timothy, bluegrass, or clover. In hot weather particularly, a field of tall rape drenched with dew is a poor run for sheep. They should be kept on the grass until the rape is dry, because first getting wet and then being exposed to the hot sun is hard on them.

Rape has a great deal of fattening power; for this reason it is a good feed during the last few weeks before the lambs are to go to market.

Rape is often sown in corn just before the corn is cultivated for the last time. When sheep and lambs are turned in the corn the rape serves as a first-rate supplement. Being hardy, it is good feed until well into the winter, provided the sheep have become accustomed to it before it becomes frosted or frozen (Fig. 182).

**Oats and Canadian peas** sown together make a good green feed for ewes and lambs, but they are better suited for soiling purposes than for grazing. The peas should be sown two and one-half inches deep and the oats covered lightly by harrowing so that they will get a start before the peas come through the ground. Sow four pecks each of peas and oats to the acre. This mixed growth is best for sheep feed when the oats are about ready to head. Before that time the oats are so soft and watery that it takes a very large amount to satisfy the appetite.

**Soybeans,** either broadcasted or sown in rows, make a fairly good forage crop in late summer and early fall. When sown in corn they serve as an excellent supplement to the corn for fattening lambs. If pastured by alternating the grazing in different parts and not allowing any particular section to be too closely eaten, a field of soybeans may be used for a fairly long period. When most of the leaves have been eaten off, it is time to move to a fresh portion of the field so that the plants on the grazed part will have a chance to leaf again. A heavy fill of wet soybean forage may cause bloat. As the pods begin to develop, the grazing must be limited to a short time each day or the sheep will get too much of the grain. Soybeans cannot withstand frost.

**Cowpeas** have many of the same qualities as soybeans, but they are not so palatable and they require a warmer climate.

**Lespedeza** is gaining rapidly in importance as a sheep pasture in many states. In palatability, lack of a tendency to

Fig. 182.—In the rape at the University of Illinois, Urbana, Illinois.

cause bloat, gain produced, ability to withstand drought, and availability during midsummer when permanent pastures are short, it deserves a very high rank.

**Sudan grass** is a rapid-growing, relatively drought-enduring plant, useful in many sections as a sheep pasture. It should be pastured sufficiently close to prevent rank growth.

Other grasses and clovers such as brome grass, Bermuda grass, and hop or bur clover are useful for grazing in sections to which they are adapted.

**Grass and Forage Crops Compared.**—It is impossible to make a clear-cut comparison between grass and forage crops as sources of green feed for sheep and lambs. Permanent pastures are old standbys which nothing else can completely replace as convenient feeding grounds, for they can be, and usually are, made use of in every month of the year. Their worst feature lies in the fact that parasites harmful to sheep accumulate in them. In many instances they become so badly infested as to be almost useless. Fortunately there are permanent pastures in regions where sheep parasites are to be found that for some reason do not become badly infested. Sheep thrive on them year after year.

On the other hand, annual forage crops and such crops as clover and alfalfa are by no means parasite proof, but if they are in a rotation system of cultivation, the chances are that they will not become so badly infested as permanent pastures.

In recent years many permanent pastures in the middle west of the United States have had to give way to grain crops. Instead of roomy pastures once so common, are now seen little cramped, overstocked grass lots. These are undoubtedly relatively less efficient for sheep than larger pastures, because the grass is not allowed to get enough leaf surface to grow well, and the ground, besides becoming badly infested with parasites, is tainted with the droppings from the sheep and other farm animals.

The circumstances related above, coupled with the fact that such pastures as bluegrass do not last through all of the grazing season, raises the question as to whether sheep husbandry can be successfully followed by depending largely on forage crops. Undoubtedly, it can. Prime lambs can be produced on farms that do not have a foot of permanent grass, and the future will furnish numerous instances of it. With clover, alfalfa, sweet clover, rye, rape, soybeans, and cowpeas to work into a scheme for handling the flock, it will be possible to produce better lambs in the central part of the United States than have been produced in that region during the last twenty years.

It is possible to raise choice market lambs in the dry lot, and the time may come when it will be found profitable in certain regions to grow them in this way. Or they may be grown on a partial dry-lot basis. That is, the ewes may be kept in the dry lot and the lambs let out to pasture, or *vice versa* (Fig. 183).

The writer would not belittle the value of permanent pasture. There are places where nothing else equals it and sheepmen living in such places are happily located. The only interest they have in forage crops is to see whether they can use them to supplement their pastures.

**Docking and Castrating Lambs.**—A necessary operation in the production of lambs is docking and castrating. Owners of farm flocks often fail to do this, but they are always criticized as being guilty of neglect. It is better to dock and castrate when the lambs are from eight to sixteen days of age, as the resulting "set-back" in growth is least at that time. For the sake of convenience, both docking and castrating should be done at the same time. Opinions vary as to whether the operation should be performed early in the day or in the evening, but it seems that the lambs bleed less if they are operated upon either before they become active in the morning or when they are about to bed down for the night. A bright clear day with a prospect of several more to follow is the best kind of

FIG. 183.—Raised in a dry lot, University of Illinois, Urbana, Illinois.

day for docking and castrating as healing proceeds faster. The operation should be conducted under sanitary conditions. Avoid exposures to storms and keep them on dry, clean bedding at night.

*In docking,* the tail should be cut about an inch from the body, leaving it a little shorter on the side next the buttock. The operation can be performed with a knife, chisel, or docking iron. The latter is an instrument with a blunt blade, which upon being heated to a dull red, burns its way through the tail and sears over the stump or dock so that there is no bleeding. Western sheepmen use the docking iron. An emasculator, which is an instrument so designed that it crushes as well as cuts, has been tried in several range bands and farm flocks. There is practically no loss of blood in its use. It requires no heating (Figs. 184 and 185).

*In castrating,* the end of the scrotum should be cut off so as to permit drainage. The testicles should be grasped firmly between the thumb and fingers and drawn out. The work should be done quickly but not roughly, and the wound should be bathed with an antiseptic wash (Fig. 186).

There are many methods of castrating and there have been prolonged controversies as to which is the best, hence, it does not seem advisable to outline any particular method.

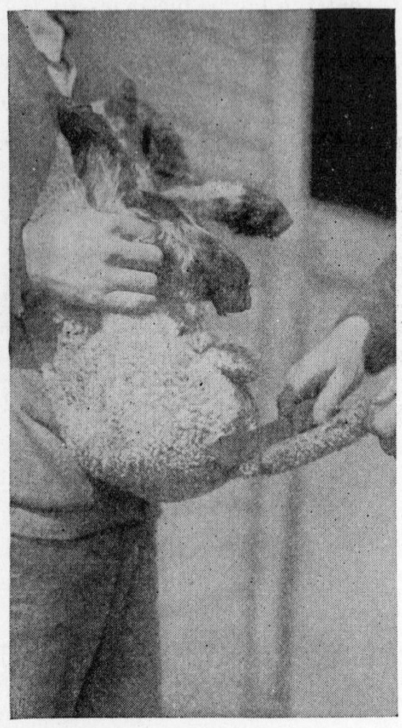

FIG. 184.

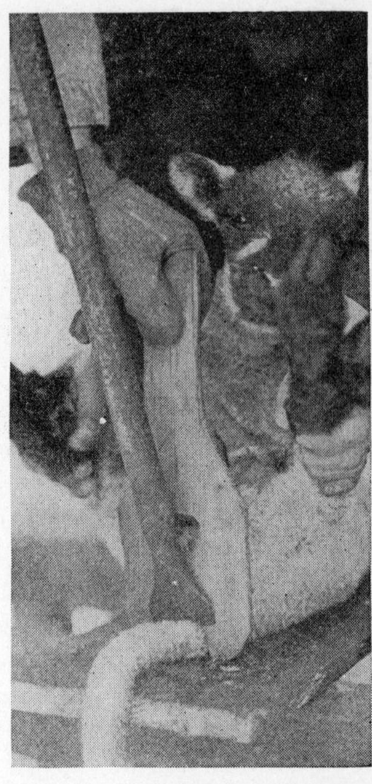

FIG. 185.

FIG. 184.—Docking a lamb with knife.
FIG. 185.—Docking a lamb with iron. The tail should be severed about one and one-fourth inches from the body.

**Market Lambs at Weaning Time.**—As a general rule, it is better to have the lambs in farm flocks come early (February or March), for then one can devote more time to them. They learn to eat grain before the grass season opens and are ready to market when they are old enough to wean, which is when they are from three to four months of age. At this time they should still have their "baby fat" and they should weigh 65 to 70 pounds. In regions where the summers are hot, lambs make very little gain through July, August, and early September, in fact they may lose in weight. During this time they are likely to become infested with parasites, and as a result some die, others lose weight, and only a few remain thrifty and plump. Some of them may be killed by dogs. If they are sold more feed is left for the ewes and the ewe

Fig. 186.—Docking with the emasculator. Lambs may be held in this position for castrating. The operator then cuts off the end of the scrotum and draws out the testicles, one at a time. The work should be done quickly and carefully.

lambs that are to go into the breeding flock. If the owner has extensive grass lands and is not in position to grow grain and hay, he may have good reason for handling late-born lambs. Otherwise the comparatively early lamb looks to be the better proposition.

**Rations for Suckling Lambs.**—The amount of feed consumed by lambs from the time they were old enough to eat until they were ready for market at weaning time is reported below in pounds per head per day.

The information given for rations Nos. 11 to 16 inclusive was obtained in experiments conducted at the Illinois Station. The lambs fed rations numbered 11, 12, 13 and 16 were by a pure-bred Shropshire ram and out of western ewes weighing about 115 pounds when pregnant. Although rations 14 and 15 are the same as rations 11 and 12 the lambs were by a pure-bred Hampshire ram and out of western ewes weighing about 115 pounds when pregnant.

*Ration No. 11*

| Age of lambs—weeks | 2-6 | | 6-10 | | 10–14 | |
|---|---|---|---|---|---|---|
| Grain Ration | Cracked corn | 20 lbs. | Corn | 30 lbs. | Corn | 60 lbs. |
| | Oats | 20 " | Oats | 20 " | Oats | 30 " |
| | Bran | 20 " | L.O.M. | 10 " | L.O.M. | 10 " |
| | L.O.M. | 10 " | | | | |

Lambs and ewes kept in dry lot

| | 2-6 | 6-10 | 10–14 |
|---|---|---|---|
| Grain eaten daily | .12 | .60 | 1.0 |
| Alfalfa eaten daily | .09 | .30 | .7 |
| Weight at beginning | 16.0 | 29.5 | 45.0 |
| Weight at close | 29.5 | 45.0 | 59.0 |

*Ration No. 12*

Same grain ration as No. 11

Lambs and ewes on rye, alfalfa and rape pasture

| | 2-6 | 6-10 | 10–14 |
|---|---|---|---|
| Grain eaten daily | .06 | .30 | .40 |
| Alfalfa eaten daily | .05 | — | — |
| Weight at beginning | 16.5 | 30.0 | 48.0 |
| Weight at close | 30.0 | 48.0 | 63.0 |

*Ration No. 13*

Same grain ration as No. 11

Lambs and ewes in dry lot first period, then on blue-grass pasture

| | 2-6 | 6-10 | 10–14 |
|---|---|---|---|
| Grain eaten daily | .14 | .10 | .15 |
| Alfalfa eaten daily | .10 | — | — |
| Weight at beginning | 16.5 | 30.0 | 44.5 |
| Weight at close | 30.0 | 44.5 | 56.5 |

*Ration No. 14*

| Age of lambs—weeks | | 2-6 | | 6-10 | | 10-14 | |
|---|---|---|---|---|---|---|---|
| | Cracked corn | 20 lbs. | Corn | 30 lbs. | Corn | 60 lbs. | |
| Grain ration | Oats | 20 " | Oats | 20 " | Oats | 30 " | |
| | Bran | 20 " | L.O.M. | 10 " | L.O.M. | 10 " | |
| | L.O.M. | 10 " | | | | | |

Lambs and ewes kept in dry lot

| | 2-6 | 6-10 | 10-14 |
|---|---|---|---|
| Grain eaten daily | .11 | .50 | 1.0 |
| Alfalfa eaten daily | .16 | .46 | 1.0 |
| Weight at beginning | 15.5 | 28.0 | 46.0 |
| Weight at close | 28.0 | 46.0 | 60.0 |

*Ration No. 15*

Same grain ration as No. 14

Lambs and ewes on rye, alfalfa and rape pasture

| | 2-6 | 6-10 | 10-14 |
|---|---|---|---|
| Grain eaten daily | .08 | .45 | .7 |
| Alfalfa eaten daily | .04 | .40 | .2 |
| Weight at beginning | 18.0 | 35.0 | 52.0 |
| Weight at close | 35.0 | 52.0 | 72.0 |

*Ration No. 16*

Lambs and ewes kept in the dry lot and given free choice of the different feeds. Compare with Ration No. 11, where the same feeds were given but the concentrates were mixed

Feed Consumed Daily

| Age of lambs—weeks | 1st Period 2–6 | 2nd Period 6–10 | 3rd Period 10–14 |
|---|---|---|---|
| Shelled corn ...... | .02 | .13 | .330 |
| Ground corn ...... | .01 | .04 | .180 |
| Whole oats ....... | .04 | .18 | .380 |
| Ground oats ...... | .02 | .03 | .007 |
| Bran ............. | .03 | .07 | .110 |
| Linseed oil meal .. | .09 | .24 | .540 |
| Alfalfa hay ....... | .25 | .45 | .570 |
| Weight at beginning | 15 lbs. | 28 lbs. | 45 lbs. |
| Weight at close .... | | | 60 lbs. |

A brief summary of three years' comparisons of rations and methods of raising lambs based on Purdue Station Bulletin 344 follows. The lambs were carefully selected and with the exception of one pair of twins each year in each lot were all single lambs. The ewes were white-faced westerns and the same rams, pure-bred Shropshires, were used all three seasons. It is significant to note that the pastures were chiefly legumes, oats, rape or timothy and that the acreage was large so that there was always a superabundance of succulent feed in the fields. It is also important to observe that these tests did not extend beyond the middle of July and that the lambs did not become infested with stomach worms during the trials.

| | *Ration No. 17* | *Ration No. 18* |
|---|---|---|
| Ration for lambs | Shelled corn<br>Alfalfa hay | Shelled corn<br>Alfalfa hay |
| Management | Lambs and ewes kept in dry lot | Lambs kept in dry lot<br>Ewes on pasture |
| Grain eaten daily | .94 | .97 |
| Alfalfa eaten daily | 1.08 | 1.23 |
| Weight at beginning | 34.5 | 34.3 |
| Weight at close | 73.3 | 77.0 |
| Daily gain | .49 | .54 |

| | *Ration No. 19* | *Ration No. 20* |
|---|---|---|
| Ration for lambs | Shelled corn<br>Pasture | Pasture |
| Management | Lambs and ewes on pasture | Lambs and ewes on pasture |
| Grain eaten daily | .19 | — |
| No. days on pasture | 79 | 79 |
| Weight at beginning | 34.1 | 33.8 |
| Weight at close | 81.3 | 80.3 |
| Daily gain | .60 | .59 |

A further test at Purdue reported in Bulletin 353 is summarized below. The lambs were by pure-bred Shropshire rams and out of white-faced western ewes. The feeds in rations Nos. 21 and 22 were mixed in equal proportion. Each group of approximately 20 ewes and 20 lambs had access to five acres of pasture. The report covers one year.

| | *Ration No. 21* | *Ration No. 22* |
|---|---|---|
| Ration for lambs | Cracked corn<br>Ground oats<br>Bran<br>Linseed oil meal<br>Molasses<br>Pasture | Shelled corn<br>Whole oats<br>Linseed oil meal<br>Pasture |

| | *Ration No. 21 (Cont'd.)* | *Ration No. 22 (Cont'd.)* |
|---|---|---|
| Management | Lambs and ewes on clover pasture | Lambs and ewes on clover pasture |
| Grain eaten daily | .50 | .58 |
| No. days on pasture | 60 | 60 |
| Weight at beginning | 36.5 | 36.9 |
| Weight at close | 73.4 | 78.4 |
| Daily gain | .61 | .69 |

| | *Ration No. 23* | *Ration No. 24* |
|---|---|---|
| Ration for lambs | Shelled corn<br>Pasture | Pasture |
| Management | Lambs and ewes on clover pasture | Lambs and ewes on clover pasture |
| Grain eaten daily | .52 | — |
| No. days on pasture | 60 | 60 |
| Weight at beginning | 38.2 | 36.5 |
| Weight at close | 77.4 | 76.2 |
| Daily gain | .65 | .65 |

The following data were secured in tests at the Ohio Station and were reported in Bulletin 270. The lambs in this experiment were by a pure-bred Southdown ram and out of grade Delaine Merino ewes weighing about 85 pounds. The lambs were developed as winter or hot-house lambs, and were fed all they would eat from December 19 to February 18 in a dry lot. Since it is very difficult to breed for fall lambs, it is almost impossible to have a considerable number of them born within a brief period. These lambs ranged from 2 to 9 weeks in age when the experiment began. They averaged 27 pounds in weight at the beginning of the experiment and they were slaughtered when they attained a weight of about 55 pounds.

*Ration No. 25*

| | |
|---|---|
| Shelled corn | .65 |
| Alfalfa hay | .65 |
| Daily gain | .44 |

Mothers were fed grain mixture consisting of corn, 4 parts; linseed oil meal, 1 part; corn silage and alfalfa hay.

*Ration No. 26*

| | |
|---|---|
| Shelled corn | .66 |
| Alfalfa hay | .67 |
| Daily gain | .41 |

Mothers were fed grain mixture consisting of corn, 5 parts; oats, 2 parts; bran, 2 parts; oil meal, 1 part; corn silage and alfalfa hay.

The lambs in this experiment were similar in breeding to those fed rations 25 and 26. They were fed 95 days, beginning December 24. Their initial weight was about 16 pounds, and since they were not intended for hot-house lambs, they were not forced so rapidly as were the lambs in the experiment given above.

*Ration No. 27*

| | |
|---|---|
| Shelled corn | .33 |
| Alfalfa hay | .34 |
| Daily gain | .32 |

*Ration No. 28*

| | |
|---|---|
| Grain { Corn—5 parts, Oats—2 parts, Bran—2 parts, Oil meal—1 part } | .33 |
| Alfalfa hay | .32 |
| Daily gain | .31 |

## QUESTIONS

1. What are the general methods of feeding lambs?
2. At what time during the suckling period should the ewe receive the most grain?
3. What feed would you use to keep up the milk flow?
4. Discuss the most useful roughages to use at this period.
5. How much silage may be fed to a ewe during the suckling period?
6. Is a variety of feed necessary for the ewes at this period? Why?
7. Give six rules that may be applied to the feeding of suckling ewes.
8. When will the lambs begin to eat grain?
9. What are lamb creeps?
10. Describe a method of starting the lambs on grain.
11. How does a pasture crop affect the consumption of grain by the lambs?
12. Of what value are forage crops in producing market lambs?
13. Name six common forage crops and the time of year they are available for pasture.
14. Is it necessary to dock and castrate? Why?
15. Describe common methods used in docking.
16. In castrating.
17. Give five reasons why it is advantageous to sell market lambs early in the summer.

## CHAPTER XXXIV

## SUMMER MANAGEMENT

**Weaning the Lambs.—Proper Age for Weaning.**—When the lambs are not taken from the ewes and sent to market, provision must be made for weaning them. They should not be weaned before they are three and one-half months old, and if they are doing well and the ewes are still furnishing them with a good quantity of milk, it may be best not to wean them until they are four or five months old.

Oftentimes the lambs are not separated from their mothers early enough. The ewes reach the point where they no longer give much milk, and the lambs, depending more than they should upon what little they can get, annoy them by persistently wanting to nurse. When a ewe without much milk nurses a pair of robust lambs weighing sixty-five pounds or more, she goes through a pretty rough experience that is none too good for her udder, because the lambs in suckling hunch at the udder so hard that the rear parts of the ewe are almost lifted from the ground. In hot weather, if only a little milk is to be had, it does a big lamb, old enough to wean, little good to keep thrusting its nose after the teat under the hot flanks of the ewe. Both mother and lamb are better off if separated. There is a natural weaning period, that is, there comes a time when the ewes will wean the lambs, but they ought to be weaned before this time comes.

If the lambs are weaned fairly early and placed on pasture or forage that has not been grazed by the sheep, they are less likely to become badly infested with parasites. This is an important consideration in places where parasitic troubles must be kept constantly in mind. If the weaning is not delayed beyond the proper time, the ewes will have time to recuperate and get in proper condition for the breeding season.

If possible, all of the lambs should be weaned at the same time, but in case there are some very late ones, they should be allowed to stay with their mothers until they are of sufficient age not to be checked in growth or stunted by being deprived of milk.

**Procedure in Weaning.**—In flocks kept primarily for producing market lambs, it is best to separate the ewes and lambs and not allow them to be together again. The ewes should be taken from the lambs, that is, the lambs should not be removed to quarters entirely strange to them. A week or so before they are to be weaned, they should be allowed to graze on the feed intended for them through the weaning period. If it is not possible to do this, they should be left for a few days on the field to which they are accustomed, as they do not seem to miss their mothers so much when they are in familiar surroundings. It is better, however, to have them where the feed is fresh and good, even though the place is strange to them, than to leave them where the feed is poor.

Another method of weaning is to get the ewes and lambs gradually accustomed to being separated. This is a very good method if it does not cost too much in labor, for one can begin when the lambs are not old enough to do without milk. A fine opportunity is afforded to place the lambs on the cleanest, best pasture while the ewes are finishing up the old second-rate pasture. By beginning early enough, and by allowing the ewes and lambs to be together only when they are in the dry lot, one can in large measure keep parasites out of the lambs. For this purpose, the plan is even better than the English method of hurdling, in which the lambs are allowed to run with the ewes and also ahead of them on fresh forage.

**Feeding Lambs after Weaning.**—In addition to the best of pasture or forage, lambs should receive some grain during the weaning period and all through the hot months. Oats, corn, wheat, and barley can all be utilized as well as such concentrates as wheat bran, linseed oil meal or cake, and cottonseed meal. Usually it is not necessary to feed more than one-half pound grain per head daily if the pasture or forage is good. Oats alone will serve as a good grain feed. If the forage or pasture is a leguminous crop, corn alone will do very well as the grain part of the ration, but usually a mixture such as oats, five parts; corn, five parts, and wheat bran, two parts, by weight, is preferable to any one feed. Linseed oil meal or cottonseed meal should not form the sole grain ration, as they are not suitable for using in large quantities in summer.

Feeding the lambs a little grain each day affords an opportunity for seeing them often and hence for detecting troubles before they become unmanageable.

Salt and good water are just as essential to the thrift of lambs at weaning time as at any other period of their lives.

**Separating Lambs.**—In case some of the male lambs are left entire, which should be the case only in pure-bred flocks, it will be necessary to place them by themselves when their sex instinct becomes marked. This is necessary because some of the older ewe lambs are likely to breed in the autumn months and also because the ram lambs will cause both themselves and the ewes to lose flesh by almost constantly teasing the ewes.

**Treatment of Ewes after the Lambs are Weaned.**—When taken from the lambs the ewes should be placed upon rather dry, scant pasture in order to reduce the secretion of milk. Every two or three days those that have full, tight udders should be milked. After the secretion of milk has been checked so that there is no danger of the udder spoiling, the ewes should be given good grazing in order to get them in fairly good condition before the beginning of the breeding season.

Ewes enjoy gleaning over the farm, and after the lambs are weaned, no other run is better for them. At this time they are active and hence able to feed over large areas. If given the job of cleaning up the neglected fence rows, nooks, and corners, they do so with much relish and to their own benefit. When handled in this way they often eat down the weeds along the fence rows to such extent that mowing is not necessary. In this way weeds are prevented from forming seeds and their spread over the farm is greatly reduced. Insect breeding places are also destroyed.

If it is not advisable to allow the ewes to glean over the farm after the lambs are weaned, they should be given good pasture. They do not need as succulent pasture, however, as is needed by the lambs, and they often fatten on what seems to be a dry, unwholesome pasture of bluegrass or timothy.

Like the lambs, the ewes should have access to salt and good water throughout the summer season.

**Shelter and Shade in Summer.**—Shade is of great importance in summer to both ewes and lambs. No field in which they are confined during the day should be without protection from the hot sun (Fig. 187).

There is difference of opinion as to what constitutes the best shade. Trees, of course, are natural provisions for escape from the intense heat of the sun, and to the lover of sheep there is no more comely sight than a well-fed flock contentedly lying beneath the widespreading branches of a big shade tree. It is not always convenient or economical to have ample shade trees in every field, besides, there is a reason for partly condemning trees for shade because they cannot be moved from place to place. On this account the grass around them is likely to become so badly infested with parasites that they are undesirable as resting places for the flock. By exercising proper precautions in guarding against parasites, this

FIG. 187.—A good shade tree.

last objection does not necessarily obtain, in which case a good shade tree should be regarded as beneficial to the flock (Fig. 187).

It is more difficult to provide shade in fields having no trees and so situated that the sheep cannot conveniently come to the buildings. In such fields, shades should be built, either temporary or permanent in nature. A cheap permanent shade can be built by simply setting posts in the ground to serve as a support to a roof made of boards. In rainy weather, however, a roof of this sort lets the water through and the resting place of the sheep becomes muddy. At somewhat increased cost, this fault can be remedied by covering the boards with roofing paper. A shade similar to the one above can be placed on dimension pieces four by six inches and thus be made movable. Roofing paper does not necessarily need to be placed on the movable shade because it can be moved when the ground beneath it becomes muddy (Fig. 188).

Light movable shades can be made by using hurdles covered with burlap. Set up such a hurdle with the length running north and south. Then lay a hurdle on top of this one so that the two form a **T**. This arrangement furnishes shade for both forenoon and afternoon, and one man can do all the work involved in setting it up.

There are still other types of both permanent and movable shades

Fig. 188.—A movable shade. A shade of this sort can be moved from time to time to the spots in the fields that are most in need of manure or to places where the circulation of air is best. It thus has some advantages over the shade tree. (From Pennsylvania State College Circular 49.)

that are quite as good, and possibly better than the types discussed here.

*Protection from Summer Rains.*—Sometimes in summer there are protracted periods of excessive rainfall to which the sheep should not be continually exposed. It is well to draw them in close around the barns and allow them to stay under shelter the greater part of the time. The severest of all times for sheep are periods of excessive heat accompanied by great humidity. Such periods are still more severe upon them if they are constantly wet from rain.

A well-arranged barn is always a convenience in summer as a refuge both from the sun and rains, and an attempt should be made to have pasture or forage near it so that in the worst periods, this can be utilized by the flock.

**Summer Enemies of the Flock.**—After the shepherd has provided ample pasture, forage, water, salt, shade, and shelter for his flock in summer, he must still remember that there are certain insidious enemies which he must guard against. Most of these enemies are parasitic in nature and hence hard to combat. The most common and the most dreaded of these parasites in farm flocks is the stomach worm.

**Stomach Worm.**—The stomach worm (*Hæmonchus contortus*) made its first deadly attack upon the flocks in the central part of the United States in 1893 and 1894. It was probably brought to this country in sheep imported from England. At any rate, it was a new enemy to those who had handled Merinos, and when the savage attack of 1893 and 1894 came, nearly all flock owners in the middle-western section of the United States were nonplussed and helpless. Thousands of lambs and many old sheep died in Ohio, Michigan, Indiana, and Illinois. Hundreds engaged in sheep raising were so discouraged that they closed out their flocks and gave up sheep forever. Since that time, a large percentage of the native lambs sent to the open markets have been badly infested with stomach worm. Being unthrifty and unfinished, they have been the object of scathing criticism on the part of commission men and buyers for the packers. Sheepmen are gradually learning how to keep the stomach worm in check, but it is still an insidious enemy that is sure to bring trouble to the farm flock owner who is not always keenly alive to the possibility of its presence (Fig. 189).

**Life History of the Stomach Worm.**—To Ransom,[1] of the Zoölogical Division of the Bureau of Animal Industry, more than to anyone else, belongs the credit of determining the life history of the stomach worm. He learned what takes place from the time the worms mate until the sheep become infested, or perhaps reinfested. The mating process takes place in the abomasum (known as the fourth or true stomach of the sheep), where all of the worms live while in the host, except a few that drift over into the duodenum. The eggs, which are microscopic, are deposited in the abomasum and pass out of the body in the feces. Heat hastens the time of hatching, which may occur in a few hours, days, or weeks, accord-

[1] Circulars 93 and 102, U. S. Bureau of Animal Industry, Washington, D. C.

ing to the temperature. Either dryness or freezing temperature will kill the eggs and the very young larvæ. The newly hatched larva feeds upon the fecal matter in which it lives until it develops into the final stage outside the sheep or host. This is called the final free living stage, and the time from hatching until this stage is reached is also a matter of temperature, ranging from a few days to a few weeks. On attaining the final free living stage the

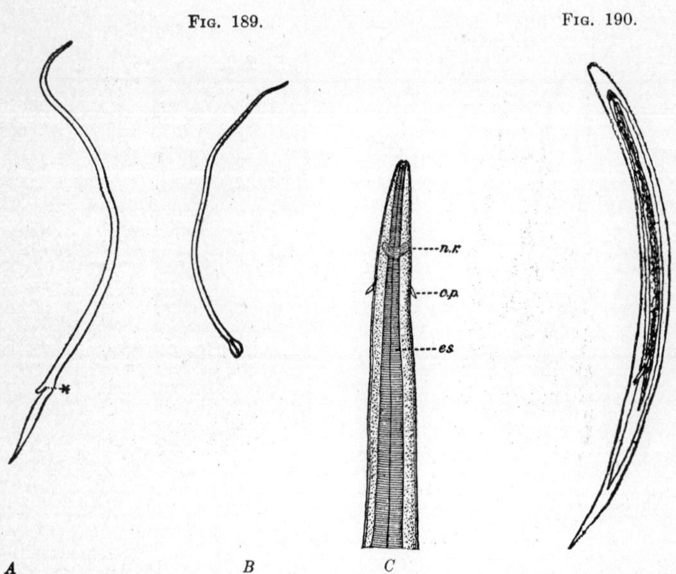


FIG. 189.—Stomach worm (*Hæmonchus contortus*). *A*, female larva × 5; *B*, male; *C*, anterior end of body showing: *n.r.*, nerve ring; *c.p.*, cervical papilla; *es*, œsophagus. (From Bureau of Animal Industry Bul. 127.)

FIG. 190.—Ensheathed stomach worm. In this stage the worm is highly resistant to hot, cold and dry weather, and hence is hard to destroy. (From 22d Annual Report South Carolina Station.)

larva becomes enveloped in a thin, horny-like coat, called a chitinous sheath, is no longer able to take in food, and hence must obtain its nourishment from material stored up in its own intestine (Fig. 190).

At temperatures above 40 degrees F. the ensheathed larva or embryo can move about, very slowly of course, and it becomes more active as the temperature rises. It is very unlike the newly hatched larvæ and eggs in that it is not killed even by long periods of freezing or drying. When the vegetation is wet from rain or dew, the sheathed larvæ crawl up grass or weed blades and stems, coming to rest when the moisture evaporates and resuming the journey when the vegetation is again wet. In this way they get up high enough to be taken in by a sheep or lamb when grazing. After being swallowed, they continue their development and attain maturity in two or three weeks (Fig. 191).

All that is known of the life history of the stomach worm has been very briefly reviewed in the foregoing. So far as the writer is aware, no one has yet determined how long an individual worm

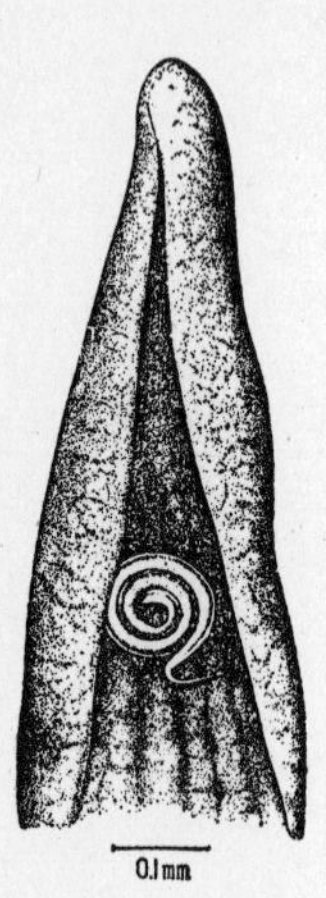


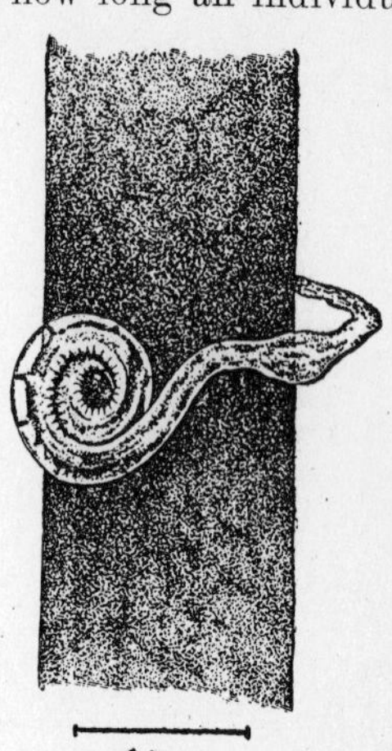


Fig. 191.—The ensheathed larva of the stomach worm on grass blades. (From Bureau of Animal Industry Circular No. 93.)

may live in the stomach of the host. If, as is maintained, none of the eggs hatch in the stomach, then it would seem possible to determine this point, and it would be valuable information. The writer has observed very heavy infestation in sheep after they have been confined continually in dry lots during the winter months. Lambs born in the same dry lots were carried through entire summer seasons without becoming infested. Therefore, it would seem that the worms that were in the sheep when they came from the pastures remained in them throughout the entire winter.

**Examining for Stomach Worms.**—Mature stomach worms are from three-fourths to an inch in length. They look like a red and a white thread intertwined. In conducting a post mortem for the purpose of determining whether there is an infestation of stomach worms it is well to examine the animal shortly after death—before it has become cold, if possible—for otherwise the worms may be dead and disintegrated beyond recognition. Before openening the stomach, it should be placed so that a slit can be cut in it which will permit of examining the liquids before they escape. If many live worms are present, they can be seen wriggling in the liquids, or attached to the inner wall of that section of the stomach joined to the small intestines.

**How the Worm Does Harm.**—It is probable that the stomach worm injures sheep and lambs in several ways. Undoubtedly one way is by sucking blood from the mucus lining of the stomach. It not only draws nourishment from the blood of its host, but its poisonous secretions, upon entering the blood of the sheep, reduce the number of red-blood cells and the hemoglobin content. After knowing the manner in which the worm lives, we can easily understand why a sheep or lamb heavily infested may have a pale skin, lusterless wool, very little blood in the veins of the white of the eye, disordered digestion characterized by a depraved appetite for dirt, or by scours. It is also easy to understand why heavily-infested animals get so thin in flesh and why lambs become so weakened that they die. When any of the above symptoms appear, an examination should be made to ascertain whether the worms are present even if it involves killing one or two of the most suspected animals. If an animal is heavily infested, thousands of worms are present. A hundred or less would of themselves check the well-doing of a lamb but little, but these show the possibility of gathering more from the pastures.

**Eradication of Stomach Worms.**—While stomach worms cannot be totally eradicated and pastures cannot be rid of them, infections may be checked so the flock will appear thrifty and the lambs will grow well.

**Changing Pastures.**—Undoubtedly changing to new pastures helps. Owners of pure-bred flocks can best afford this. Three pastures may be enough and will not require much expenditure. Temporary low fences may be used. In this method shade and water must be provided. Shades may be movable.

*Plowing the land* and sowing to forage crops upon which sheep can graze helps a great deal in keeping down infestation. For example, a pasture in which there are many stomach worms may be thoroughly plowed and sown to rye for pasture in late autumn, winter, and early spring. Then the rye may be turned under and the land sown to rape, which will furnish a great deal of green feed. But there is danger of over-estimating the protection these growths give against stomach worms. One of the worst infestations the writer has ever seen in lambs came from grazing continuously on a small rape lot for several weeks, and the veteran Shropshire breeder, George Allen, had a similar experience. In case animals are infested it is obvious that they will become reinfested just as soon as the worm eggs they cast in their feces hatch out, attain the ensheathed stage, and crawl up on the plants upon which the sheep or lambs feed. Nevertheless the man who uses forage crops rationally will have in his flock fewer stomach worms than the man who depends on old permanent pastures.

*Keeping Host Animals off Pastures.*—Is there a way of ridding an old pasture of a bad infestation of stomach worms? There is. It consists of keeping sheep and other animals which serve as host to the worm entirely off the pasture for practically one year's time. Stomach worms also infest cattle, goats, deer, American bison, etc., and therefore none of these animals should graze on the pasture, but horses and hogs could be allowed upon it.

*Drenches.*—Infestation of stomach worm can also be held in check by drenching, and there are a number of proprietary remedies (salts, powders, and liquids) which many farmers evidently believe help in keeping the worm under control. Thus far investigators have reported little success from remedies mixed with salt or administered in the feed or water. Although certain drugs given in this manner may tend to counteract the toxins liberated by the worms, tests have failed to justify their use.

(1) *Copper Sulfate or Bluestone.*—At the present time the most commonly recommended treatment for sheep and lambs infested with stomach worms is a one per cent solution of copper sulfate. This solution is prepared by dissolving one pound of pure copper sulfate crystals in 9½ U. S. gallons of water. It is better to dissolve the crystals in a gallon of boiling water and then add cold water to make the required amount. This quantity is sufficient for several hundred sheep and for small flocks the amounts of copper sulfate and water may be reduced

in proportion. Since this solution corrodes most metals, it is important that it be prepared and kept in glassware or similar containers. When administering the drench the solution should be kept well stirred. A safe dosage for a three-months-old lamb is one ounce; for a six-months-old lamb, 2 ounces; a yearling, 3 ounces; older sheep, 4 ounces. When given with due care to avoid choking the animal there is little danger in using this treatment. At the Illinois Station twice these quantities have been given without apparent ill effects and the Texas Station reports the successful use on its own flock of a 1¾ per cent solution given in the usual amounts. Although some authorities report little advantage in doing so, it is a good plan to keep the animals from feed and water for about 16 hours before and for 3 or 4 hours after drenching. When on infested pasture, sheep and lambs should be given the treatment at least once each month. Lambs should be placed on clean pasture after treatment.

(2) *Copper Sulfate and Nicotine Sulfate.*—A more drastic treatment than the bluestone alone may be prepared by the addition of Black Leaf 40 to the copper sulfate solution as prepared above. One ounce of Black Leaf 40 should be added to each gallon of the bluestone solution. This combined copper sulfate and nicotine sulfate is then administered in the same quantities as recommended for the bluestone. Because this treatment is somewhat more severe than the bluestone drench alone it is not advisable to use it for very weak animals. However, it is a safe and effective remedy when carefully prepared and administered and destroys the common broad tapeworms as well as some of the nodular and perhaps other intestinal parasites. This solution, as in the case of bluestone, should be prepared and kept in glass or earthenware containers and be stirred frequently when being used.

(3) *Iodine.*—A solution of iodine in water has been recently advocated as a vermifuge. It is known as Lugol's iodine solution and consists of 5 per cent iodine and 10 per cent potassium iodide in water. In the directions for drenching as given by Lamson it is suggested that for lambs one-half ounce of Lugol's solution be added to one quart of water and that each lamb be given from 2 to 4 ounces, depending on age and size. For large, strong lambs and sheep one ounce of Lugol's solution is added to one quart of water and four ounces given to each animal. In

some tests this treatment has been found about equal to the copper sulfate in destruction of worms.

(4) *Tetra-chlor-ethylene and Carbon Tetra-chloride.*—These substances which are given in capsules have been found to be highly efficient in the destruction of stomach worms. Opinions differ as to whether or not the heavily infested lambs do as well after these are given as following the copper sulfate treatment. Capsules containing 2½ cubic centimeters of tetra-chlor-ethylene are given to lambs and 5 cubic centimeters are used for older sheep. Capsule doses of 3 cubic centimeters of carbon tetra-chloride have been used for lambs weighing about 60 pounds. The latter substance given in one cubic centimeter dosage is con-

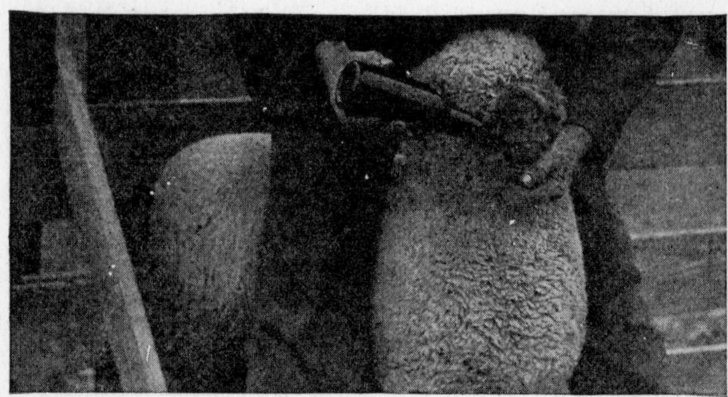

FIG. 192.—Drenching a sheep. Back the sheep into a corner so it cannot twist about, keep the head in as nearly natural position as possible, introduce the neck of the bottle at the corner of the mouth—tip the bottle up and down to prevent the liquid from running into the throat too fast.

sidered the most effective treatment for destroying liver flukes, which are troublesome in a few sections in this country but which are widely distributed in England. These treatments are generally more expensive than bluestone but have the advantage of being effective against many of the adult nodular worms.

*How to Drench.*—The animal should be allowed to stand while being drenched, as it is less likely to become strangled. It should be backed into a corner or against a wall and the man giving the drench should stand astride or at the side in order to keep it from twisting about. The nose should be lifted no higher than necessary to get the dose down, for the higher it is lifted the greater the probability of causing strangling. If the drench is given from a bottle it should have a long, slim neck which should be inserted at the corner of the mouth. In order not to give the dose too fast, the bottle containing it should be tipped gently up and down while the drench is being swallowed (Fig. 192).

A metal syringe with a nozzle about three inches long and a barrel large enough to hold one dose of the treatment is a good instrument for drenching. When the vermifuge is given in this way the liquid may be placed farther down toward the throat so that the sheep does not notice it or waste so much.

A rubber bulb syringe of the right size with a hard rubber nozzle or tube is also very satisfactory. Likewise the Australian type drenching horn shown in figure 169 is a convenient instrument to use. This is made of galvanized iron with the side opening located so as to measure the dose as the horn is withdrawn from the drenching solution.

The animal should swallow quietly and not struggle, so the dose will pass to the worms in the fourth stomach, and not to the first stomach, where it does no good.

*When to Drench.*—The whole flock should be drenched at weaning time and again about ten days later. In case the infestation is very bad, it is advisable to repeat the treatment at intervals of about 30 days throughout the pasture season, unless clean pasture is available.

**Prevention of Stomach Worms by Use of the Dry Lot.**—There is one way in which it is possible to raise lambs so that they will be practically free from stomach worms, even though their dams are badly infested. That way is to raise them in the dry lot—a lot in which no plant is to be found growing. Such lambs have all the manifestations of health and post mortems show them to be almost free from infestation. Out of a number of stomachs examined, 22 was the largest number of worms found in any individual by the writer, and this animal had a wool ball in its stomach. In case of pure-bred flocks becoming heavily infested, it may be advisable to raise a crop of lambs in the dry lot, for in so doing, clean, vigorous breeding animals can be secured. Then, too, other undesirable internal parasites may be avoided at the same time.

**Nodule Disease.**—Nodule disease is due to a parasite (*Œsophagostomum columbianum*), the embryos of which form knots or concretions inside both the large and small intestines. In the worst cases these concretions are thickly studded on the intestine along its entire course, and their harmful effects come from their interference with the processes of digestion and absorption of food materials.

The life history of the parasite which causes nodule disease is not well known. It seems that the mature female lays her eggs in the intestine, where they hatch in a short time, and in some manner pass through the mucus lining of the bowel and become embedded or encysted in the intestinal wall. As nearly as is known the irritation caused by the embryos give rise to the concretions. Dalrymple, of the Louisiana Station, found that the

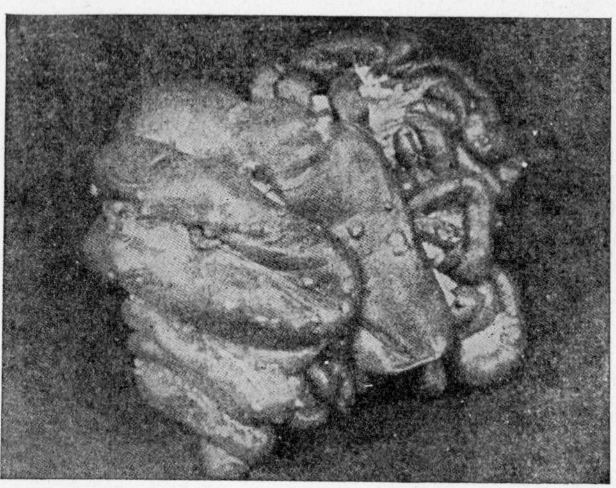

Fig. 193.—Nodule disease. Note the knots or nodules that have been caused by the parasites. (From Louisiana Experiment Station Bulletin 143.)

parasite which causes nodule disease is swallowed by the sheep while grazing; what happens to the parasite from the time it leaves the concretion in the intestine until it is swallowed by a grazing animal is unknown. Although carbon tetra-chloride and tetra-chlor-ethylene may destroy some of the adult worms, the parasites encysted in tissues are not reached (Fig. 13).

Deaths frequently result from the disease in the southern states. Its effects are most injurious when combined with other troubles such as stomach worm or tape-worm. If one has a flock badly infested with nodule disease he can keep lambs free from it by raising them in a dry lot.

**Tape-worms** are of six types. They are found in sheep in nearly all parts of the world. In the United States it is somewhat more common in the western than in the central and eastern parts, where stomach worms are worse. In the adult stage, it inhabits the small intestine, and, since it develops great length of body (some types several feet), it is needless to say that it is a greedy feeder and saps the vitality of the host. The symptoms resemble those of stomach worm, except the rapacious appetite.

The following is recommended by several writers: Oil of male shield fern, 1 dram; raw linseed oil, 2 to 4 ounces. Dose after animal has fasted 16 hours.

Some types of tape-worm infest sheep brain, liver, and muscle in the cyst or larval stage only, the adults living in dogs.

**Lungworms.**—These parasites are of two kinds and are found in air passages and in lung tissues. The thread lungworm (*Strongylus filaria*) is from one to four inches long with the intestine showing as a dark hairline throughout its length. The hair lungworms (*S. rufescens*) are about one inch in length and of a brownish red color. Affected animals show the symptoms so characteristic of parasitic troubles. In this case there is a husky cough generally followed by difficult breathing. Losses occur because of extreme weakness and suffocation. The owner of infested sheep should practice sanitation and pasture rotation.

**Grub in the Head.**—The sheep bot-fly (*Estrus ovis*) deposits larvæ instead of eggs. This occurs in the nostrils of sheep, and larvæ work up into the cavities. Flies annoy sheep when buzzing or attacking the nose. Sheep stamp their feet, duck their heads, and rub their noses in dust.

After the larvæ have reached their destination, up in the nasal cavities, they fasten themselves to the lining membranes by means of little hooks. These, along with the pressure of the growing grub, cause a great deal of irritation, and the sheep resorts to a violent snorting cough in its effort to dispel the grub. Not infrequently the grub so affects the brain as to cause death, and they always cause much discomfort and loss of flesh.

The most effective means of combating bot-fly is to keep the noses of the sheep smeared with pine tar through the summer months. The tar repels the fly and the larvæ are not deposited where they can gain access to the head. Sheep will smear their noses if salt or grain is placed in a trough containing tar.

**The Maggot Fly** (*Musca vomitorium*).—Wounds and places befouled by dung or urine are likely to attract the maggot fly. The gummy wool about the base of Merino rams' horns may attract them. The larvæ hatch out within a few hours after the eggs are deposited in the befouled places. They grow very fast and cause the sheep a great deal of discomfort. They can be killed by applying a strong solution of sheep dip or spirits of turpentine. Kerosene is also effective in killing them. The dip, mixed one part to fifty parts of water, is to be preferred to the other remedies as it is less severe on the skin of the sheep. A sheep plainly shows when it has maggots by squirming and twisting in an effort to get its mouth to the irritated spot. Maggots should not be allowed to remain on the sheep long, since they soon eat through the skin and recovery from the injury is very slow. After they have been killed, the injured place should be treated with some soothing ointment, such as carbolized oil or vaseline. Saratoga ointment, a rather expensive remedy, is very effective in restoring the broken skin and in bringing the injured part back to normal condition.

**Ticks, Lice, and Scab Mites** are external parasites that may give trouble at any time of the year. They should be exterminated in the summer or fall while the weather is warm and the wool is short.

**Lice** (*Trichocephalus sperocephalus*).—Sheep lice are white and reddish-brown parasites having almost the same color as the skin of the sheep. They are about one-twentieth of an inch long, but because of their color are rather hard to see when on the sheep. They are usually present in largest numbers on the back just behind the shoulders, but in bad cases they are on nearly all parts of the body. On account of the irritation they cause, the sheep is very uncomfortable and often rubs out a large portion of its fleece in trying to get relief. A thorough dipping will kill lice, but since the eggs are not destroyed by the dip, it requires a second dipping completely to get rid of them. It pays well to dip lousy sheep, for if it is not done, a great deal of the wool crop will be lost, and if nothing more were accomplished than the relief to the animals, the dipping would be well worth while. When dipping is not possible, Baker [2] advises rubbing the affected parts with a mixture composed of equal parts of lard and sulfur (Fig. 194).

**Ticks** (*Melophagus ovinus*).—The sheep tick is a flat, brownish, wingless fly that subsists on the blood it sucks from the skin of the

[2] Baker, "Sheep Diseases," 1916.

sheep. It travels all over the sheep's body, but it seems to have a preference for the belly and under side of the neck. In piercing the skin, it causes more or less irritation, and a sheep with many ticks on it suffers and loses in weight and strength. It also loses wool from rubbing. When the first warm days come, the ticks leave the old sheep, and take to the lambs. If they are not eradicated, the lambs are checked in growth and stunted.

Ticks seldom prove fatal to the host and are such common pests that flock-owners are many times unaware of the amount of injury they do. By consistently following the practice of dipping it is possible to eradicate them and there is no good excuse for having them in the flock.

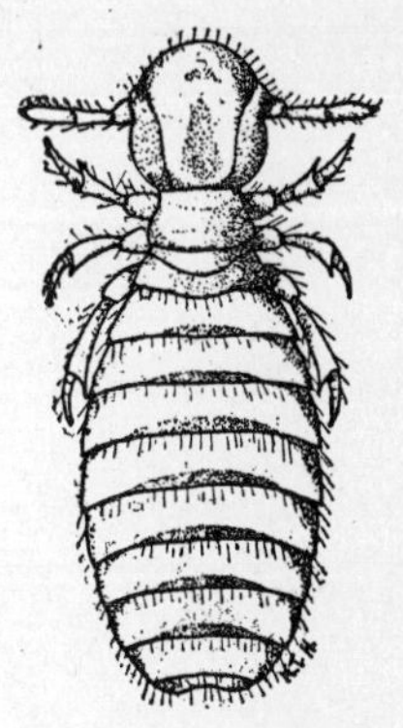

FIG. 194.—Adult sheep louse. (From Kentucky Station Bulletin No. 143.)

The whole flock should be dipped shortly after the shearing has been completed. At that time the weather is usually warm and favorable for dipping; the old sheep just out of their coats carry very little of the dip out of the vat, and most of the ticks have gone over to the lambs, making it imperative that they be dipped. Ten days after the first dipping, the whole flock should be dipped again to get rid of ticks hatched from eggs that were deposited before the first dipping. In the autumn before the warm days have passed, careful examination should be made for ticks and lice, and if any are present, the whole flock should be dipped twice as before.

When sheep are badly infested with ticks in winter, it is good practice to remove the wool if warm quarters can be provided. Many of the ticks are taken off with the wool and the sheep destroy with their teeth most of those left on the body (Fig. 195).

**The Scab Mite** (*Psoroptes communis ovis*).—Scab mites are much smaller than either ticks or lice, but if they are placed on a dark background they can be seen with the naked eye. They are light-colored and the females are about one-fortieth of an inch long and the males one-fiftieth of an inch.[3] By piercing the skin of the sheep in the act of feeding, the mite causes inflammation and irritation. As the mites multiply, serum oozes from the skin, and as the

[3] Texas Agricultural Exp. Sta. Bulletin 479.

exudation dries a scab or crust is formed. Beneath this crust the mites continue to irritate the skin and to multiply with great rapidity. As they increase in numbers, they spread over the body of the sheep until practically the whole of it is covered unless some method is adopted to check them. The wool drops off where the scab or crust forms, and the sheep presents a very haggard and sorry appearance. But the disease ought to be detected long before this stage is reached.

The first symptom of scab is uneasiness caused by itching, which

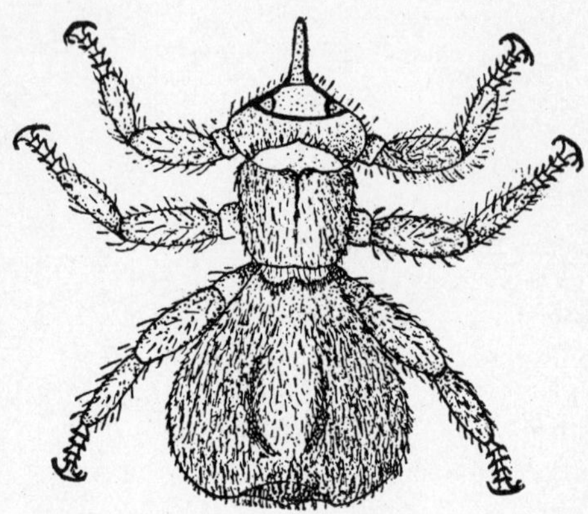

FIG. 195.—Adult sheep tick. (From Kentucky Station Bulletin 143.)

the sheep tries to allay by biting or pulling at the wool near the affected spot and by rubbing. Rubbing distributes many mites that adhere to bits of scab and wool and these mites may infest other sheep, but mites apparently do not live much more than three weeks when off the host even under favorable conditions.

When scab is found in a flock the only thing to be done is to dip the entire flock before the trouble has time to spread farther. This work must be thoroughly done. Since many of the mites are under the scabs, they are hard to reach with the dip unless the scabs are first soaked or broken down by rubbing with some rough object, such as a corn cob or piece of wood. One dipping is not sufficient in that it does not destroy the eggs. After the first dipping the sheep should be turned back into their pen, where they will continue to rub and disinfect the walls or fences. The second dipping should occur ten days after the first.

Scab has been eradicated from most sections of the United States. By enforcing dipping and quarantine, the U. S. Bureau of Animal Industry has done a splendid piece of work in cleaning up the flocks of the western states. In this work lime-sulfur dip has been used more than any other solution (Fig. 196).

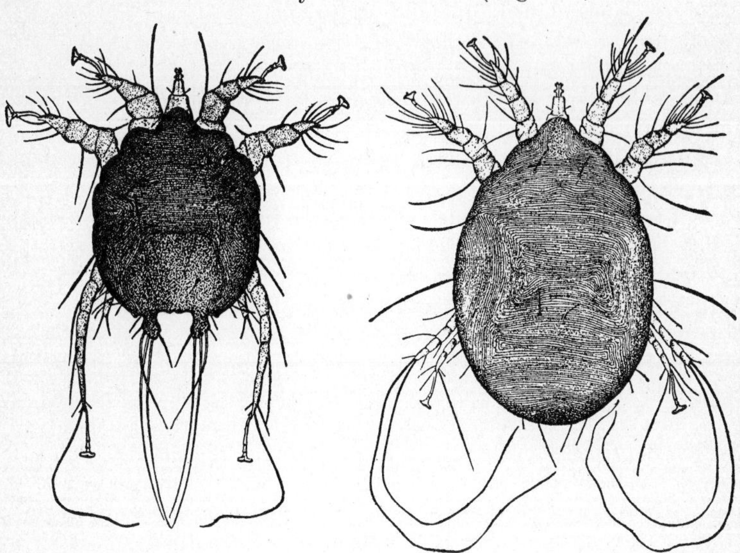

Fig. 196.—Sheep scab mite, dorsal view—male and female. (From Bureau of Animal Industry Bulletin 142.)

**Lime-sulfur Dip.**—The formula for the lime-sulfur dip used by the U. S. Bureau of Animal Industry is as follows:

| | |
|---|---|
| Unslaked lime | 8 pounds |
| Flowers of sulfur | 24 pounds |
| Water | 100 gallons |

In preparing the mixture, slake the lime in a little water, to which add the sulfur slowly and stir constantly. Transfer the mass to a vessel containing thirty gallons of hot water and boil for two hours with frequent stirring to prevent the lime-sulfur paste from caking on the bottom of the vessel. Add water from time to time to replace that lost by evaporation. The boiling causes the lime to combine with the sulfur, making calcium sulfide, which is the active agent in the dip that kills the mite. This mixture, a chocolate-colored mass, is then transferred to a barrel and allowed to settle for several hours, after which the clear solution is dipped from the top of the barrel or else drawn from it by making a hole in the side about three or four inches from the bottom. The sediment is largely uncombined lime and sulfur, and if stirred up into the clear solution will injure the wool. Enough water should be added to the clear solution to make 100 gallons. The water added should be hot enough so that the temperature of the preparation in the vat, after being well mixed, will register from 100 to 105 degrees F.

Kentucky Station Bulletin 143 gives the following comment on lime-sulfur dip:

"This well-known dip is very effective in the treatment of sheep scab. It is also one of the cheapest of dips. It does, on the whole, a slight damage to the wool, even if properly prepared—more noticeable in fine than in coarse wools. It is caustic to the operator's hands. Some dealers object to it because it gives the wool a washed appearance, consequently the sheep do not look in as good condition for immediate market as where some other dip is used.

"The U. S. Bureau of Animal Industry has reached the conclusion that it has but little effect in destroying the sheep tick, hence should not be used if the sheep are afflicted with both scab-mite and tick. However, with these objections to the lime-sulfur dip, a few of the large sheepmen in this state use it when their sheep have become badly affected with the scab mite."

**Tobacco dips** are effective remedies for scab and they are said to be non-injurious to the wool. The active agent in them which kills the scab mite is nicotine. These dips also kill sheep lice and ticks, and, therefore, can be made use of as general dips.

**Various arsenical dips** have been prepared, but as home-made decoctions prepared by a formula little use has been made of them. If the writer mistakes not the famous proprietary dip manufactured by William Cooper and Nephews is regarded as an arsenical dip.

**The various coal-tar dips** are among the most pleasant to use. They are easy to prepare; they are healing and disinfecting, and they leave the skin in healthy condition. Many of the manufactured or proprietary dips contain coal-tar products.

**Manufactured Dips.**—Various prescriptions are available for making dips at home. But in treating for lice and ticks (scab is rare in the United States, except in a few states) it is cheaper and more satisfying to rely on the manufactured dips. As a rule, they are efficient, and reliable directions for their use are always sent out with them.

**Foot-rot** is an old, old ailment with sheep, and directions for its control have been written for centuries. There are two forms: One, non-contagious, caused by too much wet weather; the other is contagious, and is caused by the microörganism, *Bacillus necrophorous.* The contagious form is hard to deal with, as in the worst cases the animal is very lame for a long time. The foot is hot and swollen around the coronary band. In this region soft, greenish spots develop which break and emit pus having a very putrid odor. A good remedy is a saturated or 30 per cent[4] copper-sulfate solution applied once or twice daily by standing the sheep in a shallow trough containing the solution. Thorough trimming of the feet is of the highest importance in preparation for treatment. The infection does not persist long on well-drained dry ground. Sheep having contagious foot-rot should not be allowed to run with the flock.

**Goitre.**—Sheep sometimes develop goitre. When it occurs in newborn lambs it denotes a deficiency of iodine in the ration of the ewes. Lambs affected with goitre or ''big neck'' have a characteristic swelling along the underside of the neck. The use of iodized salt for pregnant ewes is the most effective preventive. Tincture of iodine applied to the skin over the goitre may help.

**Overheating.**—When the temperature gets above 88 degrees F. and the humidity is great, there is danger of one or more members of the flock becoming overheated. An overheated sheep or lamb is stiff, trembles while on its feet, and is unable to walk far without lying down. First, carry it to a cool, shady place; then give Epsom salts, dissolved in water (two and one-half ounces for a lamb and four ounces for a sheep) and 10 to 20 drops of tincture of aconite.

When an overheated sheep was so badly affected that it could not get up, R. J. Stone gave the following treatment: Strychnine, one-fiftieth grain, 3 times a day for 3 days, then one-twenty-fifth grain at night, and one-fiftieth grain in the morning and at noon, and increasing gradually to one-twenty-fifth grain three

[4] Montana Station Bulletin 285.

times daily until recovery or until the animal is able to walk about. Reduce doses gradually for about one week.

It is advisable to shear an overheated sheep, but care must be used because the animal will die if it gets excited and exerts itself much.

**Predatory animals** are a menace to the flock in all seasons of the year, but especially so in summer when the sheep are in the fields far out from the winter quarters.

Of all the predatory animals, the dog is the worst in the middle west and eastern parts of the United States, but in a few places between the Mississippi River and the Rocky Mountains wolves and coyotes must be contended with.

In many places farmers have been forced to quit keeping sheep because of dogs. Were dogs controlled, farm flocks would be much more numerous than they are. In 1914, the United States Bureau of Animal Industry, upon inquiring as to what prevents the keeping of sheep on farms, received many replies, over 58 per cent of which gave dogs as the cause. These replies vividly picture the need of laws that will eliminate cur dogs and keep all other dogs under proper control. When good laws are secured, sheepmen must have courage enough to have them enforced.

There is no way of equipping the flock to insure it against an attack of dogs. Putting bells on a number of sheep assists some, but the discordant jangling characteristic of American sheep bells will not stop a bold dog bent on mischief. If the field in which the sheep are running is near the farm residence provision can perhaps be made for allowing them a road to the farm buildings, so that when they are chased by dogs they can come near enough to awaken someone to come to their rescue. But this plan cannot be depended upon, as often neither the sheep nor the dogs make enough noise to awaken persons sound asleep. One other recourse is to place the flock in dog-proof pens at night. This requires a great deal of labor, and it prevents the flock from feeding at the most desirable time.

As soon as it is discovered that sheep have been wounded and worried by dogs, they should be brought to the barns, where there are conveniences for giving them the necessary attention. The first thing to do is to locate all the wounds, including even the slightest tooth marks, and to rub them thoroughly, though gently, with carbolized oil (olive oil, 99 parts; concentrated carbolic acid,

1 part). Keep up this treatment every day until the wounds are healing nicely. Thereafter, treat occasionally to insure keeping the wounded places disinfected.

For some time after sheep have been worried by dogs they are very nervous and become easily excited even though the cause is slight. Therefore, they should be kept in a quiet place where they may receive nutritious feed and where it is not necessary to take more than a moderate amount of exercise.

Coyotes, wolves, bobcats, and mountain lions are a great annoyance and expense to the owners of sheep in the western part of the United States. The coyote is the worst in the lot, and an organized effort to exterminate it is being prosecuted. The Federal Government is assisting by appropriating money to pay trained hunters and trappers. Several states give liberal bounties for coyote scalps and the sheepmen themselves are doing all they can, not only to exterminate the coyote, but also other predatory animals.

## QUESTIONS

1. When should the lambs be weaned?
2. What are the disadvantages of weaning lambs too early?
3. Discuss the two methods of weaning as practiced by shepherds.
4. Of what value is bluegrass as a pasture?
5. What are the dangers of pasturing alfalfa and clover?
6. Discuss fully the treatment of bloat.
7. Name three common forage crops for summer pasture.
8. What feed should be given the lambs when they are weaned?
9. Of what value is shade in summer?
10. What are some of the common summer enemies of the sheep?
11. Give the life history of the stomach worm.
12. What are the symptoms of stomach worms?
13. Give a treatment for stomach worms.
14. Where does the sheep bot-fly deposit its larvæ?
15. In what way would you treat a sheep with maggots?
16. How do external parasites injure sheep?
17. How can the presence of lice be detected?
18. What is the remedy for scab?
19. What are the best times for dipping sheep?
20. What are the symptoms of overheating in sheep?
21. What predatory animals give the most trouble to the sheepman?

## CHAPTER XXXV

# THE WOOL CROP

**Importance of Wool.**—Sheep yield two products, mutton and wool; but, in many cases, the wool crop is taken as a matter of course and its value is not fully appreciated. In flocks where the production of lambs for market is the chief object, the income from the wool is about thirty per cent of the total income from the flock. This estimate is based on the assumption that the average weight of fleece is eight pounds and that there will be one lamb marketed for each sheep shorn. Records show that the wool constitutes more than thirty per cent of the total income from the flock, for the breeding ewe produces one fleece before she raises a lamb. Further, she always produces a fleece, but not always a lamb.

By giving careful attention to the wool product, the income from the flock can be materially increased. Ewes should be selected for their wool as well as for their mutton, so as to market both prime lambs and first-class wool.

**Requisites of Wool.**—Good wool (p. 54) shows purity, uniformity, strength, character, good color, moderate yolk, and is rather clean. Class and grade must be considered. The amount of yolk and dirt influence shrinkage.

**Purity.**—A fleece is not considered pure or true in structure if it contains "off colored" fibers, kemps, or hair. Fibers which are hair-like in their make-up are frequently found on the folds or wrinkles of fine-wool sheep. Kemps are abnormal fibers composed of horny material, generally of a chalk-white color; such fibers are brittle, inelastic, weak, and do not take dyes well. (Compare figures 25, 26, and 197.) They indicate inferior breeding. Kempy wools are worth several cents per pound less than others. Black fibres mixed in with white wool reduce the value in making white cloth. Little dark wool is used in its natural color, and sells at a discount. Yellowish, buff-tinged, and dingy wools are often less desirable than white because they do not always scour out pure white (Fig. 197).

**Uniformity.**—A fleece is uniform in fineness when all the fibers are about the same in diameter. It is practically impossible to get absolute uniformity in this respect throughout the fleece and it is not expected. The wool on the hips seldom equals that on the shoulder in fineness, but the variation in the wool grown on these two regions of the body is much less in some individuals than in others, and when this is the case, the fleece as a whole is much more nearly uniform in quality.

**Strength of Fiber.**—Wool is regarded as strong when individual fibers do not have a weak place somewhere in their length. These weak places are due largely to periods of sickness and undernourish-

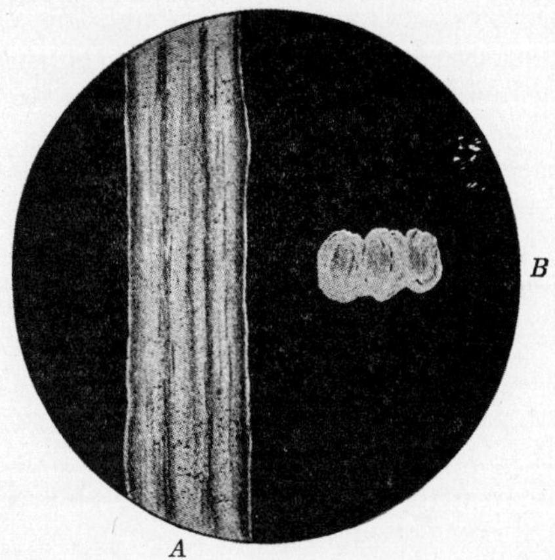


Fig. 197.—Kemp, structureless like fibers that are brittle and do not take the color dyes. *A*, longitudinal section, *B*, cross-section, compare with Fig. 24. (From "Structure the Wool Fiber," Bowman. Courtesy of The Macmillan Co.)

ment, or to abrupt changes from dry to green feed, or *vice versa,* while the sheep is growing the wool. Hence, strength of fiber is a factor which depends more or less upon good feeding and shepherding; and the kind of care necessary to produce a good crop of lambs is the best for growing wool. Tender wools, especially if they are two and one-half inches or more in length, sell for less than wools of similar length and finish because they break in the process of combing and must be used as short wools.

It is often possible to see the weak or tender place or to determine its location by pulling on a lock of wool and noting where it breaks. Such a test is only an approximation of whether the wool is too weak at its tenderest point to stand the strain of combing in the process of manufacture. Strong, well-nourished wool, upon being released from pressure, springs back to its natural bulk. It thus displays life or loftiness, a very desirable characteristic. Another way to determine the strength and life of wool is to twist a number of fibers into a cord and then note the sound this cord gives off when it is drawn tight and touched much as one would touch the strings of a violin when tuning it. If the sound is somewhat like a metallic ring instead of a dull thud, the wool is sound and strong (Figs. 198 and 199).

**Character.**—This is a term which is used in referring to the evenness and distinctness of the crimp or waviness of the wool fibers. Thus a fleece which has character shows a uniform and prominent crimp from the base to the tip of the fibers. Character may also include softness to the touch. Because character is closely associated with elasticity, it is an important matter from the standpoint of the manufacturer. Fleeces which lack character are frequently designated as "mushy" or "frowsy."

**Color.**—Wool that is of good color is said to be bright. In this respect color does not refer to the black or dark fibers but to the whiteness or tint. Wool that is yellow or stained or that is very dull in appearance may be described as defective in color. The brightness of the fine wools and the luster of the long wools are not wholly matters of color, but, nevertheless, are closely allied with and to some extent dependent upon good color. The character of a fleece is enhanced by good color.

**Condition.**—This factor depends on the amount of yolk and foreign matter in wool, and is very important in determining its value. If the amounts are excessive, the shrinkage in weight from scouring is great and hence such wools are worth less in the unscoured state than lighter shrinking wools. Shrinkage is an extremely variable but always important factor. It represents the percentage of the weight of the fleece that is lost in the process of scouring. If a ten-pound fleece weighs four pounds after scouring it has a shrinkage of 60 per cent or may be said to yield 40 per cent of clean wool. These percentages show a very wide range depending upon the breed, sex, individuality, and management of the sheep, the class and grade of the wool, and the climate and soil conditions under which the sheep are kept. Wool seldom shrinks less than 30 per cent and generally not over 80 per cent. A certain amount of "free-flowing" yolk is necessary to keep the wool fibers in good condition, but there should be no justification for breeding excessive quantities of it merely for the sake of increasing the weight of the fleece.

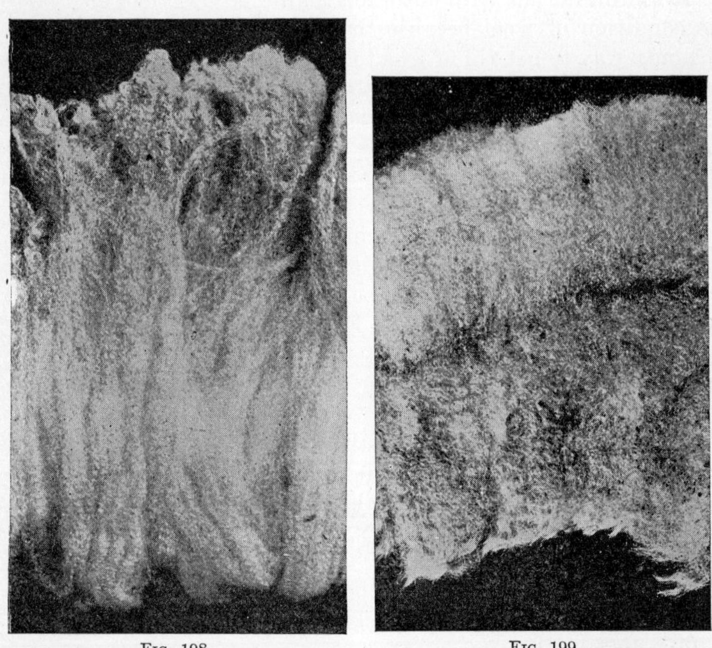

FIG. 198. FIG. 199.

FIG. 198.—Well-grown wool, even in strength with crimps of even length from bottom to top.
FIG. 199.—Tender wool, showing break caused by disease or improper nourishment.

**Cleanliness.**—Dirt, sand, burs, straw, and chaff in wool not only decrease its scoured yield, but also affect its value. It is impossible completely to scour out burs, straw, and chaff, and if the wool containing them is to be made clean it must be treated with a weak solution of sulphuric acid and heated, a process known as carbonizing and one which is likely to weaken the wool. The conditions under which the sheep must be kept may make it impossible to keep out dirt and sand; on some of the ranges in the western parts of the United States, it is not altogether possible to keep out burs, but on farms the presence of chaff, straw, and burs in wool is largely the grower's fault. Racks should be used that will not let chaff fall into the wool on top of the neck and shoulders and the flock should not be allowed to feed continually at stacks of straw.

Branding sheep with insoluble paint is very detrimental to the condition of wool because the paint cannot be scoured out. The only way to get rid of it is to clip it off, an expensive process because it must be done with hand labor (Fig. 200).

**Classes of Wool.**—Wool is classed either as combing, as French or baby combing, or as clothing. Combing wools are used in worsted manufacturing where it is necessary to place the fibers parallel to each other in the yarn. In order to meet the combing requirements, the fibers should be strong and two inches or more in length. The broken, short, and tangled fibers are discarded as "noils" to be used in the manufacture of woolens. What is known as the French combs can make worsted yarn from wools somewhat shorter than two inches; nevertheless, length and evenness in strength of fiber remain important factors in estimating the value.

Clothing wools are shorter than combing wools. They are used in the making of woolens, felts, and fabrics of similar type. No attempt is made to keep the fibres parallel; in fact, the more they can be mixed in every direction the better they serve the purpose desired.

Combing wools are worth from two to six cents per scoured pound more than clothing wools. On this account it is generally advisable to attempt to grow combing wool, but it is not always possible to secure the length and strength of fiber necessary to put wool into this class. This is especially true of wools from flocks where Merino blood predominates, and unless care is used in selecting breeding stock with wool having adequate length of fiber a considerable percentage of the fleeces in flocks where Down blood predominates (Oxford Down excepted) will be classed as clothing. Age is another factor which influences the class of wool that may be produced, for old sheep past their prime of life do not grow as much length of fiber as do young sheep of similar breeding.

Coarse, kempy, poorly-bred wool is classed as carpet wool.

It is not produced except in very small quantities, in regions where improved methods of breeding and feeding are followed.

**Grades of Wool.**—The wool that comes under each class is divided into various grades according to fineness. Trade journals giving reports of wool sales on the large markets contain a maze of quotations arranged so as to bewilder rather than to enlighten persons not thoroughly familiar with the wool trade.

The U. S. Bureau of Agriculture Economics several years ago undertook to establish "Official Wool Standards" with a view to simplifying and standardizing the grading of wools. These standards and the nomenclature used in referring to them have been in use but a few years.

Thus we are at a point of transition from one system to another. Under the old system, grading of wool in the United States was based on a blood classification, supposedly with reference to the breeding of the sheep producing the wool. However, the terms had no such meaning and were very misleading and did not allow for a sufficient number of grades for ample distinction between wools of varying fineness. The new standards are based on the British system of designating the grades by spinning counts.

In the following table are shown the old system of grades, the new "Official Standard Grades," and the length standards for the various classes.

**Grades and Length Standards for Wool**

| *New Standard Grades* | *Corresponding grade old U. S. system* | *New length standard for wool classed as:* Combing Inches | French Combing Inches | Clothing Inches |
|---|---|---|---|---|
| 80's | | | | |
| 70's | Fine | Over 2 | 1¼ to 2 | Under 1¼ |
| 64's | | | | |
| 60's | | | | |
| 58's | Half Blood | Over 2¼ | 1¼ to 2¼ | Under 1¼ |
| 56's | Three-eighths Blood | Over 2½ | 1½ to 2½ | Under 1½ |
| 50's | | | | |
| 48's | Quarter Blood | Over 2¾ | 1½ to 2¾ | Under 1½ |
| 46's | Low Quarter Blood | Over 3 | 2 to 3 | Under 2 |
| 44's | Common [1] | | | |
| 40's | | | | |
| 36's | Braid | | | |

[1] Common and braid are practically always of combing length.

"The coarser wools are represented by the lower counts, as 18's, 24's, 36's, etc., and the finer ones as 64's, 70's, 80's, etc. These numbers or counts represent the hanks per pound of top into which the wool is supposedly capable of being spun, each hank representing 560 yards. Thus, wool of 50's quality should spin 50 × 560 yards per pound to top, if spun to the limit. This is based on the worsted system of manufacture.

"As a matter of fact the top-maker's quality does not actually represent the counts to which the wool can be spun. The lower grades will not spin up to their number, while the finer ones will spin much higher than their designated numbers. Some fine American wools have been spun to 200 counts for exhibition purposes. Short wool will not spin as high as similar wools of greater length, hence this factor also influences the counts to which the wool will spin.

"Another fact worthy of mention is that the wools are rarely spun to their limit; that is, to as fine a yarn as is possible to spin. Wool can be spun several counts higher in England than it can in America. This is due to the fact that the air is moister there and that the labor of the mills is more capable than in the United States. This does not imply that American fabrics are inferior to imported, as a better cloth results if the wool is not so highly spun."—*U. S. Dept. Agr. Bul. 206.*

Montana, Wyoming, Colorado, Utah, Nevada, Idaho, and Washington wools are called "territory wools" in distinction from the clips from Texas, California, Oregon, New Mexico, and Arizona. Quotations are often given for the wools from different states. While these wools undoubtedly differ somewhat, it is almost impossible to tell in general descriptive terms what the differences are, and to be able further to subdivide the classifications given above requires an expert knowledge of the whole wool trade. Wools grown east of the Missouri river are often spoken of as farm, fleece, or native wool.

The table on grades of wool from different breeds is based on the above bulletin and California Extension Circular 12. It is made clear that in the mutton breeds particularly there are wide variations within a breed.

**Shearing.**—To a limited extent, the condition of the wool depends upon the time when the shearing is done. It is not always possible to shear at the time when the wool is in condition to most nearly suit market requirements. Oftentimes, in the western part of the United States, the shearing must be done either before the sheep are started from the winter range or

**Breeds of Sheep and Their Grades of Wools.**

| Breed | *Official Standard Spinning Count* | *Grade Under Old U. S. System* | *Class* |
|---|---|---|---|
| American Merino | 64's, 80's | Fine | Clothing, some combing |
| Delaine Merino | 64's, 80's | Fine (Delaine) | Combing |
| Rambouillet | 60's, 80's | Fine and Fine Medium | Combing, clothing |
| Southdown | 56's, 58's, 60's | Half and three-eighths blood | Clothing, combing |
| Shropshire | 50's, 56's | Three-eighths and quarter blood | Combing, clothing |
| Hampshire | 50's, 56's | Three-eighths and quarter blood | Combing, clothing |
| Suffolk | 50's, 56's | Three-eighths and quarter blood | Combing, clothing |
| Dorset | 50's, 56's | Three-eighths and quarter blood | Combing, clothing |
| Cheviot | 50's, 56's | Quarter and three-eighths blood | Combing |
| Tunis | 50's, 56's | Quarter and three-eighths blood | Combing |
| Corriedale | 48's, 50's, 56's, 58's | Quarter, three-eighths and half blood | Combing |
| Columbia | 46's, 48's | Low quarter and quarter blood | Combing |
| Oxford | 46's, 48's, 50's | Quarter and low quarter blood | Combing |
| Border Leicester | 40's, 44's, 46's | Low quarter, common, braid | Combing |
| Romney | 40's, 44's, 46's, 48's | Quarter, low quarter, common braid | Combing |
| English Leicester | 36's, 40's | Braid | |
| Cotswold | 36's, 40's | Braid | |
| Lincoln | 36's, 40's | Braid | |

while they are being moved from the winter feeding grounds to the spring or summer range. If this were not done the sheep would get so far away from railway lines that the cost of hauling the wool would be greatly increased. Besides this, various other factors are involved in determining the time when the shearing shall be done.

It is different, however, in regions where farm flocks are kept, and if good shelter is available, it is possible to shear more nearly at the time when the wool is in best condition for being removed. The usual time for shearing in the middle western and eastern parts of the United States is from the middle of April to the middle of May, after the cold weather is over and there have been a few days a little too warm for the comfort of unshorn sheep. On the whole, this is a good time to shear, as the oil has risen in the wool in sufficient quantity to make it "full of life" and the shearing easy. If shearing is deferred too long the wool becomes dead and lifeless. As a rule the wool from breeding ewes would be in somewhat better condition if they were shorn before they lamb because the feverish condition frequently resulting from lambing often causes them to lose some of their wool. Moreover the wool that is grown while they are expending so much energy in the production of milk is likely to be tender.

With early shearing there will be fever dung tags if it is done before the sheep are turned out to pasture. The extreme succulence of the fresh young grass causes the feces to soften and collect around the rear parts, and if the stained wool is not trimmed off when the feces first start to collect, a great mass will accumulate and greatly damage the wool. If the weather should be warm, the dung will also attract flies and the sheep will be attacked by maggots.

There are some objections to shearing early, one of which is that the weight of fleece is considerably lighter than it would be later on because there has not been enough warm weather to cause the yolk to rise in large quantity. Hammond, of the Ohio Station, has experimented on this point and his conclusion printed in Ohio Station Bulletin 294 is as follows: "Washed sheep shorn April 12 produced more grease wool than did washed sheep shorn June 1, while unwashed sheep shorn April 12 produced less grease wool than did unwashed sheep shorn June 1." This indicates that between these two dates there was an increase in weight of fleece due to the accumulation of yolk or other foreign matter in the wool.

In feeding a lot of western lambs, the writer [3] sheared half of them March 1 and the other half May 25. The late shorn fleeces contained a much greater amount of yolk and they averaged 2.6 pounds more in weight than the early-shorn fleeces. In this case the difference in weight was due to the difference both in the amount of yolk and in the actual amount of wool. From Hammond's conclusion, however, it is clear that there would be no advantage in securing the greater weight of fleece from late shearing if wool were purchased strictly on the scoured basis. With small lots but very little discrimination is made in this respect unless the wool is excessively heavy in amount of yolk. But, even if wool were purchased on the scoured basis, it would not always pay to shear early, for there are places where the spring season is so variable that shelter will not adequately protect the health of shorn sheep. Sudden changes from warm to cold, windy weather may cause colds in the worst form, and when this happens, fatalities are almost sure to occur.

[3] Ill. Sta. Bul. 167.

**Places for Shearing.**—Where large bands of sheep are kept, as in the western part of the United States, sheds are built solely for the purpose of shearing, but where small flocks are kept the shearing quarters are usually of a temporary nature. In arranging a place, every precaution should be taken to keep the wool clean. While the fleece is being removed the sheep should be placed on a smooth board platform about ten feet square; the sheep awaiting shearing should be penned where they will not drag manure and litter with them as they are brought to the shearing place.

**Requirements for Good Shearing.**—A good job of shearing consists in cutting the wool off smoothly close to the body.

The power machine will cut closer than the hand shears, but satisfactory work may be done with the latter if the operator is careful and possesses some skill. It is the tendency of the unskilled shearer, whether using the machine or hand shears, to fail to cut close to the sheep's body, but in advancing the shears he cannot follow the shape of the animal, and hence some of the wool is cut from a half to an inch away from the skin. He can, and usually does, back up and cut close where he failed in his first attempt. This makes what is known as second cuts. Because they are so short they are of low value for manufacturing purposes. It is also obvious that the evil of making second cuts makes the fibres in the main body of the fleece shorter and uneven in length, and therefore less desirable.

In doing good shearing it is also necessary to get the fleece off without getting it torn apart. After setting a sheep on its rump, there is a knack of holding it so that it will not kick and struggle violently. Its body should be tilted back towards the knees of the operator so that its hind legs cannot get sufficient contact with the floor to make effective resistance. It is the adjustment of this position that is equivalent to the knack of holding.

Power shearing machines are gradually replacing the hand shears. The power machine does smoother work, makes fewer second cuts, and does not cut the skin of the sheep so badly. The amateur shearer can do much better with the power machine. In various places in the western part of the United States, the hand shears are still used because the power machine cuts so close that the sheep will blister if it turns hot or they will suffer if it turns cold. If thick combs are used, however, it is not necessary to cut extremely close with the power machine.

**Tying the Fleece.**—Several things must be done to make a good job of tying the fleece. First, in order to make an honest package, all tag locks must be removed whether they be of dung, or of grease and dirt. The tags have about one-third the value of clean wool. Second, the fleece should be carefully rolled up by hand with no ends and stray locks protruding and with the flesh side out. This greatly adds to the appearance of the fleece. It also prevents mixing the wool in different fleeces. Third, the

Fig. 200. Fig. 201.

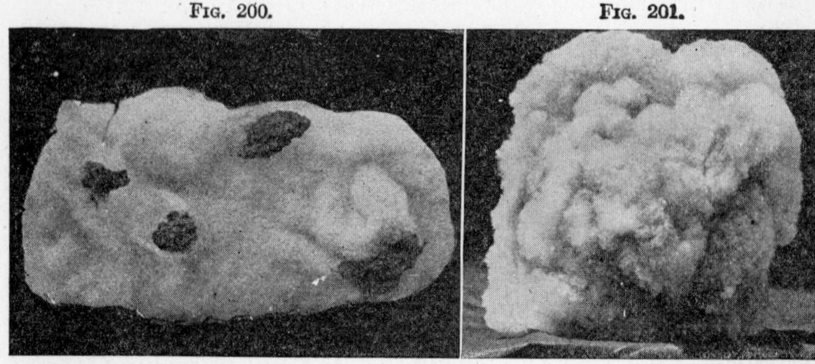

Fig. 200.—Insoluble paint in scoured wool due to paint that was used in branding the live sheep.

Fig. 201.—A fleece properly tied, the flesh side outward, no loose locks straggling, the whole fleece fluffy or soft in appearance. (From Illinois Station Circular 161.)

fleece should be tied with a hard glazed twine, not larger than one-eighth inch in diameter. Special care should be taken to make a firm hard knot that will not slip (Fig. 201).

**Tying Twine.**[4]—"The use of wrong kinds of tying twine has caused the manufacturer more trouble than any other one thing, with the wools marketed from the farms of the central and eastern United States. A hard, glazed twine should be used in order to avoid getting any of its fiber mixed with the wool. In recent years paper wool twine has been introduced which is entirely satisfactory to the manufacturer. Rough, loosely woven twine made of vegetable fiber is not desirable because some of the fiber gets into the wool. It is impossible to remove it. It will not

---

4 Ill. Sta. Circ. 161.

take the dyes used in coloring wool and it is detrimental to the strength and finish of the cloth. The only way to get rid of it is to pick it out of the finished cloth, which is an expensive process. Sisal twine is the most objectionable of all employed for tying wool. The mills have objected to it so strenuously that its use is being largely discontinued. In no event should it be used; better not tie at all than use it. There have been placed on the market jute products, called wool twine, which are not at all satisfactory. They are so loose and rough that many of the fibers cling to the wool and cause defects in the goods. Undoubtedly the wool trade the world over will institute a war against this type of twine. These so-called wool twines are also unnecessarily heavy. The best wool buyers object to excessive size and length of string. A well-known wool house in the middle west informed the writer that they had removed more than one pound of twine from a single fleece. The use of so much cheap stuff amounts to unfair packing. It is not necessary to wrap the string more than three times around the fleece—twice is usually sufficient—and the size of the string should be no greater than needed to give it the strength to stand the strain of drawing it in tightly on the wool for the purpose of tying. As stated above, it should not be more than one-eighth inch in diameter. India three-ply size No. 4½ is a type suitable for tying wool; so are the paper wool twines. Some of the latter, however, are stiff, and therefore difficult to tie in a firm, hard knot that will not slip and release the wool. In selecting from them care should be taken to secure a kind that is soft and pliable (Fig. 202).

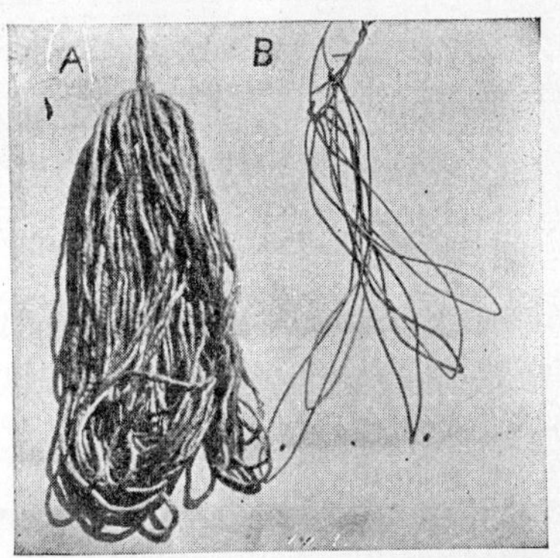


Fig. 202.—Wool twine. *A*, taken from a fleece and showing the use of an excessive quantity. *B*, showing the proper kind and quantity to use in tying a fleece. (From Illinois Station Circular 161.)

"**Packing and Storing.**—When packing, the fleeces of ewes, lambs, rams, and wethers should be packed separately. In small flocks it is hardly advisable to pack them in separate bags, but they can be separated in the bag by sheets of stiff, strong paper so that they can be easily sorted at the market. A bag containing a certain kind or kinds of wool should be marked so that its contents are known. Tags and wool from dead sheep should be packed separately.

"Black or gray fleeces should not be allowed to come in contact with white fleeces; burry fleeces should be packed to themselves (Fig. 203).

"If the wool is not sold immediately after shearing, it should be stored in a clean, dry place. It should not be left on the bare ground even though it is placed in bags. It is best to store

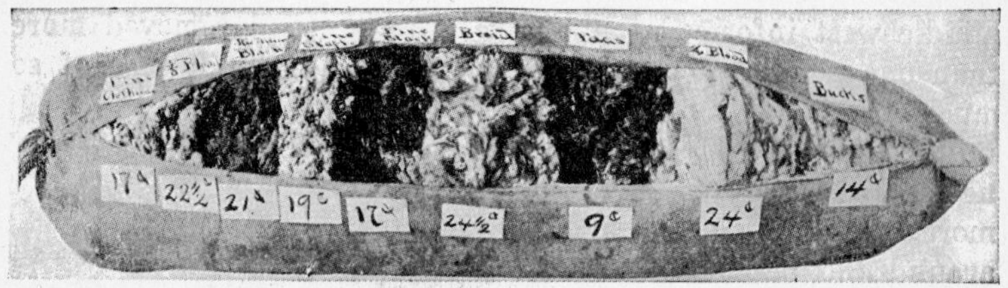


Fig. 203.—Wrong method of packing wool. Various grades and colors varying from 9 to 24 cents per pound in value packed in the same bag.

and market wool in bags, as it is the more likely to be kept clean. The bags should be closely woven, so that they will effectively keep out dust and dirt. They should also be of a type that will not shed particles of fiber into the wool. The loosely woven jute bags commonly used are satisfactory in neither particular."

**Marketing Wool.**—The claim is made that there is no open market for wool in the United States. For this reason it is difficult for the grower to know what his wool is worth. An open market would be a great help to the grower, but without a knowledge of about how much his wool would shrink in scouring, he would still be more or less in the dark. Owners of small clips are, as a rule, at great disadvantage in selling, for they cannot get in touch with agencies whose chief business consists in handling wool. With the development of more interest in farm flocks, conditions for selling small clips will undoubtedly improve.

Since very few growers dispose of their clips to the manufacturers, various agencies undertake to concentrate the clips, grade, store, and sell them at such times as the mills have need of them. The more prominent of these agencies are local buyers, wool merchants, commission houses, mill buyers, and wool growers' coöperative associations. Very few wool producers are in a position to grade or store their wool and as most manufacturers find it advisable to buy stocks at various times and considerable quantities of a particular grade, these concerns handling the wool perform useful functions.

Local buyers operate mainly in sections producing many small clips and whose owners desire to sell them for cash. Usually such buyers are engaged in other business and since their purchases are generally made at a flat rate for the locality in which they operate they need no exact or extensive knowledge of wool values. Under such a system the producer has no incentive to improve either the wool or its preparation for market.

Wool merchants handle most of the wool grown in this country. They not only purchase large quantities from producers for cash but they also handle much of that secured by local buyers. They perform a number of services, such as grading, warehousing, and the assumption of risks incident to the possession of large quantities of wool. Although they have been the object of much criticism, the wool merchants have been important agencies in the marketing of the wool grown in this country.

Commission houses, when acting on a strictly commission basis, receive wool from the grower and sell it at such time and price as is sanctioned by the owner. The grower assumes the risk of a declining market and pays the house a commission for the services which it has performed. While this plan of selling may sometimes bring higher prices than can be secured from the wool merchant, the receipt of the returns for the clip is delayed.

Mill buyers function much the same as wool merchants except that they do not buy for speculation and resale. Purchases are limited to classes and grades of wool which the mill can use.

In some instances wool growers have joined together to form

coöperative agencies for the marketing of their clips. These groups vary in the manner of organization and in the services which they attempt to render to their members. Some are merely "pools" of the clips of the members so that more buyers will be attracted by the volume of wool offered. Others go a step farther and grade the wool before offering it for sale. In its most complete development the coöperative association renders all the services of a selling agency for growers in a large territory. These associations do not buy wool, but money may be advanced to the coöperator at a stipulated rate of interest upon the receipt of his clip at the warehouse. Such organizations are primarily interested in securing a stable market and full market value for the wool which they handle. As the volume of wool sold by these societies increases they become factors of increasing importance in determining the prices which the grower receives. In some associations the members contract to deliver their wools for sale by the agency for a period of years; in others, a "retainer agreement" is being tried whereby the grower reserves the right to sell his wool in any way he may choose but agrees to pay a fee to the association in case it does not sell his wool. Such an arrangement would seem to provide the grower with a grower controlled agency and yet leave him free to dispose of his wool through whatever channel seemed at the time to be most advantageous. The advantages of coöperative wool selling lie not only in the probable increased monetary returns but in the educational work of such agencies as well.

The National Wool Marketing Corporation organized in 1930 is the leading coöperative wool selling organization in this country. Its program includes such activities as:

(1) Collecting and financing wool;
(2) Warehousing, grading and otherwise preparing the wool for sale direct to the mills;
(3) Stabilization of the wool market by selling at such times as the mills require;
(4) The promotion of wool consumption by stressing the advantages of wool:
(5) Reduction in wool marketing expense;
(6) Supplying complete information to the grower regarding his wool and the state of the market;

(7) Studying the possibility of instituting auction sales of wool after the manner of wool selling agencies of Australia.

Auction sales for the disposal of wool have recently been strongly advocated as a solution of the problems confronting the grower in disposing of his product. The proponents of this method state that auction sales would enable producers to know prices being paid and the amounts and grades of wool actually passing into consumption would likewise be known. The values would be established by those in need of the wool or that had the best outlet for it. Some advocates believe some marketing costs would be eliminated by concentrating the wool at points near to where it was grown and in such large quantities that buyers for many mills would be attracted to the sales and the open competition would tend to stabilize prices. Small concerns would have an equal advantage with large ones in buying and small growers through the combining of their clips would have as good an opportunity to sell as those with very large quantities to offer.

Some proponents of auction sales are in favor of having the sales held in Boston or in only a few centers so that buyers would be certain to attend in large numbers. Attempts are now being made to establish wool auctions and it is likely that the next few years may see a quantity of wool sold in this manner. That this system will be the final solution of the wool marketing problem is hardly to be expected.

As a commodity wool is particularly adapted to orderly

*Size of Flocks in the United States According to Number of Sheep Shorn in 1930.*

| Number of sheep shorn | Number of producers | Per cent of all producers | Pounds of wool shorn | Per cent of all wool shorn |
|---|---|---|---|---|
| 1–24 | 275,438 | 58.0 | 21,984,904 | 7.5 |
| 25–49 | 100,164 | 21.2 | 23,735,206 | 8.0 |
| 50–99 | 50,849 | 10.7 | 24,428,854 | 8.2 |
| 100–999 | 39,562 | 8.4 | 73,760,392 | 24.9 |
| 1000—4999 | 6,160 | 1.3 | 96,538,257 | 32.6 |
| 5000–50,000 or over | 744 | .2 | 55,515,893 | 18.8 |
| Total | 472,917 | 100.0 | 295,964,506 | 100.0 |

marketing as it is essentially non-perishable, deteriorates very slowly, and is far less combustible than many other commodities. A further advantage should be found in the fact that approximately ten per cent of the sheep raisers produce more than two-thirds of the nation's supply, as shown on page 329.

**Glossary of Terms Used in the Wool Trade.**—The following glossary of terms used in the wool trade are taken from various sources:

*Black Wool.*—Includes any wool that is not white.

*Braid Wool.*—Grade name, and synonym for luster wools.

*Britch Wool.*—Wool from the lower thighs of the sheep; usually the coarsest on the body.

*Carbonized Wool.*—That which has been treated with a solution of aluminum chlorid or sulfuric acid to remove vegetable matter. Carbonizing is rarely practiced with worsted wools.

*Carding.*—Consists of opening the wool staples, separating to a certain extent the fibers, and condensing and delivering the opened wool in a continuous strand.

*Carpet Wool.*—Low-grade coarse wool used in the manufacture of carpets. There is very little produced in the United States.

*Character.*—The evenness and distinctness of crimp.

*Combing.*—An operation in worsted manufacture which straightens the fibers and separates the short, weak, and tangled fibers known as noils from the continuous strand of long parallel fibers known as top.

*Combing Wool.*—Wool that is long enough to comb on English combs and that is used for making worsted goods.

*Come-back.*—In America this refers to a wool fine in quality and having more length than would ordinarily be expected. In Australia it is the result of breeding crossbreds back toward pure Merinos, one of the parents being a pure Merino.

*Condition.*—Refers to the degree of oil in grease wool. It largely regulates the price. In scoured wool it is used to indicate the degree of moisture.

*Cotted Fleeces.*—A cotted fleece is one in which the fibers are matted or tangled. The cause may be ill health of the sheep or the absence of the proper amounts of yolk or grease in the wool.

*Cow Tail.*—A very coarse fleece, more like hair than wool.

*Crimp.*—The natural waviness of wool fiber. Uniformity of crimp indicates superior wool.

*Crossbred Wools.*—In the United States the term generally refers to wool from a long-wool and fine-wool cross.

*Defective.*—Denotes that something will show disadvantageously after the wool is scoured. Fire, water, or moths may cause defective wools. California burry wool is quoted as defective.

*Delaine Wool.*—Delaine originally referred to a fine type of women's dress goods. Delaine wools are fine combing or worsted wools, from Ohio and vicinity, but not necessarily from the Delaine Merino.

*Fall Wool.*—Wool shorn in the fall where shearing is practiced twice a year, as in California and Texas. The fall wool is usually dirtier than the spring clip. It represents from four to six months' growth.

*Filling (Weft).*—Threads that run crosswise and fill in between the warp.

*Fleece Wool.*—Wool grown in the eastern and central farm states.

*French Combing.*—Wool that is shorter than strictly combing wool but long enough to comb on French combs.

*Fribs.*—Short and dirty locks of small size. Dungy bits of wool.

*Frowzy Wool.*—A lifeless appearing wool with the fibers lying more or less topsy-turvy. The opposite of lofty wool.

*Grease Wool.*—Wool as it comes from the sheep with the grease still in it.

*Hogget Wool.*—English term for the first wool from a sheep.

*Kemp.*—Not a dead hair, but an abnormal fiber made up entirely of horny material, such as is on the outside of ordinary wool fiber. It will not dye as well as the ordinary fiber and does not possess spinning qualities.

*Line Fleeces.*—Those midway between two grades as to quality or length.

*Locks.*—Heavy, manure-ladened bits of wool.

*Lofty Wool.*—Open wool, full of life. Springs back into normal position after being crushed in the hand.

*Luster Wool.*—That from Lincoln, Leicester, and Cotswold sheep. It is known as luster wool because the coarse fibers reflect the light.

*Modock.*—Wool from range sheep that have been fed and sheared in the farm states. The wool has qualities of both regions.

*Noil.*—A by-product of worsted manufacture consisting of short and tangled fibers. It is used in the manufacture of woolens.

*Off Sorts.*—The by-products of sorting. In fine staple or any other grade there are quantities of short, coarse, stained, and colored wools. These are off sorts.

*Picklock Wool.*—Formerly a grade above XXX. Picklock was the product of Silesian Merino blood. There is no American market grade of that name at present; a little of this quality of wool is produced in West Virginia.

*Pulled Wool.*—Wool taken from the skin of a slaughtered sheep's pelt by slipping, sweating, or the use of depilatory.

*Purity.*—A fleece having this property is free from dark fibers, kemp, and hair.

*Quality.*—The diameter of the wool. It largely determines the spinning quality or grade.

*Run-out Fleece.*—One that is not uniform but much coarser on the britch than elsewhere. It may be kempy.

*Scouring.*—The process by which the grease and dirt are removed from wool.

*Seedy.*—Wool that carries large amounts of seeds and chaff.

*Shafty Wool.*—Wool of good length and spinning qualities.

*Shearlings.*—Short wool pulled from skins of sheep shorn before slaughtering. Also English term for yearling sheep.

*Shivy Wool.*—A somewhat broad term. It refers to the presence of vegetable matter in the wool.

*Shoddy.*—Wool that has been previously used for manufacturing purposes. torn apart, and made ready to use again.

*Shrinkage.*—The percentage of loss in scouring grease wool.

*Skirting.*—Skirting fleeces consists in removing the pieces and the low-quality wool of the britch from the edge of the fleece.

*Soundness.*—The strength of the wool fibers.

*Spring Wool.*—Six to eight months' growth; shorn in the spring where sheep are shorn twice a year.

*Stained Wool.*—That which is discolored by urine, dung, etc.

*Staple.*—(*a*) A lock or bunch of wool as it exists in the fleece. (*b*) Western combing wool.

*Stubble Shearing.*—Shearing some distance from the skin, leaving a "stubble."

*Suint.*—Excretions from sweat glands deposited in the wool.

*Sweating Sheds.*—Sheds in which sheep are "sweated" before shearing. The purpose is to raise the yolk and make shearing easier.

*Tags.*—Large dungy locks.

*Tender.*—Wool which is unsound or weak.

*Territory Wools.*—Territory wools are in general those that come from the territory west of the Missouri River.

*Tippy Wool.*—Wool in which the tip or weather end of the fiber is more or less incrusted.

*Top.*—A continuous untwisted strand of the longer wool fibers straightened by combing. After drawing and spinning it becomes worsted yarn.

*Top-maker's Qualities or Counts.*—Top-maker's qualities or counts are the numbers used in designating the quality of certain foreign wools. They range from 12's upward. The numbers are supposed to indicate the number of hanks of yarn a pound of top will spin to. Each hank represents 560 yards.

*Tub Washed.*—Wool that has been washed after having been sheared. Very rare in America; was formerly practiced in Kentucky.

*Virgin Wool.*—Wool that has not previously been used in manufacturing.

*Warp.*—The threads that run lengthwise in cloth.

*Washed Wools.*—Those from which the suint has been removed by washing the sheep before shearing.

*Wether.*—In English wools it refers to wool other than the first clip from the sheep. In sheep, a castrated male.

*Yield.*—The amount of clean wool left after the removal of the grease and dirt.

*Yolk.*—The fatty grease deposited upon the wool fibers from the oil glands.

## QUESTIONS

1. Review Chapter V and tell how the quality of wool is determined.
2. Why is excessive yolk objectionable in wool? Burs? Chaff?
3. What kinds of twine should be used in tying wool?
4. What is kemp? Is it desirable in wool?
5. What is necessary in order to grow strong wool?
6. Of what advantage is uniformity of breeding in growing wool?
7. What is clothing wool? Combing wool? How is each used?
8. Give arguments for and against early shearing.

# PART V

## SHEEP FEEDING

## CHAPTER XXXVI

# HISTORY OF SHEEP FEEDING IN THE UNITED STATES

**Sheep Feeding Defined.**—The following discussion of sheep feeding deals with the feeding of western sheep and lambs on farms and in feed lots. Although it is taken for granted that in all cases the animals involved in the feeding process are to be purchased by the feeder and that they are to be western sheep and lambs, much of the discussion also applies to cases in which owners fatten lambs of their own raising in autumn and winter.

**Origin of Sheep Feeding.**—It is only since about 1890 that the practice of fattening western sheep and lambs has developed and become widespread. This practice had its origin around the large flour mills of St. Paul, Minneapolis, and other cities in the Northwest. Previous to 1890 the screenings or waste from these large mills was looked upon as useless material and each year thousands of tons were dumped into the streams.

In 1892 William Wyman, of Hamline, Minnesota, upon conceiving the idea of using the waste from the large flour mills for finishing western sheep, constructed a feeding yard midway between Minneapolis and St. Paul. His venture was a success, and his demonstration encouraged others to take up the business of sheep feeding. Immense yards, each accommodating several thousand sheep, were built around Minneapolis, St. Paul, Chicago and other cities where large flour mills were located.

The common practice was to fill the yards with sheep and lambs from Montana, Oregon, Wyoming, Idaho, and other western states early in October, have them ready for the market about midwinter, and then fill the yards again. The second crop was usually shorn before time for marketing, which was near the first of June.

For a few years after the practice of fattening sheep and lambs on screenings began, both the animals and feed were obtained for a small outlay of capital. Owners in the West, on account of not having enough feed to fatten their surplus sheep and lambs, were glad to dispose of them at very moderate prices, and, of course, the screenings, being a waste product, were very cheap. Screenings-fed sheep and lambs soon became very popular with the packers and commanded good prices. The result was that the business of sheep and lamb feeding netted large profits.

**The Day of the Large Operators.**—The men who built large yards and fed great numbers of sheep were known as the large operators. Most of them were located near the cities which had large flour mills, but some established themselves in Kansas and Nebraska, where corn and hay were cheap. Their business was speculative in nature, and it was easy to determine whether or not profits were made. So long as both feeds and feeder animals were cheap and there was a margin of two dollars or more per hundred-weight between the purchase and sale price of the sheep the business could not help being profitable. Its profitableness awakened the interest of people not only in the feeding of sheep, but also in screenings, the feed that was being so successfully used in the process of fattening. As a result, the demand for feeders increased and prices for them advanced. Other uses were found for screenings, and they, too, advanced in price. Therefore it was not long before the large operators had to give close attention to their sheep feeding in order to make it profitable. Following these changes they could not make profits and, worse still, many failed financially.

It is now more than a decade since the majority of the large operators around the great flour-making centers ceased operations. Occasionally a few attempt feeding in a large way at the accumulating centers which are located near the large markets on the railroads that lead in from the West. These extensive feeders may or may not use screenings. As a rule they are preferred, but the price placed on them may make it necessary to select some other feed. When prices for corn and hay drop considerably below the normal level in Kansas and Nebraska a little sheep feeding is done on the old-time plan. Colorado is the only place where large operators now feed regularly, and it is doubtful whether they will continue for many years more because the time has come when they cannot be fully assured of profits from the business (Fig. 204).

From the foregoing statements it is evident that the day of the large operator in sheep feeding is practically over. There should be no regret, for sheep feeding properly belongs to those who raise a part or all of the feed.

Fig. 204.—Sheep on feed at Ft. Collins, Colorado. The lambs in the foreground are eating grain; when they have finished they will be driven into a pen at the right, a fresh supply of grain will be put in the troughs and a fresh lot of lambs will be brought in to feed. Hay is placed along the fences at the right and the lambs thrust their heads between the boards to feed on it.

**Rise of Farmer Feeders.**—Not long after the large operators started to feed sheep farmers saw opportunities for profits in the business. Within a short time they were able to demonstrate that they were in better position to engage in sheep feeding than were the large operators. Their advantages were these: First, they owned the land on which the feeding was done, while, as a rule, the large operators did not; second, they considered the manure a valuable item, while to the large operators it was often an incumbrance. In fact, it was the need for manure which led certain farmers in Michigan to engage in sheep feeding. Their farms had been depleted in fertility by continued cropping with wheat and something had to be done to restore fertility. Profitable sheep feeding, with the attendant production of manure, caught the attention of these farmers and they began to engage in the business about 1893. Anyone who travels through south central Michigan will be impressed by the number of large red barns that have been erected for the purpose of conserving all of the roughages grown on the farm, such as hay, straw, corn stover, and bean hulls, and for housing sheep and lambs to which the roughages are fed. Most of the concentrates are shipped in. Thus more fertility is carried back to the land in the form of manure than was taken away from it in the form of roughages. The crops produced on the farms where the large red barns are located bear ample evidence that something has been done to restore fertility, and those acquainted with conditions unhesitatingly give the credit to the feeding of sheep.

Since farmers own the land on which they do their feeding they have still another advantage over the large operator in that they produce a great deal of their own feed. In the early days, when screenings were ridiculously cheap, this was not such an advantage, but now that a market has been established for them, the man who grows all or a part of his feed near the base of his operations is in better position to feed than the man who is compelled to buy all of his feeds.

Again, the landowner, particularly in the corn belt, usually has a great deal of growth on his land which he considers waste unless consumed by some such animal as the sheep. The utilization of this growth gives the farmer or landowner a tremendous advantage over the large operator, for whatever gain the sheep make from it is counted clear profit. With this and the other advantages enumerated, it is clear that in time sheep feeding must be almost entirely in the hands of the farmer feeders, or of those who feed on a similar basis. In fact, the great bulk of the sheep feeding of to-day is done by owners or operatcrs of land who feed from a few hundred to a few thousand sheep and lambs in a season. At the present time probably 95 per cent or more of the sheep fed are lambs.

## QUESTIONS

1. When did the sheep-feeding industry originate?
2. Who first practiced the feeding of sheep on mill screenings?
3. How did the large feeders operate?
4. Why did the farmers become interested?
5. In what ways do farmer feeders have advantage over the speculative feeders?

## CHAPTER XXXVII

# MARKET CLASSES OF SHEEP

THE sheep feeder should have a comprehensive knowledge of the classes of sheep sold on the open markets and of the requirements for the grades within these classes.

The following is a condensed tabulation of a recent outline developed by the Bureau of Agricultural Economics, (U. S. Dept. Agr. Bul. 1360).

Lamb and Sheep Schedules

| *Class* | *Subclass* | *Age Selection* | *Weight Selection* | | | | *Grade* |
|---|---|---|---|---|---|---|---|
| | | | *Light*[1] | *Handy* | *Medium* | *Heavy* | |
| Lambs | Slaughter | Spring Lambs | 70 | All Weights 70–80 | 80–90 | 90 up | Prime<br>Choice<br>Good<br>Medium<br>Common<br>Cull |
| | Feeder | All ages | 60 | .... | 60–70 | 70 up | Fancy<br>Choice<br>Good<br>Medium<br>Common<br>Inferior |
| | Shearer | All ages | 70 | .... | 70–80 | 80 up | Choice<br>Good<br>Medium |
| Ewes | Slaughter | Yearling | 90 | .... | 90–100 | 100 up | See slaughter lambs |
| | | 2 yrs. or over | 100 | 100–120 | 120–140 | 140 up | |
| | Feeder | All ages | .. | All Weights | .. | .. | Choice<br>Good<br>Medium<br>Common<br>Inferior |
| | Breeder | Yearling | 90 | .... | 90–100 | 100 up | Fancy<br>Choice<br>Good<br>Medium<br>Common |
| | | 2 and 3 yrs. | 100 | .... | 100–125 | 125 up | |
| | | 4 yrs. or over | 100 | .... | 100–125 | 125 up | |
| Wethers | Slaughter | Yearling | 90 | 90–100 | 100–110 | 110 up | See slaughter lambs |
| | | 2 yrs. or over | 100 | 100–115 | 115–130 | 130 up | |
| | Feeder | Yearling | .. | All Weights | .. | .. | See slaughter lambs |
| | | 2 yrs. or over | .. | All Weights | .. | .. | |
| Rams | Slaughter | Yearling | .. | All Weights | .. | .. | Good<br>Medium<br>Common |
| | | 2 yrs. or over | .. | All Weights | .. | .. | |

[1] Weights below this are acceptable and the weights are often quoted as 70 pounds down.

The chief difference between the old and the new systems in reference to the classes and subclasses is that the old classes were based on the use of the animals, as mutton, feeder, and breeder. This is the basis of the present subclasses. The present listing of classes is made on the basis of sex with the exception of the lamb class, which in reality is an age classification, as ewe, wether, and ram lambs are found in this group. Lambs are not grouped according to sex, as the influence of this factor on form, quality, or condition is not very noticeable in very young animals. Ram lambs are often sold separately from the ewe and wether lambs after they have reached the age of 5 or 6 months, as male characteristics have developed. The castration of the males is advised.

*Lambs* include all sheep under 12 or 14 months of age except those that are so forward in their development of body as to resemble mature sheep. If any of the temporary teeth have been replaced by permanent teeth the animal would not be classed as a lamb. Lambs constitute over 90 per cent of the sheep sold for slaughter. They are preferred to older sheep as meat is tender, of delicate flavor, and cuts are of convenient size.

A division on the basis of age into *spring lambs* and *lambs* is used to distinguish very young lambs dropped during the winter months and marketed when from 3 to 5 months old, weighing 55 and 70 pounds, from the more mature lambs of the previous year which may be found on the market at the same time. After July 1, the lambs from the previous year are sufficiently mature to be classed as ewes or wethers. Spring lambs are then known in market parlance as lambs.

*Wethers* are castrated males that are too mature in development of body and too advanced in age to class as lambs. Yearlings are more numerous than those of greater age, but at the present time do not constitute more than about 3 per cent of the market offerings.

As a mutton product yearling wethers are used as a substitute for lamb, and in order to serve this purpose they must bear considerable resemblance to lambs in form, quality, weight, condition, and immaturity. They are identified by the two broad teeth in front of the lower jaw and by the epiphyseal cartilage, or "break joint." To determine this presence of the latter, grasp the foreleg between the forefinger and thumb and rub up and down just above the pastern joint, where a rather sharp prominence will be felt if the cartilage has not disappeared.

By removing the forefoot of the carcass at the epiphyseal cartilage a reddish indented surface is exposed which is quite different in appearance from the surface exposed when the foot is removed at the regular joint of mature sheep.

*Ewes* are females too far advanced in maturity to class as lambs; the class includes all ages from yearlings up. Yearling ewes do not sell as well as yearling wethers because they mature earlier and often fail to show the "break joint" soon after they pass out of the lamb class.

*Backs and stags* are a small class of entire males too mature to class as lambs, and castrated males showing the coarseness of mature rams.

**Grades.**—Each class, bucks and stags excepted, is divided into from 3 to 6 grades, the full list for slaughter groups being prime, choice, good, medium, common, and cull. The term "prime" is replaced by the term "fancy" in feeder and breeding classes. A prime animal represents the best and a cull one the worst in a given class. In some cases the lower grade is omitted because animals corresponding to that grade are classed as feeders. The term "fancy" is applied only to the best grade of lambs in the feeder class and to the best grade of ewes in the breeding class, and it is but seldom used in these classes. Inferior refers to the lowest grade of lightweight feeder lambs and feeder ewes. All rams are included in three grades.

**Grades of Mutton Sheep.**—The grade to which a sheep in any of the subclasses of mutton or slaughter sheep belongs is determined by its form, quality, and condition. Of these factors, quality and condition are the most important. Animals deficient in any factors grade below prime.

In all particulars except weight the following description of a prime mutton lamb, taken from Illinois Station Bulletin 129, serves fairly well as a description of prime slaughter animals in the other classes of sheep:

"It is understood that when lambs are graded as prime they are the very best of the class on the market. Prime lambs are taken largely for fancy city market, hotel, and restaurant trade. Such lambs are practically above criticism in quality, condition, and weight. They are usually secured by sorting the best out of a band. Before a lamb is graded as prime it is determined by sight and touch that it possesses the form, quality, and condition demanded by the best dealers.

"**Form.**—The butcher demands form showing development in loin, back, and leg of mutton, from which high-priced cuts are secured. The animal should show depth and breadth, and not be paunchy, which adds to the percentage of waste. Prime lambs present a general fullness and smoothness of outline, with thickness and evenness of flesh and absence of roughness. The appearance of the carcass must be attractive when placed on exhibition in the market. It is generally conceded that form is enhanced if the body is supported by short legs. However, many prime lambs have only moderately short legs. Very long legs detract from the dressed yield and from the appearance of the carcass when displayed, and on this account lambs that are decidedly upstanding do not grade as prime.

"**Quality and Condition**—(1) **General Quality.**—The degree of development in quality is one of the most important factors in determining the value of fat lambs. General quality is indicated by a medium-sized, clean-cut head, ears of fine texture, fine but strong bone, a light pelt, and full, well-rounded outlines. All these attributes suggest a freedom from that degree of coarseness which adds to the waste in dressing, and from the unattractiveness which works against the value of the carcass.

"Of the items of general quality enumerated, lightness of pelt is the most essential. By pelt is meant the skin and wool combined. With a light-weight pelt, the skin will be comparatively thin and free from folds or wrinkles, and the wool not very dense or oily. The only time when the heavier weight of pelt seems to be favored is in the spring, when both shorn and unshorn sheep and lambs are being marketed. During these months the difference in price between shorn and unshorn lambs varies from seventy-five cents to one dollar and twenty-five cents per hundredweight in favor of the unshorn lambs. The amount of difference depends on the condition of the wool market and the time in the season when the lambs are slaughtered. The difference usually becomes less as the hot weather approaches, because it is believed that the carcasses of unshorn lambs deteriorate in quality on account of the discomfort the lambs suffer in hot weather from being left in their fleeces. It should be remembered, however, that this discrimination in favor of the heavier pelt holds only when shorn and unshorn sheep or lambs are compared. Of two lambs in the wool, the one with the lighter pelt is always preferred, if equal in other respects.

"The question is often asked why sheep or lambs with heavy pelts are discriminated against when they carry a greater weight of wool than those with light pelts. This question arises naturally because wool is worth a great deal more per pound than mutton, and it would seem that lambs with heavy fleeces should be credited with the greater amount of wool which they produce. In a large packing plant the slaughtering department usually delivers pelts having wool at about the same stage of growth to the wool pullery department at a uniform price. Hence the department buying the lambs does not discriminate in favor of those having heavy fleeces. If the buyer for the packer were required to base his bids upon the wool as well as the mutton yields his task would be greatly complicated because, in estimating the yield of wool, he would be obliged to determine how much of the pelt was wool and how much of it skin. Hence the packer instructs the buyer to be governed chiefly by the percentage of marketable meat which the lamb will yield and not by the combined product of mutton and wool.

"The weight of pelt may differ appreciably according to the amount of foreign material and moisture in the wool. Should lambs be very wet, buyers may refuse to bid on them until they become nearly dry; and if bids are made on lambs whose wool contains an unusual percentage of moisture, the buyer attempts to allow for it by the price he offers. Foreign material, such as mud, sand, or dung, may be lodged in the wool, and in such case the buyer protects himself from loss by bidding less per pound than if clean. Such bids usually work against the owner, and hence it pays to market lambs in clean condition.

"Occasionally the general quality of lambs may be developed to such a marked degree that they will sell as prime even though they are somewhat deficient in form. A notable example is the fat Mexican lamb. From the standpoint of form, the Mexicans are not especially attractive, since they have narrow, upstanding bodies and long necks, but they are unequalled in fineness of features and lightness of pelt. Without their high development of general quality they would not receive favorable consideration from buyers, but because of it, when fat, they top the market.

"(2) **Quality of Flesh and Condition.**—The terms 'quality' and 'condition' are frequently used interchangeably on the market, chiefly because the quality of the flesh of an animal is largely dependent upon condition. By condition is meant degree of fatness. The reasons why a lamb should be fat are: (*a*) other things being equal, there will not be so high a percentage of offal as in the half-fat or the thin lamb; (*b*) the fat adds to the attractiveness of the carcass and thus makes it more inviting to the purchaser; (*c*) the comparatively fat carcass loses less in weight in the process of cooling out in the refrigerator and also in cooking; (*d*) some fat on the outside of the lean meat and a considerable amount deposited through it adds to its palatability by making it more juicy and of better flavor.

"Desirable quality of flesh is indicated by firmness along the back, at the loins over the sides and at the leg of mutton. 'Hard as a board' is a favorite phrase with many sheepmen to describe a back having a desirable quality of flesh, but with this single idea in mind bareness or lack of flesh might be mistaken for firmness of flesh. While the flesh should have that firmness which would seem hard to an inexperienced man, it should have just enough springiness to yield slightly to the touch.

"It rarely happens that lambs are made too fat for the prime grade, but very often they fail to grade as prime because they are not fat enough. Because lambs are finished for market before they have ceased growing, they do not have the tendency to lay on fat in large, soft bunches at the rump and in rolls at the girth, and hence it is difficult to carry them to the point of excessive fatness. The development of fat essential to the prime lamb is indicated by a thick dock, a full, mellow purse, thickness and smoothness on the back and over the ribs, fullness at the neck and a plump well-filled breast.

"By merely looking at a lamb in the wool, one can not tell its condition with exactness, and hence it is necessary to judge condition by placing the hands on the animal. Experts rely upon placing the hand but once; for example, by spreading the hand so that the back and ribs will be touched by one stroke, or by grasping the loin, or by getting the thickness and fullness of the dock; but none risk their judgment upon sight alone. A great deal is determined by the stroke that touches the back and ribs because it not only reveals the condition as evidenced by the degree of smoothness present, but also the amount and quality of the flesh by the thickness and firmness of it. This stroke also aids in determining the kind of pelt a lamb may have with respect to thickness of skin, density of wool, and presence of foreign material.

"**Weight.**—Weight is a factor that varies somewhat with the different seasons of the year, but, in general, the lamb of prime quality and condition and weighing 80 pounds sells at the highest price. When spring lambs first appear on the market they weigh little more than 60 pounds; but if they have the quality and the finish they easily command top prices. During the summer months, when people are apt to eat less meat, consumers of mutton, as a rule, desire small cuts, and this gives rise to a strong demand for lambs ranging in weight from 65 to 70 pounds. There never is a time, however, when lambs weighing 80 pounds will not sell as prime provided they are prime in

Fig. 205.—Prime lambs, uniform, shapely, showing general quality, fat and no wrinkles.

form, quality, and condition. Occasionally native lambs showing the best form, quality, and condition, will sell at top prices even though they reach 100 pounds in weight. Such cases are exceptional, and no one could expect to market lambs of this weight regularly and always have them sell so well.

"Quality and condition are of direct interest to the packer in that they influence the percentage of marketable meat secured, but weight is a factor regulated almost entirely by the consumer, who may be very exacting if prices are high. It is believed that in the combination of tenderness, juiciness, and flavor the flesh from the lighter lamb is not superior to that of the heavier lamb. But in making selections from the lighter carcass the average consumer feels more fully assured that he is getting lamb and not mutton, and the size of the cuts from the smaller carcass is more convenient for his use.

"What has been said in the above discussion about the form, quality, and condition of the prime lamb is in the main true of any class of slaughter sheep. Any animal that is markedly deficient in either form, quality, or condition will not meet the demands of the dealer, and not grade as prime" (Figs. 205-208).

**Common and Cull Grades.**—Animals in common or cull grades are nearly always very deficient in condition, as shown by lack of covering over the back and ribs. Coarseness and

FIG. 206.—Prime yearlings, tidy and not much larger than lambs.

overweight, as frequently occurs with ram lambs, may cause them to be graded as common lambs or culls. Wethers in medium to good condition, but having heavy pelts and coarse features, may be graded as common. Advanced pregnancy in ewes and lack in condition or quality may place them in the common grade (Figs. 209-211).

The intermediate grades—choice, good, and medium—indicate various degrees of deficiency in condition, quality, and form. Animals markedly deficient in either condition or quality rarely grade higher than medium, but bad form, unless accompanied by paunchiness, is not so much discriminated against. Weight has a variable influence in determining the value. When the supply of a class is not great enough to satisfy the demand, it has little influence, but if there is a plentiful supply its influence is marked.

FIG. 207.—Prime wethers, showing the quality and thickness required of prime heavy mutton, fed by J. Orton Finley, Oneida, Illinois.

The most desirable weights of slaughter sheep are those which are known as light, or handy weights. Under conditions now existing in the eastern half of the United States some have taken this to mean that there is no advantage to be found in keeping

FIG. 208.—Prime ewes.

FIG. 209.—Common lambs. Thin in flesh, not docked and castrated. (Ill. Sta. Bul. 129.)

some of the larger, coarser breeds with lambs that do not attain a good market finish at a light weight. Very different considerations are important in western sections.

The dressing percentage of animals in the prime grades of unshorn sheep ranges from 52 to 54 per cent. Very fat animals will dress out as much as 60 per cent of carcass to live weight, but when the dressed percentage is this high the mutton is too fat to be used economically.

**Feeder Sheep.**—Condition or the amount of flesh is the one thing which determines whether or not sheep belong in the feeder class. When they are too thin to suit the needs of the packer they are classed as feeders, provided they are healthy western sheep and not extremely coarse and advanced in age. Occasionally a few natives are taken out as feeders, but so rarely and in such small numbers that they can not be listed as belonging to the feeder class.

Fig. 210.

Fig. 211.

Fig. 210.—Common wethers. Thin in flesh, heavy pelts. (From Illinois Station Bulletin 129.)

Fig. 211.—Common ewes. Very thin in flesh. (From Illinois Station Bulletin 129.)

**Grades of Feeders.**—The grade to which a feeder sheep belongs is determined by its form, quality, constitution, and condition. In most particulars the following description of choice feeder lambs is from Illinois Bulletin 129 (Figs. 212, 213):

**"Choice Feeder Lambs.**—Choice feeders should develop into choice and prime mutton lambs. Of all the grades that generally come to the notice of buyers, this one is probably more uniform than any other.

"What the buyer expects of choice feeders is the ability to finish into prime or choice mutton lambs, and to produce gains at economical figures. The selection of such lambs is based upon form, quality, constitution, condition, and weight.

**"Form in Feeder Lambs.**—In general, the form should be deep, broad, well-knit, of medium length, and low-set. This con-

FIG. 212.—Choice feeder lambs thrifty and free from coarseness.

FIG. 213.—Choice feeder lambs showing compactness and quality.

formation indicates early maturity, good constitution, capacity for growth, and a likelihood of finishing into an attractive carcass with a relatively high percentage of valuable cuts. Very leggy, gaunt, narrow, loosely-made lambs usually fatten slowly and lack the ability to make economical gains or to reach choice mutton finish. The choice feeder should be of medium length rather than very long or very short. Great length is usually attended with general ungainliness and a tendency to finish slowly. Since lambs of this conformation are usually very long in the coupling, they lack, when at their best, the compactness desired in the choice mutton lamb. On the other hand, the unusually short lamb as a rule behaves on feed as though it had been stunted. It is often fastidious in its eating; it frequently presents a paunchy appearance and improves but slightly during the feeding period. It has been said that choice feeders should be low-set, but only a comparatively small number of strong, western lambs have legs that would be termed short. In making selections, the less leggy type should be preferred.

"**Quality of Feeder Lambs.**—Quality is a very important consideration in the selection of feeder lambs. It is characterized by a medium-sized, clean-cut head; medium-sized ears; bone that is free from coarseness at the joints; skin, thin and without folds or wrinkles. A smooth skin without folds or wrinkles and carrying wool of moderate weight is the most important requirement of desirable quality in feeder lambs. Lambs with heavy pelts are discriminated against because they do not, as a rule, gain so rapidly as lambs with smooth skins, and they never command top prices when returned to the market fat, because the excessive weight of pelt materially reduces the percentage of the dressed weight.

"**Constitution of Feeders.**—The conformation which indicates a strong constitution is described above under form. A wide, deep chest, fullness in the heart-girth, and depth and breadth of body indicate sufficient space for well-developed vital organs, which means a strong constitution. Another important point, which if not a part of constitution is closely akin to it, is thrift. The intelligent buyer of choice feeders rejects all lambs that appear in the least unthrifty, such as lame ones and those inclined to lag behind when the band is moving.

"**Condition.**—While it is understood that no grade of feeder lambs is what we would call fat, choice lambs should be fairly full in their outlines and without any suggestion of emaciation. Such condition is of importance for two reasons: First, the exceedingly thin lamb usually does not finish in a normal feeding period; and, second, a lamb of this description often fails to make gains as economically as those in higher condition.

"**Weight to be Considered in Feeders.**—The question of weight should receive consideration. Choice lightweight feeder lambs range in weight from 55 to 60 pounds. Lambs weighing less than this are regarded as either too young or too much retarded in growth to be desired by many feeders. It is expected of choice lambs that they finish with desirable weights in a normal feeding period, which is from 75 to 120 days, and hence the initial weight should not be much less than 55 pounds."

FIG. 214.

FIG. 215.

FIG. 214.—Common feeder lambs. Very thin, and unthrifty in appearance. (From Illinois Station Bulletin 129.)

FIG. 215.—Common feeder yearlings. Very heavy pelts which are objectionable in any class of feeders. (From Illinois Station Bulletin 129.)

In determining the proper form of a feeder sheep, it is not to be expected that the amount of depth and breadth in proportion to the length is to be as great as in the fat lamb in high condition.

Fancy selected feeder lambs (one grade higher than choice

lambs) are usually above 60 pounds in weight and lacking only 10 to 15 pounds to put them in prime condition for mutton.

**The Common Grades.**—The following may cause feeder lambs to grade as common: Lack of thrift, light weight (35 to 45 pounds), extreme weight of pelt, and coarseness in features. Common feeder yearlings are so heavy in pelt and heavy in weight that they may be classed as wethers when fat. Common feeder wethers may be very thin, advanced in age, coarse, and pelty. Common feeder ewes are very thin, and as a rule have defective teeth (Figs. 214 and 215).

**Shearer Lambs.**—Lambs that are somewhat deficient in condition but carry fairly heavy fleeces are sometimes taken from the markets to nearby feeding stations where they are shorn and put on a short feed which is intended to add the extra condition necessary to make them sell well for slaughter. Lambs for shearing are purchased most freely when there is a relatively high price for wool and the purchaser thinks that he can make a profit by selling the wool and lambs separately. Since the shorn lambs sell for less per pound than those in full fleece, buyers of shearing lambs are most active when they foresee a rising market. In many cases lambs that are bought primarily for feeding are shorn before they are returned to market.

## QUESTIONS

1. What is the important difference between mutton and feeder sheep?
2. What are the most important factors in determining the grade of a mutton lamb?
3. What does the market mean by pelt?
4. Why are lambs preferred to older sheep?
5. What are yearlings?
6. How are they used in the mutton trade?
7. What grade is applied to the best mutton lamb? The worst?

## CHAPTER XXXVIII

# CONSIDERATIONS IN SHEEP AND LAMB FEEDING

**Sheep and Lamb Feeding Conducted in Autumn and Winter.**—Most sheep and lamb feeding is conducted in the autumn and winter. There are two reasons for this: (1) many persons are not prepared to feed except then, and (2) feeder sheep and lambs are not shipped from the range to the markets in large numbers until autumn.

Feeder sheep and lambs reach the markets in largest numbers in the autumn, because the moving of the sheep at this time from the summer ranges in the mountains to smaller winter ranges on the plains furnishes one of the best opportunities to dispose of surplus stock, a fair percentage of which is classed as feeders.

As a rule the autumn and winter are the best seasons for farmers to feed. General farm work does not then require so much attention and feed and labor are more plentiful.

**Principal Costs in Feeding Lambs.**—Of the items which enter into the costs incurred in fattening western lambs those of initial cost of the lambs and the cost of the feeds used constitute from 86 to 93 per cent of all charges. The government data show that the purchase price of the lambs makes up 52.5 per cent of the costs of open yard feeding in Colorado and Nebraska and of barn feeding in Michigan and Indiana, and accounts for 73 per cent of the charges of field feeding in Iowa and Nebraska. Thus the need for the exercise of good judgment in purchasing lambs if excessive cost is to be avoided. Feed charges varied from 20 per cent in field feeding to over 34 per cent in barn feeding. Marketing costs varied from 1.7 per cent to a little over 5 per cent, while miscellaneous items such as labor, interest, risk, taxes, and use of equipment varied from 4.7 to 11 per cent of the total.

**Types of Sheep and Lamb Feeding.—The Dry Lot.**—Feeding altogether on harvested or stored feeds is commonly referred to as dry-lot feeding. It is practiced in various places. In Michigan it is the common practice to place the sheep or lambs in barns and keep them there through the period. In other places the plan is frequently modified by providing a run in an outside lot in addition to the shelter. Where the weather is usually dry, the animals are kept entirely in open lots. In the western beet-growing districts lambs are fed on beet tops and beet pulp with barley, oats or corn, and alfalfa hay. The yards are filled in fall and feeding lasts for 4 or 5 months. As lambs reach a suitable market condition, they are "topped out" and shipped.

As a rule, Michigan feeders produce the necessary roughage, but the greater part of the concentrates are purchased. Just what concentrate is procured depends largely upon cost. Tons of salvage are used (salvage is damaged grain, such as corn and wheat taken from elevator fires), but good corn is frequently shipped in.

Those who feed entirely under shelter would prefer to finish two different bands of sheep or lambs each season, the first sold early in the new year, the second coming soon after. When scarcity of feeders prevents feeding two bands in a season, they purchase one shipment rather late, and market them after shearing. It is not an uncommon practice for Michigan and other feeders east of Chicago to buy the unfinished sheep and lambs from the stalk fields further west.

Feeding under shelter has several advantages which other methods lack. First, there is no waste of feed. Second, there is no waste of manure. The latter, though overlooked hitherto by many feeders, surely will not be disregarded much longer. Third, adverse weather conditions are not so serious a matter where the feeding is done under shelter. Fourth, certain types of feeders, such as little, weak, cheap "peewee" lambs can be handled, which could not be use at all under any other method. An attempt to feed them in the open would be an immense risk.

The disadvantage, if any, of feeding under shelter lies in the cost of equipment.

**First Over Fields and Then Under Shelter.**—This is a type of feeding practiced by those who have a great deal of land and who produce nearly or quite all of their feed. They have a great deal of feed left in the fields which either could not be harvested or which they do not see fit to harvest. By allowing the sheep to run on these fields, at least a part of this feed is consumed and the cost of finishing the animals is thereby lessened. When the weather turns bad they are brought to barns and finished on stored feeds.

Those who follow this method usually feed out but one shipment of sheep or lambs in a year. Generally they ship back to market rather early, but may not market until after shearing.

**Feeding Altogether in Fields.**—This plan is becoming more and more widely practiced, but when it consists solely in feeding

FIG. 216.—Sheeping down corn. Rape, soybeans, the clovers, or pasture grasses form good supplements to use with the corn.

in corn stalks, it is usually a failure. When sheep eat down corn in which rape or soybeans are grown economical gains and prime finish may be secured, or if good pasture can be utilized in connection with the corn, the feeding operation can be made successful. Other means consist of providing legume roughages or protein concentrates in racks in the fields or in adjoining shelters. Death losses are greater in field feeding than in dry lot feeding. (Fig. 216).

In feeding altogether in the fields, the feeding period may be either short or long. A long period amounts really to a rather extended period of stocking through the winter and a short fattening period in the spring.

**Specialized Plants.**—The feeding stations or accumulating stations mentioned in the previous chapter are to be classified under specialized plants. In such places all the feeds are purchased and the manure, instead of being hauled out on the land, is put through a drying and pulverizing process and sold as commercial fertilizer. Those who feed at the accumulating stations are persons who either are attempting to do business as did the old-time operator, or have started to feed at some other point and for some reason have been obliged to move. Feeders in the far West sometimes exhaust their supply of grain and then move up to the accumulating stations for finishing.

There are also specialized plants quite different from the accumulating station, of which the plants located at pea canning factories are good examples. At the time the peas are canned, the pea hulls and vines are made into silage by a very simple and inexpensive process. No silo is needed, and all that is necessary is to stack them neatly and tramp them well. The silage is unusually palatable to sheep and lambs and when used with fattening concentrates and a little dry roughage produces an excellent market finish.

**Nature of the Business of Sheep Feeding.**—Whoever undertakes to feed sheep and lambs should realize that there is a hazard in the business. In other words, both risk and chance are involved in it to a certain extent. Risk arises from the probability of losses during the feeding period and of low gains for the feed consumed. Chance arises from the probability of high prices for feeders and of low prices for fat sheep or lambs or *vice versa.* It is hardly fair, however, to call the business of sheep feeding purely speculative when conducted by those who follow it regularly year after year. But it is speculative when it is conducted by those who do not intend to follow it up regularly, and who engage in it only because they have an impression that the conditions surrounding it are such as to assure large profits irrespective of the lack of skill with which it is conducted.

It has often been said that the success of the feeding operation depends largely upon buying well and selling well. By this is meant that the selling price per hundredweight should be considerably higher than the purchase price. Unless the market for feeders be unusually low, no one can be reasonably sure of a much higher market for fat sheep and lambs than for feeders. There are certain indications, however, as to the future of the market which should be studied. Some of these indications are as follows:

First, the number of feeder sheep and lambs that are being sent to the country from the markets. If the supply of feeders seems to be small it is more than likely that prices will be high both for feeders and for fat sheep and lambs. Under such circumstances, one should exercise caution in buying, and he should be reasonably sure that the total supply of feeders is small before he makes his purchase.

Second, the supply of feed in the regions where feeding is done. If there is a heavy supply of feed, prices are likely to be high for feeders and low for the finished animals. Whenever there is an abnormally large supply of feed inexperienced persons are inclined to take up feeding. As a rule they are wanting in discrimination, both in buying and in selling. They boost the prices for feeders and depress the prices for fat sheep and lambs.

A large supply of feed does not necessarily indicate that one should not engage in feeding. But it does indicate the need of exercising care in buying and of planning to avoid the probable weak spots on the market. If there is a hungry demand for feeders to eat off a fall growth, it is probable that there will be a heavy run back to market late in the autumn or early in the winter. In such a season one should plan to market his animals late in the winter or during the spring months.

Third, the supply of other meat animals. If there is a scarcity of cattle or of swine, one may be reasonably sure of a good market for sheep. This is not always a safe indication because some abnormal situation may exist which causes such a heavy marketing of sheep as to be detrimental to prices.

Fourth, the price of wool. Undoubtedly high prices for wool tend to stimulate the prices for fat sheep because the packer is anxious to handle the wool of the sheep sent to slaughter. If the prices of wool were low the prices offered for feeders would be somewhat lower.

Fifth, the general prosperity of the people. If the prosperity of the people is threatened, prices for sheep and lambs are likely to be on a low level. Owing to the flurry in Wall Street late in the autumn of 1907, the prices for mutton and lamb were low throughout the following winter. It has been said that mutton and lamb are for the tables of the rich, but adverse financial conditions indicate that they are also for the tables of the salaried and wage-earning classes.

FIG. 217.—This man, who is sorting out the fat sheep to send to market, realizes that feeding is a fattening process.

Sixth, the general level of meat prices. Meat can soar too much in price. After it reaches a certain point, people begin to refuse to buy and the result is a lowering of prices. The level of meat prices is a consideration only for the very near future. That is, if one should be feeding a band of lambs that is just about ready to market, and should the market be growing stronger each week, attaining higher and higher levels, it is best not to be too optimistic as to the continuance of the rise, for so high a level may be reached that people will refuse to buy.

**Feeding a Fattening Process.**—Before starting to feed sheep or lambs one should fully realize that the object of the feeding operation is to convert animals in thin flesh into a finished product for slaughter. It would seem that no one would entertain any other idea, but each year thousands of western sheep and lambs are turned back to the large markets from corn-belt farms in unfinished condition. In fact, many of these sheep and lambs must be resold as feeders. Although many reasons can be given for this lack of finish, experience has shown that many feeders are not impressed as they should be by the importance of finish. They do not realize that in order to sell well, their offerings must be well fattened (Fig. 217).

**Equipment for Feeding.**—Supply of feed. Any one who is contemplating the feeding of either sheep or lambs should make a careful study of how well he is equipped to engage in the work. First of all he should ascertain whether he has an adequate supply of the proper kind of feed, both grain and roughage, to make his animals fat. In case his supply of feed is not adequate he should know definitely whether he can purchase it at a price that will justify his using it in the feeding process. Lack of feed is one of the reasons often given for so many sheep and lambs returning to the market in unfinished condition. In the corn belt, particularly, too many persons attempt to feed when they know they do not have enough of the proper kind of roughage. Their supply is exhausted before their sheep or lambs are finished and since concentrates alone can not be used, the feeding operation is carried on at a loss. Attempts to fatten on grass and roughages alone are rarely profitable because in fall and winter the feeding of some concentrate feed is required to make sheep or lambs fat. Therefore, it pays to look over the supply of feed carefully, and make sure that one does not purchase more sheep or lambs than he can finish to good advantage.

**Bedding.**—There is a variance of opinion as to the amount of bedding required by fattening sheep. Many provide nothing but the roughage waste. If there is a large quantity of this waste, it is quite sufficient, but if there is not, extra bedding should be provided. To the Michigan feeder, however, who mows away all of his straw for sheep feed it may seem like extravagant waste to use it for bedding. But in regions where so much straw is wasted, it is good economy to use it for bedding, because it will not only keep the sheep in better condition, but it will serve its purpose better as a fertilizer.

**Water.**—Fattening sheep or lambs need clean, wholesome water, every day. In cold weather, lambs that are receiving nothing but dry feeds will drink a half-gallon (four pounds) daily, and on warm days they will drink much more. Care should be taken to keep the watering troughs clean and sweet. The water can be kept in more wholesome condition if the troughs are located out of doors, but if this is done, some provision has to be made to keep it from freezing.

**Salt.**—All sheep kept on feeds that are produced in the Middle West and East crave salt. The reason for this is that there is not enough of this mineral in the feeds to satisfy the demands of the body for it. Salt may be given periodically, say twice a week, or it may be kept before the sheep all the time. As a rule the latter is the better practice, as it more nearly insures that the animals will get all the salt they need. But it should not be kept before them constantly until they have become accustomed to it. Cases have been reported of sheep and lambs dying because of their almost constant consumption of salt. Such cases do not seem to be numerous, but should a few animals in a band have a craving for salt which cannot be satisfied it would be better to feed it periodically.

**Sheds and Lots.**—Suitable feeding grounds and sufficient shelter are of importance in successful sheep and lamb feeding. Practically all feeders emphasize the need of having dry, well-drained feeding grounds. Sheep dislike mud. A prominent Illinois farmer who has been successful in feeding sheep and lambs for the past fifteen or twenty years has made the statement that rather than let a band of lambs wade through a muddy gateway, he would make a passage for them by tearing down a section of fence where it is not muddy.

Opinions differ as to the value of shelter for sheep and lambs on feed in regions where the fall and winter climate is variable. A few advocate no shelter whatever, while others maintain that the feeding process is more profitable if conducted entirely under shelter. Still others, in fact the majority, take the intermediate position, which is that sheep and lambs should be provided with enough shelter to protect them from storms, but that in fair weather they should be allowed to run in lots or in fields.

Those who believe shelter is not essential to successful feeding usually have some natural protection, such as timber or hills, to which the animals may go during stormy periods. With the aid of this protection they endure all but the worst storms without going back in condition, and many a band of western sheep

Fig. 218.—A sheep feeding shed at feeding yards, Kirkland, Illinois.

Fig. 219.—A suitable trough for feeding sheep.

and lambs has been made fat in the Middle West without having had access to shelter.

Shelter is essential to the most successful feeding. There are seasons when persons who have the best natural protection find it hard to handle their sheep and lambs because of the frequent and long storm periods. At such times, these men would be much better equipped if they had sufficient shelter to house the animals on feed. There is a saying common on the Chicago market to the effect that farmers will start shipping half-fat sheep and lambs when the first snow flies, which means that they attempt to do their feeding in the cornstalks and are not adequately equipped with shelter. Daily reports of the livestock markets have frequently called attention to the fact that sheep and lambs from the cornstalks in the Middle West have been returned to market in lower condition than they were when they were sold out as feeders. No stronger statement can be made to indicate that such a practice is unprofitable, and perhaps no stronger statement can be made to emphasize the fact that in general shelter should be provided for feeder sheep and lambs wherever the climate is variable.

If the shelter is constructed for no other purpose than for housing fattening sheep, it need not be of an expensive type. From five to seven square feet, exclusive of space for racks, should be allotted to each sheep and the chief consideration should be to provide a shelter that is dry and well-ventilated. There is no need of extra effort to make it warm (Fig. 218).

If outside lots are desired they should be located adjacent to the sheds or barns in order to prevent the sheep from taking needless exercise. These lots should be well drained, free from mud and not very large. It is a good plan to bed them deep with stalks or straw in order to keep a clean footing. The writer recalls an instance where sheep were given a run to an outside paved lot. In rainy weather the dung became a semi-liquid mass injurious to the feet of the sheep. Large lots cause too much exercise and a great loss of manure. The lots furnish an outlet for the sheep and thus keep down barn odors which tend to depress the appetite of the animals.

**Troughs and Racks.**—Sheep need troughs and racks that can be kept clean, for they will rarely eat feed befouled by dung. Many feeders locate those for grain outside the barns or sheds or in feeding lots. In this way the feeding place for grain is kept clean and appetizing. Some successful feeders wash the troughs occasionally with lime water to keep down odors (Fig. 219). Troughs and racks should be constructed so that sheep cannot walk in them. In nearly every band of feeders there are a few animals that desire to stand in the troughs and racks while they eat.

**Length of Feeding Period.**—This depends upon the age, weight, and condition of the animals to be fed. As a rule it does not pay to keep sheep or lambs on harvested or stored feeds for a long period. Yet there are justifiable exceptions to this statement. If the feed is rather low in grade the period may be long. Those who buy little, weak lambs have no other alternative than a long feeding period; yet good profits have been made with such lambs by those equipped with comfortable shelter and nutritious feeds. In general, however, the motto of feeders who follow the dry-lot method is large daily gains and rapid finish. They finish wethers in from 30 to 70 days; yearlings in from 40 to 80 days, and lambs in from 75 to 120 days.

In case a large number of animals are being fed, some of them may be sorted out and sent to market in 25 or 30 days after the feeding period begins. All of the feeders purchased are rarely in the same condition, and it requires little to make some of them ready for market. If there are enough to make one or more carloads, and if the market is satisfactory, it is better to market them before the thinner animals are ready to go.

**First Steps in Feeding.**—Sheep and lambs should receive very close attention for the first two or three days after they arrive at the place of feeding. The reason for this is that, as a rule, they have been through several days of rather rough treatment while enroute to the market and passing through it. During this time they may not have had enough feed to satisfy their appetite and perhaps not enough water to quench their thirst. Care should be taken not to allow them to rush to the watering troughs and drink all they can hold; it is better to allow them to drink a little every few hours until their thirst is satisfied. In mild weather it is well to scatter the first feed on the ground. If fed from racks, allow ample space and place feed in advance, to prevent "piling up" in their anxiety to get the feed. Nothing but dry roughage should be given at first. Succulent feed is likely to cause scours, and western sheep and lambs are not accustomed to much grain. Supply plenty of choice roughage as soon as they arrive at the place of feeding. Alfalfa hay may prove an exception as too much causes scours or bloat.

The chief problem is to get them accustomed to feeds which are new and might cause disorders. Clover hay is usually new to them but fortunately they may eat all they want of it from the very first. On the other hand, all heavy concentrates, except linseed meal fed in cool weather, must be fed in moderate quantities at first. Nor is it well to feed silage heavily at first.

The following table from the Illinois Station shows daily feeds per lamb each week of feeding and how fast feeds should be increased. Too much caution was taken with corn and silage in the first two weeks, as the lambs lost instead of gaining. The lambs averaged 65 pounds at first.

*Changes in Rations for feeding period of Seventeen Weeks.*

| | Sample Ration No. 1 | | | | Sample Ration No. 2 | | | | |
|---|---|---|---|---|---|---|---|---|---|
| Week | Shelled corn | Clover hay | Water | Daily gain | Shelled corn | Corn silage | Clover hay | Water | Daily gain |
| | *lbs.* | *lbs.* | *lbs.* | *lbs.* | *lbs.* | *lbs.* | *lbs.* | *lbs.* | *lbs.* |
| 1........ | .22 | 1.70 | 2.85 | .15 | .20 | .32 | 1.43 | 2.38 | .38 |
| 2........ | .45 | 1.70 | 3.43 | .05 | .40 | .80 | 1.24 | 2.19 | .14 |
| 3........ | .78 | 1.35 | 3.37 | .34 | .36 | 1.18 | 1.06 | 2.79 | .34 |
| 4........ | .81 | 1.39 | 3.68 | .05 | .75 | 1.03 | 1.00 | 2.89 | .11 |
| 5........ | .96 | 1.37 | 4.12 | .23 | .83 | 1.29 | 1.05 | 3.25 | .25 |
| 6........ | 1.06 | 1.26 | 4.09 | .25 | .94 | 1.50 | .94 | 3.47 | .32 |
| 7........ | 1.19 | 1.14 | 3.96 | .34 | 1.06 | 1.75 | .92 | 3.27 | .57 |
| 8........ | 1.36 | 1.03 | 4.55 | .29 | 1.06 | 1.98 | .72 | 3.66 | .29 |
| 9........ | 1.38 | 1.02 | 4.36 | .16 | 1.06 | 2.00 | .69 | 3.45 | .23 |
| 10........ | 1.47 | .96 | 4.14 | .39 | 1.13 | 2.38 | .56 | 3.70 | .59 |
| 11........ | 1.59 | .98 | 6.17 | .43 | 1.22 | 2.63 | .51 | 4.51 | .41 |
| 12........ | 1.71 | .98 | 4.82 | .45 | 1.34 | 2.63 | .52 | 4.47 | .39 |
| 13........ | 1.81 | .97 | 5.45 | .54 | 1.44 | 2.63 | .43 | 4.38 | .41 |
| 14........ | 1.81 | .97 | 4.96 | .21 | 1.44 | 2.44 | .51 | 3.10 | .27 |
| 15........ | 1.82 | .94 | 2.90 | .14 | 1.48 | 2.63 | .55 | 2.58 | .68 |
| 16........ | 1.71 | .93 | 5.13 | .54 | 1.63 | 2.61 | .52 | 4.08 | .27 |
| 17........ | 1.87 | .93 | 5.45 | .36 | 1.63 | 2.63 | .53 | 3.95 | .38 |

**Increasing Feed.**—If possible, the increases should be made on clear, cool days, when the appetite of sheep is keenest. Warmth and humidity are depressing.

When are sheep or lambs on full feed? This is indicated when they fail to eat, within a few minutes, all of the concentrate part of their ration. They have more than needed if they leave palatable roughages, such as clover hay, alfalfa, and corn stover.

The self-feeder method was generally used by the old-time operators and it is still employed in many large feeding plants. With this method the sheep or lambs are on full feed almost from the beginning of the feeding period. A large quantity of feed is placed in racks or feed boxes to which the animals have free access. The feed is usually, but not always, a mixture of concentrates and chaffed roughage. At the beginning of the feeding period, the proportion of roughage is much greater than the concentrates. As the feeding period advances this proportion is changed gradually.

**Manner of Giving the Ration.**—The concentrates should be fed first and should be eaten in a few minutes; then comes the succulent feed, if used, and finally the roughage. If combination grain and hay racks are used, the succulent feed may be placed in the troughs. If there is danger of freezing, withhold roughage to cause succulence to be eaten promptly.

Feed regularly and twice each day. If the animals receive their feed at a set time, they remain quiet and contented at all other times. It is better to give all feeds twice each day, because in this way there is less chance to gorge the stomach with any one feed. It is well to feed silage three times a day. If other work about the place does not make it necessary feeding before daylight should not be done. Sheep or lambs will lie at rest until daybreak if not aroused, and rest should not be disturbed.

**Importance of Even Conditions.**—Sheep quarters should be kept quiet or in one condition with respect to noise. It is better to move about in the barn in a straightforward, deliberate manner than to tiptoe cautiously about. Unusual noises and circumstances may cause sheep to jump to their feet and stampede.

**Animals "Off Feed."**—In spite of good care, good feeds, and good water, fattening sheep or lambs will go "off feed" occasionally. If they are indifferent to feed it is advisable to reduce the amount, it being well to omit the concentrate for one or two feeds. In case a few refuse to eat, they should be placed in a pen by themselves and drenched with Epsom salts. Use just enough water to get the salts into solution. It may be advisable to reduce the quantity of concentrates for two or three feeds.

**Troubles in the Feed-lot.**—Many feeders of lambs expect to experience a death loss of about three per cent during the feeding period. Certain diseases which affect lambs call for the services of the expert and the feeder who can obtain the help of a competent veterinarian is, indeed, fortunate. The following diseases often cause excessive losses and since many of them arise through lack of care and sanitation, these points should have the constant attention of the feeder.

*Hemorrhagic septicemia* is an infectious, contagious disease characterized by dullness and loss of appetite with a discharge from the nose and eyes, rapid breathing, and fever, often followed by pneumonia. Under certain conditions of good weather, good housing, and good feeding, the trouble may subside within a week or two. The usual treatment after the identity of the trouble has been established is to immunize those lambs which are not yet affected. This is the safest procedure to follow.

*Dysenteries* have caused some severe losses. Lambs suffering from these disorders become dull and feverish and a diarrhea which is usually bloody manifests itself. As the condition may be due to the presence of various contagious organisms, the ailing animals should be separated from the rest of the flock. Treatment varies with the cause and usually consists of the administration of laxatives and intestinal antiseptics. A light diet of oats, bran and alfalfa hay should be given.

*Diarrhea* may be found at some time in some lambs in practically every lot of feeding lambs. Many cases of scours are the result of indigestion due to improper feeding. It is very difficult if not impossible to prevent some lambs from eating too much even when the very best feeds are used. Lambs that are seriously affected should be removed from the lot and given a tablespoon of castor oil and fed lightly on oats and hay.

*Soremouth* is an infectious disease caused by a filterable virus.[1] In severe cases the mouth becomes a mass of scabs which make it impossible for the lambs to eat, and they lose weight rapidly. Death sometimes results. The disease runs a course of three to four weeks at the end of which the scabs have completely disappeared. Medical treatment is unsatisfactory although the lips may be kept more flexible by the application of an ointment or salve. Vaccination establishes an immunity which endures for two or three years. Vaccination of infected lambs shortens the course and lessens the severity of the disease.

*Pneumonia* has a variety of causes. When in the form of an epidemic, the hemorrhagic septicemia organism is the most likely cause. Exposure, chilling in transportation, and housing in damp, poorly ventilated quarters seem to render the animals liable to the disease. Avoidance of these conditions aids in prevention. Few affected lambs recover and treatment seems to avail little.

*Urinary calculi* are small granules that form in the kidneys, bladder, and urinary passages. The trouble seems to be confined to males. Symptoms are depression, some distention of the abdomen, and straining. Root crops have been suspected of causing the trouble but this is unlikely, as the "stones" consist largely of calcium and phosphate materials found to only a minor degree in roots. Treatment often fails and death usually occurs.

---

[1] Texas Station Bulletin 504.

## CHAPTER XXXIX

# SOME IMPORTANT FACTORS AFFECTING THE RATE AND ECONOMY OF GAIN IN FATTENING SHEEP AND LAMBS

**The Effect of Age.—On Rate of Body Development.**—The rate of growth in sheep decreases as they approach maturity. Senequier,[1] in investigating the body development of ten ewes of the milking breed of Larzac, observed that the most rapid increase in weight was during the first two months, and three-fourths of the increase was made during the first year. During the second year the rate of gain was slower and it was still slower from the twenty-fifth month to maturity. The weight at two months was about one-third of the average weight at maturity; at the fifth month, one-half; between the sixth and seventh months, two-thirds; and between the eighth and ninth months, three-fourths of the adult weight. They were considered mature at the completion of the second dentition, which was reached at from thirty-eight to forty-one months.

**Fattening Sheep of Different Ages.**—Lambs of feeder age (above five months) and in feeder condition gain somewhat more rapidly in weight and make considerably more economical use of feed than do older sheep. But since they grow as well as fatten, they require a little longer feeding period and a ration containing a higher percentage of protein. As compared with yearlings and wethers, they are not so well adapted to handling coarse feeds and feeds in slightly damaged condition, although it is seldom good policy to give feed of poor quality—as musty or mouldy feed—to any class of fattening sheep. Lambs also require a little more careful supervision than do yearlings and wethers, for they are more likely to go "off feed," and they are not quite so well adapted to running in the open without shelter.

As a rule, feeders who are properly equipped with shelter and feed, prefer to handle lambs because they not only make more gain

[1] "Annales Agronomiques" 21, 1885, No. 9.

from a given weight of feed, but they sell better as a prime product. That is, one year with another, the margin on prime lambs is likely to be greater than the margin on the prime grade of older sheep. Feeder lambs cost more per hundredweight than do yearlings and wethers, but in cases where the margin between cost and selling price is the same, the higher cost is an advantage.

Yearlings and wethers, provided the latter are not greatly advanced in age, are about the same in their rate of gain and in the amount of feed they use to produce a pound of gain. Both are well adapted to making use of rations rather low in protein. At the Illinois Station the writer fed a lot of yearlings for 84 days on corn, corn silage, and oat straw, that made almost as much gain and were judged to be equal in market finish to a lot fed corn, corn silage, and alfalfa hay.

Care must be exercised in feeding yearlings, for they will sell as wethers if they are made too heavy for the mutton yearling class, or if they become too mature to break at the epiphyseal cartilage (break joint) when they are slaughtered.

Only a few feeder yearlings and wethers can be purchased on the open market. They have largely disappeared because in many places in the West where wethers were kept, sheep husbandry has been superseded by other types of agriculture, and in many other places in the West, conditions have changed so that breeding ewes are regarded as more profitable than wethers. There is a demand and hence a market for yearling and wether mutton, but in times of normal supply they are not logical mutton products, for if everything goes well so that the wether lamb is a fit product for mutton, it should be sold before it passes out of the lamb class.

Old ewes make very good use of feed if their teeth are in good condition, but if they cannot masticate their food well, they must receive close attention. Their grain should be ground and their roughage should be of good quality. In Colorado it has been found that they make good use of beet pulp, and undoubtedly silage would serve well as one of the roughages in their ration.

The following data obtained by Shaw at the Montana Station [2] show the results of fattening sheep of different ages. Particular attention should be given to the amount of hay each class consumed daily for a period of 88 days.

---

[2]Montana Station Bulletin 35.

*Fattening Sheep of Different Ages.*

| Animals | Initial weight | Feed per head per day | | Gain per head per day | Feed required for one pound gain | |
|---|---|---|---|---|---|---|
| | | Barley | Clover hay | | Grain | Hay |
| | *lbs.* | *lbs.* | *lbs.* | *lbs.* | *lbs.* | *lbs.* |
| Lambs......... | 63 | .68 | 2.05 | .27 | 2.53 | 7.63 |
| 1 year wethers.. | 95 | .68 | 3.77 | .27 | 2.56 | 14.15 |
| 2 year wethers.. | 116 | .68 | 4.05 | .28 | 2.48 | 14.67 |
| Aged ewes..... | 92 | .68 | 2.33 | .177 | 3.86 | 13.18 |

The writer,[3] in a study of the effect of age and weight on the rate and economy of gains, fed three lots of native lambs for a period of 98 days. The results are given in the following table:

*Rate and Economy of Gains with Lambs of Different Weights.*

| Lot | Age at beginning of experiment (months) | Initial weight | Average feed consumed daily | | Average daily gain | Feed required for one pound gain | |
|---|---|---|---|---|---|---|---|
| | | | Grain, Corn 4 parts: oats 1 part | Clover hay | | Concentrates | Clover hay |
| Lambs: | | *lbs.* | *lbs.* | *lbs.* | *lbs.* | *lbs.* | *lbs.* |
| 1–10 | 8.5 | 95.4 | 1.71 | 2.25 | .28 | 6.0 | 8.0 |
| 2–10 | 7.0 | 77.9 | 1.59 | 2.06 | .28 | 5.6 | 7.3 |
| 3–10 | 5.5 | 62.6 | 1.39 | 1.57 | .30 | 4.6 | 5.6 |

**The Influence of Sex.**—Sex is a consideration chiefly in feeding lambs as this is the only class in which ewes and wethers are placed together. Wether lambs are inclined to gain a little faster than ewes, but since the ewes are slightly superior in general quality, they attain market finish quite as soon as the wethers and sell for as much per hundredweight. Both sexes are practically the same in the consumption of feed.

Carcasses from wethers are slightly thicker in lean meat than those from ewes, but in the general meat trade no distinction is made between ewe and wether lamb mutton.

Mature wethers usually sell for more per hundredweight than ewes because they dress out a higher percentage of carcass to live weight and their carcasses are somewhat more shapely.

[3] Thesis—Illinois Agricultural College.

The following comparison between wether and ewe lambs fed for a period of 90 days is taken from Illinois Station Bulletin 167:

*Comparison of Wether and Ewe Lambs as to Feed Consumed and Gains Made.*

| | Proportion of corn to hay | Shelled corn per head | Alfalfa hay per head | Gain per head |
|---|---|---|---|---|
| Fed alike: | | *lbs.* | *lbs.* | *lbs.* |
| Lot 1( 20 wethers)......... | 1:0.99 | 111.6 | 110.4 | 27.05 |
| Lot 5 (20 ewes)............ | 1:1.00 | 110.4 | 110.4 | 27.14 |
| Fed alike: | | | | |
| Lot 2 (20 wethers)......... | 1:1.36 | 94.3 | 127.7 | 24.22 |
| Lot 6 (20 ewes)............ | 1:1.34 | 93.5 | 125.3 | 22.05 |

**The Influence of Shearing.**—Where good housing facilities have been available, shearing before the fattening period has become far advanced has been extensively practiced chiefly for the purpose of stimulating the appetite and increasing the rate of gain. This practice undoubtedly increases the appetite, but it does not materially increase the rate of gain unless the animals are made more comfortable by removing the fleece. When the barn is large and the system of ventilation such that cold draughts can be avoided, a large number of sheep crowded in close will probably be more comfortable out of the fleece even in cold weather. But it seldom pays to shear when the weather is cold except under such circumstances as the necessity of getting more sheep into the shelter available or of getting rid of ticks.

If the feeding period advances into the spring months, after the weather has become warm enough to make sheep in the fleece uncomfortable, then it will pay to shear, for the rate of gain will be considerably increased.

It may pay to shear just before marketing. More sheep can be placed in a car, and if the margin between clipped and unclipped sheep is small, some money may be made by removing the fleeces. But before proceeding to do it, the feeder should be sure that a good weight of desirable wool will be secured, and he should know something of how to dispose of it.

**Self-feeders.**—When the practice of feeding western sheep and lambs first began, nearly all of the large operators used self-feeders and they are still used in various places. Whether or not the self-feeder can be successfully employed depends upon the nature of the feed to be used. Chaffed or finely cut roughage mixed with the concentrates serves to lighten the ration and when this is done good results are generally secured. Feeders who use mill screenings begin the feeding period with light screenings; that is, those containing a proportionately large amount of straw and chaff; then as the period advances, they gradually work up to the heaviest type of screenings they can secure, and frequently they mix in some ground corn. Usually roughage of some sort is available in separate racks.

Where large numbers are fed, the self-feeder undoubtedly saves labor, and shortens the feeding period, but the losses are usually greater, and experiments show that more feed is required to produce a hundred pounds of gain where the self-feeder is used than where the feed is given in definite quantities twice a day. After 60 or 70 days on the self-feeder, sheep and lambs tend to go "off feed."

In order to feed corn and alfalfa in self-feeders it would be necessary to grind the corn, chaff the hay, and mix them. The cost of doing all this would be almost or quite as great as the cost of feeding twice daily and the amount of gain from the feed consumed would be less. Therefore, the use of the self-feeder is not advisable where the cost of preparing the feed is an item of considerable expense.

**Proportion of Grain and Roughage.**—Sheep are regarded as animals unusually well adapted to the consumption of roughage and even in the process of fattening they can make economical use of relatively large quantities of it. But the attempts that have been made to fatten entirely on dry roughage have not resulted in producing enough finish to satisfy the demands of the market. On the other hand, when an attempt is made to feed entirely on concentrates, the animals go "off feed," and if roughage is not supplied serious digestive disorders develop. The digestive tract of the sheep is adapted to bulky feed, therefore roughage cannot be dispensed with. It is possible, however, successfully to vary the proportion of concentrates and roughage in the ration of fattening sheep and lambs. This is a matter of importance, for in some seasons the supply of grain is relatively large while in others the opposite situation exists. Then, there are regions where the supply of the best of roughage always overbalances the supply of grain and the problem in fattening consists in determining how little grain can be used with hay supplied *ad libitum.*

In fattening lambs at the Illinois Station,[4] the writer found that it was possible in a period of 98 days to feed 100 pounds of corn to every 86 pounds of alfalfa hay. This ration produced a prime market finish and was satisfactory in all respects except that it required close watching at times to keep the lambs from going "off feed." In the first third of the feeding period, 100 pounds of corn was fed to every 157 pounds of hay; in the last third, 100 pounds was fed to every 66 pounds of hay. In a period of 90 days it was not possible to get lambs fed 100 pounds of corn to every 242 pounds of hay in choice market condition. The gains made seemed to be more in the nature of growth than of fat. But lambs fed 100 pounds of corn to every 203 pounds of hay for a period of 98 days were graded as prime.

Results reported by the Kansas Station are essentially such as to confirm the above statements. The table which follows gives further details of the Illinois experiments.

*Average Feed, Gain Per Lamb Per Day, and Feed Required Per Pound Gain*
(All weights expressed in pounds)

| Lot | Proportion of corn to hay (corn : hay) | Average corn per lamb per day | Average alfalfa hay per lamb per day | Gain per lamb per day | Corn required for one pound gain | Alfalfa hay required for one pound gain |
|---|---|---|---|---|---|---|
| Experiment No. 1.—Feeding period 90 days, Oct. 23 to Jan. 20. Twenty wether lambs in each lot. Approximate initial weight per lamb, 69 pounds. | | | | | | |
| 1 | 1:0.99 | 1.24 | 1.22 | .300 | 4.12 | 4.08 |
| 2 | 1:1.36 | 1.05 | 1.41 | .269 | 3.89 | 5.27 |
| 3 | 1:2.42 | .71 | 1.71 | .216 | 3.27 | 7.91 |
| 4 | 1:3.45 | .54 | 1.87 | .203 | 2.66 | 9.18 |
| Experiment No. 2.—Feeding period 98 days, Feb. 19 to May 27. Twenty wether lambs in each lot. Approximate initial weight per lamb, 65 pounds. | | | | | | |
| 1 | 1:0.86 | 1.36 | 1.17 | .331 | 4.11 | 3.53 |
| 2 | 1:1.31 | 1.14 | 1.49 | .320 | 3.56 | 4.66 |
| 3 | 1:2.03 | .88 | 1.78 | .294 | 2.99 | 6.06 |

**The Form in Which Feeds Should Be Given.**—The grinding or crushing of grain does not materially improve it as a feed for

[4]See table on this page.

fattening sheep and lambs having sound teeth. Apparently the reason for this is that the sheep so thoroughly masticates its feed that very little of it passes into the stomach without being prepared for the various processes of digestion. It may be of some advantage to grind very small or unusually hard seeds if the grinding does not make them less palatable. Faville[5] in feeding bald or hulless barley to lambs noticed that some of it was passed undigested; and Cochel at the Kansas Station secured a given amount of gain from less feed with ground kafir than with whole kafir corn.

**Grinding** seems to reduce rather than increase the palatability of grain. If not consumed soon after grinding it is likely to become rancid or musty, and even if it is fresh it is usually not eaten with so much relish as whole grain because it gets into the nostrils and also forms a pasty mass inside the mouth. Cooke[6] found the latter to be an objection to ground bald barley.

**A heavy grain like corn** should be ground when it is to be mixed with lighter feeds and placed in self-feeders. If whole corn were mixed with chaffed hay or with wheat screenings, it is possible for the animals to sort out the corn and leave the other feed, or *vice versa*. Even when whole corn and whole oats form a mixture, it is possible for the animals to take one and leave the other.

Under the conditions in which most sheep feeding is done, corn is most convenient to use when it is in the shelled form, but it can be used as ear corn, shock corn, or ground corn. When it forms the sole concentrate in the ration, grinding never improves its feeding value for sheep able to masticate it. When fed as corn-and-cob meal, the cob replaces a little hay, but the total feeding value of the corn is reduced. Ear corn is as efficient as shelled corn for producing gain, but when feeding in lots or sheds it is difficult to keep the sheep from wasting feed by dropping some of the ears on the ground and there is a tendency for the ears to roll up and bunch up so that there is an unequal distribution of feed in the troughs. Shock corn is better suited to feeding on grass sod than in barns or lots. When placed in racks the ears are likely to be very unevenly distributed.

At the Illinois Station the writer conducted an experiment in

---

[5] Wyoming Station Bulletin 103.
[6] Colorado Station Bulletin 40.

which clover hay and corn in various forms were fed for a period of 98 days to lambs weighing 65 pounds. The results are shown in the following table:

*Methods of Preparing Corn for Fattening Lambs.*

| Lot | Average ration | Daily gain | Feed for 100 lbs. gain | |
|---|---|---|---|---|
| | | | Corn | Roughage |
| | | *lbs.* | *lbs.* | *lbs.* |
| 1 | Ear corn, 1.6 lbs.; clover hay, 1.3 lbs....... | 0.293 | 439* | 453 |
| 2 | Shelled corn, 1.3 lbs.; clover hay, 1.3 lbs... | 0.295 | 432 | 449 |
| 3 | Ground corn, 1.3 lbs.; clover hay, 1.3 lbs... | 0.264 | 483 | 505 |
| 4 | Corn-and-cob meal, 1.5 lbs.; clover hay, 1.2 lbs.................................. | 0.264 | 489* | 475 |
| 5 | Shelled corn, 0.06 lb.; clover hay, 1.0 lb.; shock corn, 2.7 lbs ...................... | 0.247 | 23 | 406<br>1,111† |

* Reduced to shelled corn basis.
† Shock corn, containing 53 per cent of ears.

The widely-used protein concentrates, linseed oil meal and cottonseed meal, are in more convenient form to use with whole grain if they can be secured in the form of what is known as pea-size cake. They are also more palatable in this form because they do not get in the nostrils or become sticky in the mouths of the animals.

**Roughages.**—Most roughages should be fed in the form in which they are harvested and stored. Coarse, stemmy hay may be consumed with less waste if it is cut or chaffed. Should bloating result from the use of alfalfa the trouble may be obviated by cutting or chaffing the hay. Shredding or cutting corn stover makes it more convenient to feed in racks, but if it is shredded there is some danger of indigestion from eating the pith in the stalks.

The economical use of roughage depends mainly upon feeding no more of it than the sheep want, and in having racks that will prevent it from being wasted. In feeding choice clover or alfalfa, there is no need of wasting any hay, but as a rule the more or less unpalatable roughages such as oat and wheat straw can not be fed up so closely.

**Succulent Feeds.—Silage.**—Sheep utilize silage to best advantage when the corn plant is cut very fine. In making the silage, all of the knives should be in the cutter and they should be kept sharp. The use of mouldy and frozen silage should be avoided.

**Roots,** such as turnips and mangels, should be cut or chopped before they are placed in the troughs, for if fed in the whole form, they roll about, and in cold weather they are likely to freeze before they are eaten.

**Condition of Feed.**—Mouldy, musty, and frozen feeds should not be given to fattening sheep because they are likely to cause serious digestive disturbances. But salvage (grain damaged in elevator fires) is frequently used by experienced feeders. Stack-burned clover and alfalfa hay, although lower in feeding value than sound hay, have been found to be very palatable and useful.

**The Digestible Nutrients in the Fattening Ration.**—The digestible nutrients in a ration made by properly combining corn and legume hay represent what is commonly regarded as the standard requirement for fattening sheep and lambs. A ration of this sort produces about three-tenths of a pound gain per sheep per day and puts the animal in prime condition in 80 to 100 days. The following table compiled from Illinois Station Bulletin 167 indicates the digestible nutrients in rations made by combining corn and alfalfa hay in different proportions. These rations were fed for a period of 98 days to lambs with an initial weight of 65 pounds, and since the lowest daily gain per lamb was 294 thousandths of a pound, each ration was satisfactory for the purpose of fattening.

*Digestible Nutrients in Each Day's Ration.*

| Lot | Average feed per day | | Digestible nutrients per day | | Nutritive ratio | Daily gain per lamb |
|---|---|---|---|---|---|---|
| | Corn | Alfalfa hay | Protein | Carbohydrates and fat * | | |
| | *lbs.* | *lbs.* | *lbs.* | *lbs.* | | |
| 1 | 1.36 | 1.17 | .258 | 1.651 | 1: 6.4 | .33 |
| 2 | 1.14 | 1.49 | .281 | 1.641 | 1: 5.8 | .32 |
| 3 | .88 | 1.78 | .290 | 1.460 | 1: 5.0 | .29 |

* Fat reduced to carbohydrate equivalent by multiplying by 2¼.

The lower rate of gain in Lot 3 as compared with Lot 1 was in all probability due to the greater amount of roughage and the smaller amount of grain in the ration rather than to the proportionate amounts of protein and carbohydrates and fat. In fact, various experiments tend to show that the rate of gain is slightly increased when the corn and legume hay combination is supplemented so that a nitrogenous concentrate such as linseed oil meal or cottonseed meal forms about 15 per cent of the concentrate part of the ration.

Apparently sheep are adapted to making good use of comparatively large quantities of protein. At the Illinois Station, Carroll [7] fed three lots of lambs from the time they were old enough to eat grain until they were about ten months old as follows:

| Concentrates | Roughage |
|---|---|
| Lot 1, Corn 50 per cent; linseed oil meal 50 per cent | Alfalfa in green and dry form. |
| Lot 2, Corn 75 per cent; linseed oil meal 25 per cent | |
| Lot 3, Corn 95 per cent; linseed oil meal 5 per cent | |

The lambs given the largest quantity of protein were the heaviest and they were thrifty in every respect. But owing to the high price of linseed oil meal, the cost of growth was greater than in the lots where more corn was consumed.

The Lemar Brothers of South Omaha, Nebraska, after years of experience in feeding lambs on a large scale have come to use a ration composed of linseed oil meal and prairie hay. The oil meal is placed in self-feeders and the lambs are brought in direct from the market and allowed to eat all they want. After about two weeks have elapsed, the self-feeders are filled with a mixture half corn and half linseed oil meal. This ration which seems to be so greatly overbalanced with protein is regarded by the Lemar Brothers as the best they have ever used. They get very rapid gains and the lambs are ready for market after a short period of feeding. They report a little larger percentage of losses since they have adopted this system, but these are more than offset by the increased rate of gain over other methods they have employed. The larger losses are not due to the large percentage of protein in the feed, but rather to the fact that the lambs are allowed to eat all they want of a heavy concentrate from the beginning of the feeding period.

On the other hand, skillful Michigan feeders, when feeding corn or salvage, use equal quantities of straw and legume hay. That is, they give hay at one feeding and straw at the other, and they think that they get as good results as they do when they use legume hay altogether as roughage.

---

[7] Doctor's thesis, under direction of Prof. Grindley.

In a compilation from various experiments on lamb feeding, Henry and Morrison [8] show that when corn silage (a carbonaceous succulent which would reduce the percentage of protein in the ration) has been fed in conjunction with corn and clover hay, the lambs fed silage ate six-tenths of a pound less hay and one-tenth of a pound less corn daily and yet gained slightly more than those fed clover hay and shelled corn. Experiments conducted by Skinner and King,[9] however, show that when cottonseed meal formed from 12 to 19 per cent of the grain part of the ration, the rate of gain was increased from 1 to 2 per cent.

In general, such a balance in digestible nutrients as is to be found in a ration composed of corn and clover hay is about what is required for fattening lambs. The advisability of using a larger amount of protein depends chiefly on whether it can be procured at such a price that it will pay to use it. If a palatable succulent, such as corn silage, is used to supplement corn and legume hay, the amount of digestible protein can be reduced somewhat and the ration will still be satisfactory for fattening purposes.

Older sheep can be fattened on rations containing relatively less protein than is contained in those suitable for lambs. From investigations by Bull and Emmett [10] of the Illinois Experiment Station the following feed requirements for fattening lambs have been determined, and the requirements for the third group (lambs weighing from 90–110 pounds) may be regarded as similar to the requirements for sheep.

*Variation in Rations for Lambs of Different Weights.—Per Day Per 1000 lbs. Live Weight.*

| Weight of lambs | Nutritive ratio 1: | Dry matter | Digestible crude protein | Total digestible nutrients |
|---|---|---|---|---|
| *lbs.* | | *lbs.* | *lbs.* | *lbs.* |
| 50– 70 | 5.0–6.0 | 27.0–30.0 | 3.1–3.3 | 19.0–22.0 |
| 70– 90 | 6.7–7.2 | 28.0–31.0 | 2.5–2.8 | 20.0–23.0 |
| 90–110 | 7.0–8.0 | 27.0–31.0 | 2.3–2.5 | 19.0–23.0 |

**Concentrates for Fattening.—Grains.**—Corn, barley, wheat, emmer, kafir corn, and oats are the grains used in the United

[8] "Feeds and Feeding," 1916.

[9] Indiana Station Bulletins 162, 168, 179.

[10] Illinois Station Bul. 166.

States for fattening sheep and lambs. All of these give best results when supplemented with a legume roughage. If they are fed with carbonaceous roughages, a nitrogenous concentrate such as linseed oil meal or cottonseed meal should form from 20 to 25 per cent of the grain part of the ration. There may be exceptions to this when sheep (not lambs) are fed and when a succulent such as silage forms part of the roughage.

Of the various grains, corn, the feeding value of which has already been discussed, is the best and most widely used. Wheat is seldom used unless it is in such condition as to be of low value for milling purposes. It compares favorably with corn, as it produces about the same gains with only 2 per cent more feed.

**Barley** is most used in the west and north. It is generally given a value of 75 to 85 per cent that of corn on a pound basis. It sometimes seems equal to corn. It is similar in composition and combines well with alfalfa.

**Emmer** is being used as a sheep feed in the Dakotas and in the northern Rocky Mountain states. Experiments show more feed needed and gains are more rapid than with corn or barley. Nevertheless, it is a useful feed for fattening.

**Kafir, milo, feterita, darso, sorgo, hegari,** and **schrock** are coming more and more into use in dry regions where they grow well, and they have been compared in a number of trials. Although not equal to corn in rate of gain or degree of finish produced, kafir and milo are a little better for fattening lambs than the others mentioned. They are deserving of the consideration of feeders in those areas. Five years' work at the Texas Station shows these feeds to be suitable as whole or ground concentrates when fed with protein supplements and alfalfa hay. (See Texas Bulletin 379.)

**Oats** are not widely used as a sole concentrate in fattening sheep and lambs because they produce growth rather than fat. If they do not add too much to the cost of the ration, they can be used to advantage when mixed with other grains. If they are mixed with corn their bulk serves to "lighten" the ration, and the amount of roughage consumed is usually reduced.

When two or more of the grains mentioned above are available, there is no objection to making a mixture of them. In fact, there is some advantage when variety is added to the ration.

It is doubtful whether oats should be a large part of the ration.

**Peas and Beans.**—These are nearly always too high in price for fattening sheep, but being rich in protein, can often be used as supplements to corn. Field peas and soybeans are palatable and help increase the consumption of feed. In Idaho and other sections of the west, cull beans are sometimes added to a ration of barley and alfalfa hay. The rate of gain is said to be increased and the requirement of other feeds is lessened. Soybeans in large amounts tend to cause scouring. Grinding soybeans lowers their palatability and they soon become rancid.

**Commercial Concentrates.**—Linseed and cottonseed cake or meal are used in sheep feeding for balancing rations too low in protein. They both have practically the same value for this purpose. Soybean oil meal is a satisfactory supplement which is apparently equal to linseed or cottonseed meal. Usually mixtures of 2 or 3 protein supplements are not found superior to one alone. They may be fed at the rate of 1 part of supplement to 7 parts of corn or barley.

**Wheat bran,** wheat middlings, gluten feed, dried distillers' grains, fish meal, dried blood, and tankage are not widely used for fattening sheep. Wheat bran is palatable and, if price allows, it may be used to "lighten" the grain ration. Gluten feed is not palatable and hence is little used. Morrison and Kleinheinz [11] found that tankage when fed with corn and poor quality, overripe blue-grass hay, 10 per cent tankage was equal to 18 per cent linseed meal in balancing the ration.

**Beet by-products** are carbonaceous in nature. Dried beet pulp compares favorably with corn as a fattening feed. In Nebraska it is used with cottonseed meal, silage, and alfalfa hay. Beet tops may replace silage.

**Various molasses products** are used to some extent and are appetizing. Both cane and beet molasses fed in small amounts with corn in a well-balanced ration are credited with being slightly more valuable per pound than corn. Molasses is sometimes added to poor quality roughages to induce the lambs to eat more of them.

**Wheat screenings,** from elevators and mills are a complete

---

[11] "Feeds and Feeding."

sheep feed. The chaff and bits of straw in them may replace roughage. The value is variable. Feeders may learn to judge their feeding value, and use them when prices are reasonable.

**Comparison of Concentrates.**—This table from "Feeds and Feeding" gives feed values in concentrates used for sheep:

*Composition of Various Concentrates.*

| Feeding stuff | Total dry matter in 100 lbs. | Digestible nutrients in 100 lbs. | | | | |
|---|---|---|---|---|---|---|
| | | Crude protein | Carbohydrates | Fat | Total | Nutritive ratio 1: |
| *Concentrates* | *lbs.* | *lbs.* | *lbs.* | *lbs.* | *lbs.* | |
| Dent corn | 89.5 | 7.5 | 67.8 | 4.6 | 85.7 | 10.4 |
| Corn-and-cob meal | 89.6 | 6.1 | 63.7 | 3.7 | 78.1 | 11.8 |
| Gluten feed, high grade | 91.3 | 21.6 | 51.9 | 3.2 | 80.7 | 2.7 |
| Wheat, all analyses | 89.8 | 9.2 | 67.5 | 1.5 | 80.1 | 7.7 |
| Wheat bran, all analyses | 89.9 | 12.5 | 41.6 | 3.0 | 60.9 | 3.9 |
| Oats | 90.8 | 9.7 | 52.1 | 3.8 | 70.4 | 6.3 |
| Barley | 90.7 | 9.0 | 66.8 | 1.6 | 79.4 | 7.8 |
| Emmer (spelt) | 91.3 | 9.5 | 63.2 | 1.7 | 76.5 | 7.1 |
| Kafir grain | 88.2 | 9.0 | 65.8 | 2.3 | 80.0 | 7.9 |
| Cottonseed meal, choice | 92.5 | 37.0 | 21.8 | 8.6 | 78.2 | 1.1 |
| Cold-pressed cottonseed cake | 92.1 | 21.1 | 33.2 | 7.4 | 70.9 | 2.4 |
| Linseed meal, old process | 90.9 | 30.2 | 32.6 | 6.7 | 77.9 | 1.6 |
| Linseed meal, new process | 90.4 | 31.7 | 37.9 | 2.8 | 75.9 | 1.4 |
| Bean, navy | 86.6 | 18.8 | 51.3 | 0.8 | 71.9 | 2.8 |
| Cowpea | 88.4 | 19.4 | 54.5 | 1.1 | 76.4 | 2.9 |
| Pea, field | 90.8 | 19.0 | 55.8 | 0.6 | 76.2 | 3.0 |
| Soybean | 90.1 | 33.2 | 24.7 | 16.1 | 94.1 | 1.8 |
| Beet pulp, dried | 91.8 | 4.6 | 65.2 | 0.8 | 71.6 | 14.6 |

**Roughages for Fattening.**—**Legume hays** are good for fattening sheep as they are palatable and supplement corn or other grains. Red clover and alfalfa are widely grown and are not so coarse as hay from soybeans and cowpeas. Furthermore, there is no grain in the hay to make the adjustment of the ration more or less difficult. Alsike clover compares favorably with red clover, but English or mammoth clover is stemmy. Tests comparing sweet clover and alfalfa hays show the two almost equal unless the sweet clover is very stemmy.

Owing to the large proportion of stems in soybean and cowpea hays, about 20 per cent greater quantities must be fed to secure the same gain as obtained with alfalfa or clover. Soybean hay has 3 times the value of soybean straw.

Field bean straw and bean pods are prized by feeders in Michigan as they are valuable substitutes for clover hay.

**Carbonaceous Roughages.**—In making use of carbonaceous roughages, the concentrate part of the ration as stated elsewhere should be comparatively rich in protein. Corn stover is palatable and it is a good roughage if the corn plant is cut fairly early, cured well, and kept in good condition. On account of the coarse stalks the percentage of waste is high and the discarded parts do not make very good bedding.

**Sorghum hay** is about like corn stover in feeding value.

**Sudan grass** hay has been shown by the Kansas Station (Circ. 123) to have little more than 50 per cent of the value of alfalfa hay when fed with shelled corn.

**Oat and wheat straw** are unsuited as the sole roughage in the fattening ration. They can perhaps be used to best advantage in combination with corn silage, or with legume hay. Feed straw in small quantities as sheep eat more of it when so fed.

**The value of straw for feed** depends in large part on its quality. Short, fine, and bright oat straw, cut before the oat plants are thoroughly ripe, is almost as palatable as legume hay. Straw of good quality is often available at one-third of the cost of legume hay. It will pay to feed some of it 2 or 3 times a week. It furnishes a harmless change.

**Timothy hay,** market value considered, is an exceedingly poor roughage for sheep as it is unpalatable and constipating. A mixture of timothy and clover, however, makes a very good roughage provided at least half of the mixture is clover. Marsh hay ranks with timothy as poor roughage and below good oat straw.

**Prairie hay** has been used extensively in fattening sheep where self-feeders are used. It is fairly palatable, but considerably lower in feeding value than the legume hays. A combination of legume hay and good bright straw should give better results than prairie hay.

**Roots and Silage.**—Roots and silage are succulent feeds suitable for being used as supplements to grain and dry roughage. On account of the cost of production, very little use is made of roots in fattening sheep and lambs in the United States, but if they should be available, 3 to 4 pounds per head daily could be used to advantage. It has not been considered safe to feed mangels for a long period to males, for fear of causing calculi or stones which obstruct the urinary tract, but no disorders have been found in an 8-year trial at the Illinois Station.

Of late years, corn silage has come into pretty general use in many sections of the country as a sheep feed. It is not a concentrate and it is a mistake to regard it as such. Experiments have also demonstrated that it is not a complete roughage. It has been used as the sole roughage, but the appetite is better, the animals are easier to keep "on feed," and the gains are larger if some dry roughage is used with it. Roughages of rather low feeding value, such as wheat and oat straw, added to grain and silage, materially increase the effectiveness of the ration. In fact, one of the best ways to make good use of these roughages consists in supplementing them with silage and a concentrate comparatively rich in protein.

As a rule silage when added to a well-balanced ration such as corn and legume hay lowers the cost of fattening, but it does not materially increase the gains. Evidently the succulence has a beneficial effect which is offset by the carbonaceous nature of the silage, for when a nitrogenous concentrate is added the rate of gain is increased. At the Illinois Station about .3 pound daily per lamb of a mixture of 80 pounds soybean oil meal, 10 pounds each of powdered limestone and salt with shelled corn and silage equaled corn and legume roughage.

Over a long period of years the Purdue (Indiana) Station found a ration of corn, protein supplement, legume hay, and corn silage to be one of the best used. The silage may be 1.5 pounds per day. It replaces about 0.1 pound of corn and 0.6 pound of hay. If the supply of dry roughage is limited, more silage may be fed. Sorghum silage has been used in the southwest with good results.

Sunflower silage is used in some western areas that are too cool or dry for the successful production of corn. In general it is not equal to corn silage but may be used as a means of reducing costs.

Pea silage has been successfully used in fattening sheep and lambs in the vicinity of canning factories. This silage is greatly relished and lambs can eat as much as 7 pounds daily at the beginning of the feeding period without scouring or going "off feed." Several years ago the writer inspected the feeding operations of the Columbus Canning Company, Columbus, Wisconsin. This company was putting what the market calls fancy-finish on lambs by feeding screenings and corn in self-feeders, a little hay and all the pea silage the lambs would take.

**Roughages Compared.**—The following table taken from "Feeds and Feedings," by Henry and Morrison, gives the digestible nutrients in various roughages for sheep.

*Composition of Roughages.*

| Feeding stuff | Total dry matter in 100 lbs. | Digestible nutrients in 100 lbs. | | | | |
|---|---|---|---|---|---|---|
| | | Crude protein | Carbohydrates | Fat | Total | Nutritive ratio 1: |
| *Dried Roughage* | *lbs.* | *lbs.* | *lbs.* | *lbs.* | *lbs.* | |
| Clover, red, all analyses | 87.1 | 7.6 | 39.3 | 1.8 | 50.9 | 5.7 |
| Clover, alsike, all analyses | 87.7 | 7.9 | 36.9 | 1.1 | 47.3 | 5.0 |
| Clover, mammoth red | 81.3 | 6.4 | 37.2 | 1.8 | 47.6 | 6.4 |
| Alfalfa, all analyses | 91.4 | 10.6 | 39.0 | 0.9 | 51.6 | 3.9 |
| Soybean hay | 91.4 | 11.7 | 39.2 | 1.2 | 53.6 | 3.6 |
| Cowpea, in bloom to early pod | 89.4 | 12.6 | 34.6 | 1.3 | 50.1 | 3.0 |
| Corn stover (ears removed), very dry | 90.6 | 2.2 | 47.8 | 1.0 | 52.2 | 22.7 |
| Corn stover, medium in water | 81.0 | 2.1 | 42.4 | 0.7 | 46.1 | 21.0 |
| Corn stover, high in water | 59.0 | 1.4 | 31.1 | 0.6 | 33.9 | 23.2 |
| Kafir stover, dry | 83.7 | 1.7 | 43.1 | 1.3 | 47.7 | 27.1 |
| Red top, all analyses | 90.2 | 4.6 | 45.9 | 1.2 | 53.2 | 10.6 |
| Timothy, all analyses | 88.4 | 3.0 | 42.8 | 1.2 | 48.5 | 15.2 |

**Succulent Feeds Compared.**—This table from the same source gives nutrients in succulent feeds for sheep.

*Composition of Succulent Feeds.*

| Feeding stuff | Total dry matter in 100 lbs. | Digestible nutrients in 100 lbs. | | | | |
|---|---|---|---|---|---|---|
| | | Crude protein | Carbohydrates | Fat | Total | Nutritive ratio 1: |
| *Fresh Green Roughage* | *lbs.* | *lbs.* | *lbs.* | *lbs.* | *lbs.* | |
| Beet pulp, wet | 9.3 | 0.5 | 6.5 | 0.2 | 7.4 | 13.8 |
| Beet, common | 13.0 | 0.9 | 9.1 | 0.1 | 10.2 | 10.3 |
| Mangel | 9.4 | 0.8 | 6.4 | 0.1 | 7.4 | 8.2 |
| Rutabaga | 10.9 | 1.0 | 7.7 | 0.3 | 9.4 | 8.4 |
| Corn well matured, recent analyses | 26.3 | 1.1 | 15.0 | 0.7 | 17.7 | 15.1 |
| Sorghum | 22.8 | 0.6 | 11.6 | 0.5 | 13.3 | 21.2 |
| Pea-cannery refuse | 23.2 | 1.6 | 11.6 | 0.8 | 15.0 | 8.4 |

## QUESTIONS

1. What effect has age on the rate of growth in sheep? Upon the utilization of feed?
2. What factors influence the efficiency of a ration for fattening sheep and lambs?
3. Would you attempt to fatten sheep solely on silage and dry roughage?
4. Would you attempt to fatten sheep solely on grain?
5. Of what advantage are self-feeders in fattening sheep? In what particulars is hand-feeding more advantageous?
6. When would it pay to shear fattening sheep and lambs just before marketing?
7. How much gain should a fattening lamb make in 90 days?
8. How much corn and alfalfa hay will it require to feed a fattening lamb for 90 days?
9. How much corn, corn silage, and clover hay will it require to feed a fattening lamb for 90 days?
10. Construct a fattening ration for sheep from clover hay, oat straw, corn, and linseed oil meal.
11. What is the distinguishing difference between a legume and a carbonaceous roughage?

## CHAPTER XL

# FEEDING SHEEP AND LAMBS IN THE FIELD THROUGH A PART OR ALL OF THE FEEDING PERIOD

Only rugged sheep and lambs should be selected for feeding in fields and they should be purchased before the feeds have deteriorated greatly in feeding value through exposure to winds, rains, and frosts. Hard frosts lessen the value of clover and similar growths and high winds and heavy rains rapidly reduce the value of corn stalks.

**Usefulness of Various Field Feeds.—Grass.**—Grass is a very great help to the man who feeds sheep on his fields. A successful feeder in central Illinois has said: "I have found that I must have an area of good grass in order to fatten sheep or lambs in the fields. I once tried plowing up all of my pastures in order to grow more corn. I thought that sowing rye in the corn stalks would take the place of my fields of grass, but I was mistaken. I was obliged to reëstablish my pastures."

**A bluegrass pasture** that has been rested through the summer furnishes palatable feed which has a great deal of fattening power. A pasture of this sort is also an excellent place on which to scatter such feeds as ear corn and shock corn, and no better place can be found in the open for the sheep or lambs to rest and sleep.

Bluegrass fits in very well with the other feeds available on the farm. Being palatable and succulent, it is a splendid alternate feed with corn or stalks, and if the sheep or lambs are given a chance to run on both corn stalks and bluegrass they will divide the time between these runs each day. Early in the autumn, before it is time to turn in on the corn stalks, bluegrass alternates well with clover. As the sole feed, green clover is too sappy to make a good rate of gain, but sheep and lambs make good use of it if it is fed with bluegrass, field corn or corn stalks.

**Timothy** is also a good grass for fattening purposes and no better pasture can be found than one composed of several grasses and legumes, such as bluegrass, timothy, rye grass, and the clovers.

**Rape** makes a very heavy growth in fertile soil if there is plenty of moisture and light, and when combined with grass it will fatten sheep or lambs without the use of any other feed. In Missouri a number of feeders have finished lambs at very low cost by running them on blue-grass and in corn fields sown to rape and cowpeas. They purchase the lambs early in the autumn and turn them first on the blue-grass and cowpeas. The cowpeas are fed first because the leaves drop after the first frost. After they are gone, the lambs alternate between the blue-grass and the rape. By the time the greater part of the rape is consumed the lambs are fat enough to send to market. If the corn stands up well, the lambs eat very little of it; hence the blue-grass, cowpeas, and rape produce the gains.

Rape is best in fall, but is pastured into the winter, if lambs are used to it before it freezes. At first pasture only when dry, about noon; later they may stay on it all day.

Three generally practiced ways of getting rape for fall fattening are as follows: First, by seeding it in the normal way as the sole crop in the ground; second, by sowing it with oats at the rate of two pounds of seed to the acre; and, third, by seeding it at the rate of about three pounds per acre in corn at the last cultivation. When there is sufficient moisture, rape sown in oats grows rapidly after the oats are cut and furnishes feed that is ready to be pastured by the first of September. A good growth of rape in corn depends on seeding early, on the supply of moisture and the density of the corn foliage, but if the corn is to be pastured with sheep it usually pays to sow rape for pasturing by the middle of September or the first of October. Renk and Sons, extensive feeders in Wisconsin, plant the rape in the corn rows in spring for fall feed.

**Corn Fields.**—If the corn plants are tall, and if they stand well, lambs may run in the corn fields before the corn is husked without doing much damage to the corn crop. They feed on the lower blades, weeds, and grass, and make good gains.

Sheep and lambs are often used to harvest the corn crop. Several years ago Baker Brothers, large sheep feeders in Illinois, made this a regular practice. They sowed rape in their corn, got their lambs in early, and kept them in the fields until practically all of the corn was consumed. When the rape was pretty well eaten out they broke down some of the corn stalks in order to encourage the lambs to eat the corn. Late in the season all stalks with ears beyond the reach of the lambs were broken down. After the lambs were removed from the fields pigs were allowed to gather up what corn had been left. Baker Brothers were fairly successful, but made it their chief business. They kept lambs in lots or in pastures at night to get salt and water. As the lambs became fat they were sorted out and shipped. The unfinished ones were finished in lots (Fig. 220).

Another Illinois feeder, G. Firoved, has successfully harvested corn with sheep, where seeded to rape. He gives the animals access to half the area required to fatten them. He turns them on the second half before the supply of feed in the first half becomes too low. He has pastures to use when corn is

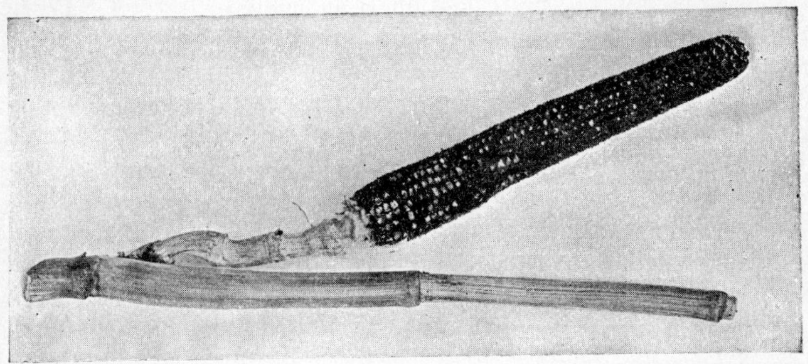

Fig. 220.—All that was left of an ear of corn and a corn stalk after the sheep were through with them.

consumed, and uses hay. Success depends on plenty of grass, forage, and hay.

The Fauts Brothers, successful feeders in Indiana, follow the practice of seeding soybeans in the corn and harvesting both the corn and the beans with lambs. They have been so successful with this method of feeding that their operations have become noted.

**Corn Stalks.**—All corn gatherers leave some corn. This, together with the dry blades on the stalks, makes good feed for sheep and lambs for a time. Stalks are of greatest value as sheep feed in comparatively dry autumn and winter seasons. Wet weather deteriorates their feeding value and mud is hard on the feet.

**General Suggestions for Feeding in Fields.**—Sheep feeders may well observe these suggestions:

1. Inspect animals daily, watching for bloat, scours, and lameness.
2. Supply salt and good water.
3. Supply new fields often, never graze too closely.
4. Avoid running sheep in deep snow as in stalk fields.
5. Never drive sheep too much; it prevents fattening.

**Gains** in fields vary with the feed and weather conditions but should amount to 6 or 10 pounds for each lamb a month.

**Shifting to the Dry Lot.**—Some feed ought to be given in the dry lot before the feeds in the fields are exhausted. Otherwise, the sheep or lambs may go back in condition before the feed in the fields is gone. Feeding ear corn on blue-grass is a good start toward the transition from fields to dry lot. If the shift is made at the right time one will find that the gains made on very cheap feeds in the fields will materially reduce the cost of gains and hence make the feeding operation more profitable.

**Corn-field and Dry-lot Compared.**—Within the past few years the Ohio, Nebraska, Illinois, and Colorado Stations have reported the results of experiments to determine the best methods of field feeding and to learn how such feeding compares with dry-lot feeding. For the most part the results confirm the statements made above. In the Ohio and Illinois trials very low gains were obtained when lambs were fed in corn fields alone without supplementary feeds such as pasture, legume roughages, or protein concentrates. Rape or soybeans as an intercrop in the corn practically doubled the gain. Allowing the field-fed lambs a small amount of legume roughages or ¼ pound each of protein grain daily resulted in gains but little below those obtained in dry lot with a ration of corn and legume hay, and aids in minimizing losses. Dense-fleeced, strong lambs withstand exposure to inclement weather if well fed in the corn belt. Convenient shelters are, however, advisable.

## QUESTIONS

1. Discuss the usefulness of grass to the feeder.
2. Of what value is rape in the corn belt?
3. Is it advisable to turn sheep and lambs in the corn field before the corn is harvested?
4. When should corn stalks be pastured?
5. How much gain can be expected from field feeding?
6. Review treatment for bloat, Chapter XXXIII.
7. Review the discussion on forage crops, Chapter XXXIII.

# PART VI

## SHEEP MANAGEMENT ON THE RANGES IN THE WESTERN STATES

## CHAPTER XLI

# NATURE OF THE RANGE AND OF THE SHEEP

**Nature of the Range.**—The sheep ranges of the West are often arranged in three geographical groups as follows: (1) the southwestern ranges of Texas, New Mexico, Arizona, and Colorado; (2) the ranges of California; and (3) the northwestern ranges of Wyoming, Montana, Idaho, Utah, Nevada, Washington, and Oregon. These groups differ most in climate, but they are also somewhat different in the methods employed in raising sheep and in the quality of their mutton and wool products.

**Types of Land Utilized as Range.**—The unenclosed types of lands over which sheep are herded are plains, foothills, and mountains. In order to have ideal conditions all three types of range should be available. Plains serve as an excellent winter range, but in summer they are too hot and too dry. Mountains furnish ideal range in summer because they are cool, well supplied with water, and comparatively luxuriant in plant and shrub growths, but with the exception of a few places in the southwest, they cannot be used in winter because of severe snowstorms. Foothills are located between the summer and the winter range and hence furnish feed during spring and fall. On each type of range, three to fifteen acres are required for one sheep.

**Plains.**—In practically every state in the West there are vast stretches of arid and semi-arid plains which present a monotonous picture of sage and sand. To the person accustomed to running sheep on luxuriant pastures, these plains would seem entirely inadequate, for as a rule, the edible plants and shrubs are small and thinly distributed on the ground. The scanty growth on which the sheep feed, however, has the power to produce growth and fat to a degree which always surprises those who have had no experience with it. The sheep grazing over a large area in the course of a day nip off a grass blade or a weed here and there, or trim an occasional palatable shrub, but they come to the bedding ground at nightfall with a fairly well-satisfied appetite (Fig. 221).

**Foothills and Mountains.**—As a rule the feed in the foothills and mountains is more luxuriant and succulent than that on the

Fig. 221.—On the plains for winter grazing.

plains because there is more moisture. There is a greater variety of feed; hence, foothill and mountain districts are more suitable for growing and fattening lambs than the plains. In fact, lambs are almost never sold for mutton directly from the plains while those grown on the best mountain ranges frequently attain suitable condition and weight for slaughter when only four and five months of age (Figs. 222 and 223).

**Cultivated Areas.**—In a few regions cultivated areas are utilized as sheep range. In California, alfalfa fields, wheat stubble, and even vineyards, serve for a part of the year as feeding grounds. After the last crop of grapes has been harvested for the year in the great vineyards around Hanford and Fresno, sheep are turned in to feed on the leaves. On the whole this practice is regarded as beneficial to the vines, for the sheep consume the thrips, little insects that would do a great deal of damage later through their attacks on the new foliage (Fig. 224).

In many places the winter range is supplemented by harvested crops. There are two reasons for this practice: First, there are storm periods during which the snow is so deep that the sheep can not get to the feed on the range; and second, owners frequently do not have enough winter range to carry their sheep. In recent years, carloads of corn from Kansas and Nebraska have been sold for winter feed to the sheepmen on the eastern slope of the Rockies, and now cottonseed cake is becoming so popular that in various places in the northern part of the Rocky Mountains it has almost entirely replaced corn. Alfalfa hay is used extensively in Washington, Oregon, Montana, Idaho, Utah, Wyoming, and Colorado to supplement the winter range (Fig. 225).

**Ownership of the Range.**—The ranges consist of public domain, National Forest, Indian reservations, reclamation lands, state lands, and lands owned by corporations and by private individuals. The only free land is the public domain. Practically all of this consists of plains or winter range, as nearly all of the foothills and mountains not owned by private individuals and by corporations are included in the National Forest.

The National Forest is under the control of the Department of Agriculture and is in the direct charge of the Forest Service. In all cases where sheep are allowed to graze on it, a definite allotment is made to the owners and a charge per head fixed for a specified period of grazing. For example, an owner with 5000 ewes

FIG. 222.—Springtime on the hills of Wyoming.

Fig. 223.—In the mountains for the summer, when good feed and temperate weather make lambs grow rapidly.

and their lambs may be charged twenty cents per ewe on a definite allotment which he may use from June 15 to November 1. To a certain extent the rate charged depends on the quality of feed on the allotment and the length of time it may be used.

FIG. 224.

FIG. 225.

FIG. 224.—Lambs in clover in Oregon. Here and there in the West a more intensive method than herding on the open range is being practiced.

FIG. 225.—Supplementing the range when snow is on the ground with corn, cottonseed cake and hay.

In every state of the range country, all sections of land bearing the survey numbers 16 and 36 are at the disposal of the commonwealth. They are often leased to sheepmen, the price depending on the location and the quality of feed growing on them. As a rule the sheepmen have little to say in adjusting rentals on these lands because they are so distributed among the other lands they propose to use that they are obliged to pay the price asked, whether or not it is reasonable.

**Railway Land Grants.**—When the various railways were projected through the West, the companies received encouragement from the Federal Government in the form of great land grants which extended in alternate sections for 20 miles or more on either side of their roads. Although much of the land in these grants has been disposed of, the railway companies still own large areas which are leased for grazing purposes. Should the alternate sections still be public domain the person leasing from the railroad will have twice as much land as he leases, but he can make little use of fences for it is unlawful to fence public domain. In recent years, however, many of the intervening sections have been occupied by homesteaders who, as a rule, do not care to rent their land for pasture; this makes the railroad land inconvenient to use.

**Other Lands.**—In addition to the above there are certain lands in the control of the National Reclamation Service and there are the lands in the various Indian reservations which may be leased for grazing; and finally, there are lands owned by private citizens. In the Southwest, and in New Mexico particularly, there are large tracts of land that were granted to private individuals at an early time by the Government of Spain. A number of these tracts are leased for grazing purposes. In many cases the sheepmen own considerable tracts of land. Usually these tracts are strategically located so that the owner may control extensive lands which he does not own.

**Cost of Leases.**—From the foregoing it is clear that a sheepman may be so located that he must have his pockets full of leases and permits before he can operate. The cost of leases on land grants, reclamation lands, reservations, and private lands ranges from two and one-half cents to twenty-five cents per acre per year. This applies to wild range or uncultivated lands. Cultivated lands rent at much higher prices and according somewhat to the urgency of the sheep owner's need of them. Permits in the National Forest cost from about 12 to 40 or more cents per sheep per season. At present the tendency is to increase the rates of rent for sheep on all types of range.

**Breeding of the Sheep on the Range.**—In general, range sheep should be of a type that produce both mutton and wool of good market quality under range conditions; they should be hardy, that is, they should be able to thrive when kept in large flocks or bands, and they should have the habit of staying close together while grazing.

**Breeds for Range.**—Until a few years ago range breeding ewes were largely or altogether of Merino parentage, but at present there is a disposition greatly to reduce the percentage of Merino blood in breeding stock and a belief is growing that it ought to be dispensed with in some regions. The Merino has been popular because it is hardy and better adapted to herding than any other breed. Its wool, being dense and oily, has been better than that of any other breed for withstanding alkali dust and the penetrating dryness of a semi-arid climate. The recent decline in the popularity of Merino blood is traceable to a number of factors. Methods of handling sheep in many parts of the West have improved so much that the extreme hardiness, characteristic of the Merino, is no longer indispensable. The high prices paid for lambs during the past five years have stimulated the desire to produce as much mutton as possible from a given number of ewes. This has given rise to a demand for rather large, strong, deep milking ewes, capable of raising a large percentage of lambs and growing them rapidly. Trials with lambs carrying a preponderance of mutton blood have shown that they make rapid gains and attain heavy weights on mountain range by the time they are old enough to wean. In addition to all of these influences, the conditions surrounding the sheep business have been such as to thoroughly arouse the interest of sheepmen in such matters as breeding, and this interest of itself has had some bearing on changes in breeding.

At this time it is difficult to predict how much change will ultimately be made in the breeding of range sheep. Aside from the herding qualities which all range sheep must have, the kind of sheep wanted is a type that represents the most effective combination of mutton and wool. It has been found that an excellent market lamb can be produced by crossing a pure-bred mutton ram on a grade Merino ewe, but the trouble with this practice is that it makes no provision for the future supply of the ewe stock. It was once possible for the mutton lamb raisers to renew their breeding ewes from regions that were not well adapted or located for raising lambs for the market, but very few such regions exist at the present time.

So long as sheep are herded on open ranges, it is improbable that Merino blood will be dispensed with. The percentage of it in bands of breeding ewes may be reduced or the type may be changed so as to suit more nearly the needs of range sheepmen, but the Merino has characteristics which are too valuable to justify anyone in supposing that its blood will be wholly discarded.

**Mutton Breeds for Range.**—Of the various mutton breeds that have been used in the West, the Cotswolds, Lincolns, and Hampshires seem to have given best results. The cross between the longwools (Cotswolds and Lincolns) and Merinos makes a very good sheep for both mutton and wool. The fleece is long and heavy and does not pull out badly when the sheep graze on brushy range. At present the Hampshire is very popular because of its ability to produce a big, strong lamb that is ready to market as mutton at weaning time. Shropshires are to be found in large numbers in Colorado, New Mexico, and California. Romney Marsh and Corriedales have been imported from New Zealand and Australia, and are now undergoing trial. Suffolks are also being used to some extent in the northwest.

The Rambouillet is most popular of the Merinos.

**Sheep of All Classes.**—Breeding ewes, yearlings, rams, wethers, and lambs may be found on the ranges, but ewes and lambs lead in numbers and importance. After they are five years old ewes begin to decline in wool production and they are usually drafted at this age and sent to market where they are disposed of as mutton, or for breeding or feeding purposes. In a few regions, however, they are retained until they are seven or eight years old. When from four to six months of age, the lambs are sent to market, where the fat ones are slaughtered for mutton while those in thin condition are sent to farms and feed lots to be fattened. Yearlings that are not intended for breeding on the range are no longer produced in large numbers. They are grown by those who are not in a position to make their lambs fat enough to sell well when four to six months old. In a very few regions wethers are kept for their wool product and for the growth they make, but they should be marketed before they are five years old as they become coarse and decline in condition after that age.

## QUESTIONS

1. Classify geographically the three general divisions of the range country.
2. What are the types of land utilized as range? Discuss each.
3. Who claims ownership of the range country? How leased?
4. What distinct characteristics do range sheep possess?
5. At what age do rangemen usually begin to cull their ewes?

## CHAPTER XLII

# MANAGEMENT OF SHEEP ON RANGES IN THE WEST

**Basis of Management.**—The management of sheep on the ranges of the West is based on the handling of a band which varies in size from 1200 to 3000 animals, depending on the nature of the range and the kind of sheep. For instance, if the grazing has to be conducted over narrow stretches of land part of the time, the band has to be comparatively small, for if it is not, the sheep in the rear will find very little to eat. Ewes and lambs have to be kept in small bands, because the lambs are inclined to stray out where predatory animals may get them, and caring for a very large band of them requires more work than the average herder can do. It is customary to place 1250 ewes and their lambs in one band. In total this amounts to a considerable number, but as a rule sheepmen regard bands of ewes with their lambs as being small.

Large bands are composed of dry sheep, that is sheep not suckling lambs. After the lambs have been weaned and the sheep placed on the winter range, the bands are usually of good size, provided the range is extensive and narrow stretches of grazing can be avoided. Under such conditions as many as 3500 sheep can be placed in a band.

**Labor Required to Handle a Band of Sheep.**—Aside from the lambing and shearing periods, only two men, a "herder" and a "camp-tender," are required to manage a band.

**The Herder.**—It is the duty of the herder to care for the sheep. If he is faithful and efficient, he is up and after them as soon as they begin to move in the morning, which is usually at daybreak. For two or three hours he guards and guides them or until they are ready to lie down and to chew the cud. He takes this opportunity to prepare his breakfast unless he arose early enough to eat before his sheep started from their bedding ground. Really the latter is a better procedure, for by carrying his lunch with him, he can be near his sheep throughout the day. The herder plans to select some time during each day the bedding ground for the night. Although it was long customary to bed down in the same place for a number of nights in succession, one-night bedding grounds are now used on many ranges. A good herder never rushes his sheep to camp and beds them down early for he knows that they will do better if given their time to come in, and also that they will not move out so early in the morning. During manorial days in England, it was a common saying that lame men were the best shepherds. So, too, the quiet, patient type of herder on the western ranges outclasses the nervous irascible type.

Although caring for the sheep is the chief duty of the herder, he also has part responsibility in the preparation of food for himself and the camp-tender. Many herders are adept in the cooking and baking of the plainer forms of food, such as bread, meat, potatoes, beans, and dried fruit.

**The camp-tender's** duties consist in keeping the camp provided with food and other necessities for himself and the herder, feed for the horses or burros, and salt for the sheep. He also attends to moving camp, assists in the cooking, and counts the sheep. As camp-mover he assumes considerable responsibility, as he must first select a camp site, which should be located where the feed is good. His count of the sheep is more nearly like an estimate than an actual count. It is made by counting the black or partially black sheep, of which there are a few in every band, and since each sheep maintains about the same position in the band day after day, the camp-tender merely ascertains whether all of the black sheep are present and whether their position in the band seems normal.

Of the two, herder and camp-tender, the latter has the more responsibility, and usually he receives more pay. When the sheep go to the mountains for the summer, the camp-tender is often given the privilege of drawing checks on the owner's account to pay for whatever is needed.

Should the owner have several bands of sheep on an extensive, undivided range, one camp-tender may be sufficient for as many as three bands. Under such conditions, a comparatively large store of provisions is kept at ranch headquarters, hence the distance of hauling is not very great. Usually, too, these conditions exist on the plains, where hauling is much less difficult than in the foot-hills and mountains (Fig. 226).

**Kind of Men Employed as Herders and Camp-Tenders.**—On the southwestern ranges nearly all herders and camp-tenders are Mexicans. It takes a larger number of them to handle a given number of sheep than it does of other types of laborers and they do not stick continuously to herding for more than three or four months at a time, but while they are in the employ of the ranch, they can, as a rule, be depended upon to stay with the sheep. Numerous cases have been cited of Mexican herders having lost their lives through faithfully caring for their sheep in severe storms.

Fig. 226.—Meal time in summer sheep camp in the mountains.

**Mexican herders** receive lower pay and they do not require so large an expenditure for provisions as do other types of herders. Their demands for provisions, however, depend somewhat on whether they are working for Mexicans, Spaniards, or Anglo-Saxons. Mexican employers may keep a man on sixty per cent of that demanded of an Anglo-Saxon employer.

Mexican herders require less mutton as they seldom keep dogs and often use goat meat. In northwestern ranges herders eat about two muttons per man per month.

On many ranches in the west it is customary to permit

herders and tenders to kill sheep for consumption in camp but on others mutton is furnished from ranch headquarters as it is needed.

**The herders and camp-tenders in California** are either Spanish and French Basques, or Anglo-Saxons. Basque herders often become proprietors. Camp-tenders often receive higher wages than herders. While the cost of wages and provisions per man is from 25 to 40 per cent greater than in the southwest, the cost per 1000 sheep is perhaps less, as the number per man is greater.

**The herders and camp-tenders on the northwestern ranges** are mainly of Anglo-Saxon stock. As a rule they receive much higher wages than are paid in the southwest and their provisions cost a great deal more. Articles of food are supplied to the sheep camps of the northwest which are probably unknown in the majority of camps in the southwest. Some of these articles are butter, eggs, honey, canned goods such as peas, beans, high-grade fruits, and maple syrup. It is a common saying that the bills of fare equal those in the best hotels.

**Labor Required to Handle a Band of Sheep in Shearing and Lambing Seasons.**—Shearing is always done at so much per head by parties who make it a business. The cost varies a great deal, according to the region in which the shearing is done and the kind of sheep to be shorn. Extra charge is made for sheep having many wrinkles in the skin and double charges are usually made for shearing rams. Before the war the costs were 8 to 18 cents per head. They now reach 12 to 27 cents or more.

**Lambing** extends over a period of from 4 to 6 weeks. The amount of labor required to lamb a band of 1250 ewes depends on the efficiency of the laborers and on the conditions under which the lambing is conducted, probably from 2 to 10 men. Wages are higher at lambing time as extra hours are required.

**Ranch Headquarters** are maintained where holdings of sheep are large, and other laborers are required for such tasks as making hay, seeing after watering places, cooking, etc. A superintendent is usually required for a large holding. The following table shows that the labor expense per sheep is rather high.

**Equipment Required for a Band of Sheep.**—The equipment necessary for handling a band of sheep may be divided into three classes as follows: winter, summer, and lambing

*Camp Expenses, per Month.*

| | Superintendent | Camp-tenders | Herders | Extra labor | Number of sheep to one man |
|---|---|---|---|---|---|
| Arizona | $84.80 | $50.38 | $49.18 | $49.38 | 867 |
| California | 94.05 | 68.75 | 54.18 | 55.13 | 1335 |
| Colorado | 76.24 | 45.83 | 41.44 | 37.20 | 897 |
| Idaho | 101.98 | 69.03 | 66.66 | 65.70 | 1359 |
| Montana | 102.22 | 68.39 | 62.70 | 62.72 | 1788 |
| Nevada | 111.50 | 64.93 | 59.42 | 63.02 | 1088 |
| New Mexico | 66.21 | 39.61 | 33.03 | 32.72 | 755 |
| Oregon | 85.52 | 62.52 | 58.04 | 57.87 | 1418 |
| Utah | 89.08 | 63.06 | 64.34 | 62.13 | 1247 |
| Washington | 89.60 | 61.33 | 60.85 | 57.54 | 1100 |
| Wyoming | 113.80 | 69.00 | 64.64 | 66.61 | 1112 |
| The region | 90.72 | 59.82 | 52.40 | 50.37 | 1119 |

equipment. In some places topography of the summer and winter range is so nearly alike that the same equipment will serve for both.

**In winter** when the sheep are on the plains, the equipment centers about the sheep wagon, which is a large, strongly-built vehicle with a canopy top. It has to be capacious, for it serves as a dwelling for two men, and it must be strong in order to withstand the strain incident to travelling over rough ground. It provides room for a bed, a stove used both for cooking and heating, a complete kit of the utensils necessary for cooking and eating, and a store of food for the men, and grain for the horses. Two good draft horses with harness are needed.

In addition to the horses for the wagon there must be at least one saddle horse which a camp-tender uses in various ways. Frequently two light horses and a spring wagon form a part of the equipment, to bring provisions for the camp.

The cost[1] of a fully equipped sheep wagon, which will wear from four to seven years according to the treatment it receives and the nature of the ground over which it is drawn, is approximately $350. The teams used on these wagons cost from $400 to $600 and they wear about as long as do horses at other types of draft work. As a rule the horses used under saddle or at light wagons cost from $80 to $125 and they wear out in three or four

[1] Costs obtained before the United States entered the war.

years. Saddles vary in cost from $35 to $60, and light wagons cost approximately $125. Saddles last many years, but light wagons are soon junk. Thus one sees that the cost of equipment for handling a band of sheep in winter is $800 or more.

**In summer** when the sheep are in the mountains, equipment and stores have to be carried on pack horses or burros because the travelling is too rough for wagons (Fig. 228).

Fig. 227.—Camp wagons, which are really dwellings on wheels, are used on the plains in wintertime

Fig. 228.—Trailing to the mountains in California where burros and horses must be used to carry supplies because the surface is too rough for wagons.

If burros are used, as is the case in many parts of the southwest and in California, five are required for each band of sheep. Three horses, two to be used as pack animals and the other as a saddle horse, are needed with each band. The pack horses carry the equipment and stores, which consist of a tent, blankets, a cooking and an eating outfit and food supplies. Large quantities of the latter can not be carried so the camp-tender has to make frequent excursions with his pack horses to a base of supplies.

The following enumerates the summer camp equipment, cost and wear:

| Article | Cost | Wear |
|---|---|---|
| 3 horses | $450 | 3 years |
| 1 saddle | 40 | 5 years |
| 2 pack saddles | 20 | 1 season |
| 1 tent | 16 | 1 season |
| 4 pairs of blankets | 40 | 2 seasons |
| 3 sets of hobbles | 6 | 2 seasons |
| Cooking and eating outfit | 16 | 2 seasons |
| | $588 | |

The above equipment does not serve for as many sheep as the winter sheep wagon because summer bands are usually smaller.

**Extra Equipment Needed at Times.**—First of all, there is extra equipment in the way of tents, blankets, and cooking utensils for the extra help in lambing time. Extra horses are needed for carrying or hauling provisions or perhaps for hauling water. Often extra wagons are needed for various purposes. Many lanterns must be on hand to guide the workers at night and to scare away predatory animals. Guns and ammunition are also needed to guard against coyotes and other animals. In some places there must be a supply of lambing tents to house ewes and their new-born lambs, or buildings are constructed especially for this.

**The equipment in lambing** varies so much under different conditions that estimating cost is difficult. Generally it consists of extras to regular equipment, but barns and sheds may be used only then.

**Fall and Winter Management.**—This begins when the sheep are moved from the mountains to the plains, about October. This is no small task, as often the distance is great and the range along the trail is limited. Trails are often closed and transfers are made by rail. Surplus stock, such as lambs, cast ewes, yearlings, and wethers are then disposed of at shipping points. Upon reaching the plains, the lambs and wethers are separated from ewes until after the breeding season.

**The Breeding Season.**—This occurs in either November or December on most ranges, although earlier breeding than this is now common in Idaho, Washington, and California. Rams are placed with the ewes at the rate of $1\frac{1}{2}$ to 3 to every 100 for 4 weeks. This makes a short lambing period of 5 weeks, and all the lambs are of about the same age.

**Care of Rams.**—Since the breeding season is a strenuous period for the rams (rams are always called bucks in the West) many owners practice feeding them liberally with grain in order to keep them in fairly good condition and vigor. Often when the ewes are grazing across an extensive plain the rams are shipped to them and, when the breeding season is over, shipped back to ranch headquarters.

Either very cold or very dry weather seems to affect the ability of rams adversely for service. Sheepmen in eastern Colorado have observed that rams will desert the ewes in very cold weather and stand about the corrals in search of feed.

Men who have used both Merino and mutton-bred rams claim that the latter are the more vigorous in breeding season and capable of more service. Some have maintained that it takes only half as many of them as Merinos for a definite number of ewes.

Since rams on the western ranges live under hard conditions they are useful in service for only about three years. Except in breeding season, they are run in what are known as buck bands. Frequently owners combine their buck flocks and put them in the care of a herder who finds range for them at so much per head per month or for the season. Some owners merely let them run at large without a herder, and when left to themselves, the rate of loss among them is very large. Then, too, range rams fight amongst themselves a great deal and this is a source of depreciation and loss.

**Winter Management.**—After the breeding season winter herding is on extensive plains which can be used only when snows furnish water. Bands of ewes go as far out as 200 miles from the home ranch. In most places, however, the winter range is not so extensive. The supply of feed may be so limited, or the periods of snowstorms so bad, that hay and grain have to be fed part of the time. In fact, shelled corn and cottonseed cake are stored for emergency use. Alfalfa and grain, such as barley, oats, and wheat, are available in regions formerly having only wild range.

**Shearing.**—This is an event which marks the transition from winter to spring management and often precedes lambing. As stated elsewhere, shearing is done by men who make it a profession. Early in March they are busy in Arizona and New Mexico, and they finish in Montana late in July. Shearing is then over except for a little fall work in California and some winter shearing in the feeding stations tributary to markets.

**Shearing camps,** equipped with shearing pens, corrals and sacking frames or balers are located on the trail between winter and summer range, if possible beside a railroad, to save long hauls in wagons. Shearing is done in a few hours if the plant is fairly large and well-equipped. Owners having several bands to shear endeavor to have but one band at a time in the corrals, to save feeding.

**Both hand and machine shearing** are practiced. The latter is the more rapid, saves more wool, and perhaps causes fewer cuts in the skin of the sheep. But when a sudden drop in temperature is likely to occur, unless thick combs are used, machine shearing takes the wool entirely too close to enable the sheep to go through such periods without injury. In some other places the hot sun may blister the skin.

In practically all shearing camps, helpers called "wranglers" drive the sheep into small pens bordering the shearing floor, so that by merely turning about the shearers find the sheep within their reach. If machines are used the fleeces are tied and the shearing floor kept clean by laborers called "tyers" and sweepers. In camps where hand shearing is done it is common for the shearers to tie the fleeces. In such camps there is seldom a common shearing floor, but a series of pens in which half of the ground space is floored. The shearing is done on the floored part while the sheep awaiting shearing stand on the unfloored part. After the fleeces are tied they are pitched into a long, flat-bottomed trough, thirty inches wide, to be sacked.

**Hand shearers** vary widely as to the number they are able to shear in a day. The poorest may not shear more than 50 by beginning at seven in the morning and ending at five in the evening while the best may shear 125 and sometimes more. Expert machine shearers will shear 200 sheep in a day. The number depends on the size of the sheep, the nature of their skins with respect to wrinkles, and the density and oily condition of their wool. A big, strong ram requires more time. For these reasons, extra charges are usually made for rams and for bands of sheep with more wrinkles and folds than is common.

On the whole shearers in the West do fair work, but long, ugly cuts in the skin should be matters of less occurrence than they are. Then, too, shearers are too careless in catching their sheep and setting them down. In plants having machines, particularly, the shearer retains his hold on the shearing shaft and brings his sheep down by grasping a hind leg and giving the animal a vicious swing. Such handling should not be tolerated, and it is no wonder that those who practice having their ewes shorn while pregnant do not like to place them in plants where machines are used. In a few sheds constructed according to the general plan used in Australia, swinging doors between the shearing floor and the sheep make it impossible for the shearer to drag a sheep in by the leg. He must pick it up and carry it in. This plan is greatly appreciated by sheepmen (Fig. 229).

Fig. 229.—Shearing shed at Bitter Creek, Wyoming, modeled after a type common in Australia

**Shearers.**—Operators of shearing plants often have difficulty with shearers. Many nomadic shearers leave if they hear of better wages or of easier shearing further on. The operators have them sign a contract which keeps them till the last band is sheared. Sheep shearing is hard work and it requires strong men whose backs are as untiring as springs of steel. They must be well fed and comfortably quartered. Since they live a nomadic life they seldom save much, for gambling prevails.

**Marketing Wool.**—Soon after shearing the wool is usually removed from the ranch and shipped by rail to market. Formerly the wool was moved from shearing shed to railroad by wagon trains, but now it is transported largely by truck. Many buyers travel through the range areas and visit flock-owners before and during shearing to purchase the clips. (See also pages 326-329.) (Fig. 230.)

**Contracting.**—Wool is sold in a number of ways in the West. In some years it is contracted at so much per pound before it is sheared. Money may be advanced to sheepmen financially embarrassed. Commission firms, speaking for themselves, say that they buy in order to accommodate sheepmen who are badly in need of money, while sheepmen and others think they buy because there is a strong prospect for a marked advance in the wool market.

**Commission Houses.**—Much wool is consigned to some eastern commission house after shearing. The house may sell

Fig. 230.—Wool graded, baled and awaiting shipment from a shearing shed.

at once or may hold. Should the consignor desire money, the house will advance a loan charging interest. Such speculative features add to the uncertainties of the business.

The most prevalent method is to sell the wool to agents of dealers' houses and manufacturers who first inspect the wool either in the shearing camps or in warehouses at shipping points. This is about as satisfactory to the grower as any method of selling. He can sell and feel that it is over in a short period.

**Auction Sales.**—This plan has been conducted in warehouses at shipping points. Agents inspect the wool and turn in sealed bids to the proprietor of the warehouse, who opens them on the day of sale in the presence of the owner, who passes judgment on them. He may reject all of them or he may select any bid made on his wool. If he is not present, the proprietor of the warehouse follows his instructions relative to probable bids. Payment is made by the purchasing agent, who, as a rule, accepts the warehouse weights. Those concerned with the organization of auction sales were for two purposes: (1) the securing of competitive bidding, and (2) furnishing to owners an opportunity to compare the selling merits of their wool. It is doubtful whether much has been accomplished through the latter.

**Coöperative Selling.**—Recently coöperative associations, organized by wool growers for the purpose of securing a square deal in disposing of their wool and for cutting down the intermediate costs, have become increasingly important in wool-marketing circles. Some of these handle several million pounds of wool annually. They undertake to teach their members better methods of preparing for market and to assist them in other ways. They are meeting, as they justly deserve, with a measurable degree of success in their purposes. In 1935, the coöperative wool-marketing associations handled over 70,000,000 pounds.

**Expense of Marketing Wool.**—There is a great deal of expense involved in preparing and marketing wool in the West. Charges for shearing, sacking, storing, and shipping make large inroads on the gross receipts. The cost of shipping wool by rail to Boston, the leading wool market, varies from $1.50 to $2.66 per 100 pounds; the cheapest transcontinental rate is on the Pacific Coast, where the railways meet the competition of water transportation. In marketing wool through coöperative associations, the charges for storage, grading, insurance, and so on, generally are held down to about 2¾ cents per pound.

**Spring and Summer Management.—The Lambing Period.**—In general, one may say that spring management begins with the lambing period. Preparation has to be made in such matters as help, equipment, and in locating and preparing the lambing ground.

**The location** should be where feed and water are plentiful as a large number of sheep are restricted to a small area for a considerable length of time, and because good feed and water are essential in starting the ewes to suckle well after the lambs are born. In some regions, the Yakima Valley in Washington being one, harvested feeds are the chief reliance during lambing. In the southwest it is not uncommon to haul water five to ten miles and store in tanks. Owners of large areas often set aside tracts for lambing on which they erect buildings or corrals and dig wells. Natural shelter from cold winds and storms is preferred, but when this is not possible, sheds or tents are provided. In the northwest, where the weather is often cold and stormy, immense barns are constructed at heavy cost. Farther south, brush and small trees are often cut and arranged for protection against chilling winds. Corrals and pens are always needed for sorting ewes and lambs from time to time.

In many regions it is impossible to locate lambing grounds where the attacks of such animals as coyotes, wolves, bob cats, mountain lions, and bears will not be a serious problem. Young lambs are toothsome morsels to these animals, and they will risk a great deal to get them. Owners sometimes make the mistake of locating in an isolated region far away from other lambing bands, and as a result, predatory animals from far and near prey upon them.

As a rule, extra men guard against the animals that would play havoc among the ewes and lambs. They kill as many of these predatory prowlers as they can by shooting, trapping, and placing poisoned bait, and scare them away at night by firing blank cartridges, building fires, and hanging out lanterns.

**Method of Handling.**—During lambing the method of handling consists in dividing the band up into small groups as the ewes lamb, and of combining these groups as the lambs grow old enough to keep from becoming lost from their mothers when placed in larger groups. The smallest groups are the "day drop" and the "night drop." That is, the ewes which lamb through the day constitute one group and the ewes which lamb at night form another. About 24 hours after the "night drop" these two groups are combined and in 72 to 96 hours this newly-formed group may be combined with another made by combining the succeeding day and night drops. To make the above clearer, suppose the day and night drops of Monday are combined on Wednesday morning and the day and night drops of Tuesday, on Thursday morning. Then the two groups made by combining the day and night drops of Monday and Tuesday may be combined on Friday or Saturday morning. This process of combining into larger and larger groups continues according to the judgment of those in charge until the whole band is together and ready to move from the lambing grounds (Fig. 231).

**Rate of Lambing.**—Usually the rate of lambing is greatest during the second or third weeks of the period. When the rate of births is at its highest the lambing camp is a very busy place and there is seemingly more or less crudeness in the way much of the work is done. As a rule, a greater supply of trained laborers would save more lambs and cut down the loss of ewes, but trained laborers are very scarce and in many instances it is impossible to get an adequate force. In these days when much depends on a successful lambing period most sheepmen do their best to get a large percentage of lambs. Still, in all but a comparatively few regions, a large percentage of twins is not wanted because, first, the feed on the range is not plentiful enough to permit a ewe to grow two lambs well and secondly, one of a pair of twins is likely to become lost from its mother through the confusion which necessarily exists in the lambing band. Such a lamb becomes a "bummer" and gains a living by stealing from several ewes. It does not develop well and it hinders the growth of those lambs from whose mothers it steals.

Fig. 231.—A permanent lambing camp consisting of a wooden frame and canvas roof and walls.

**Last Task of Lambing.**—Finishing the docking and castrating is the last task of the lambing period. All the lambs not docked and castrated are gathered together in a corral and handed out to operators, who work on them at a rate of speed which varies with the size of the task and the familiarity of the operators with it. A skilled operator can keep two men very busy catching lambs for him. The testicles and tail are removed in a remarkably short time and the lamb is in a large measure saved from the nervous exhaustion which results from a slow bungling operation. As a rule, lambs are operated upon when they are about fourteen days old.

**Percentage of Lambs.**—Immediately after docking a count of the tails is made, from which the percentage of lambs is determined. This figure depends, however, upon the percentage of ewes that lambed as well as upon the success in saving the lambs born. A 90 per cent crop of lambs is considered very successful, indeed, for more often it is very much lower.

The following tabulation shows the investigation of the agents of the Tariff Board with respect to the percentage of lambs saved in various flocks in the different western states. The figures are based on the total number of ewes of breeding age owned and the number of lambs raised to market age.

| State | Percentage of lambs | State | Percentage of lambs |
|---|---|---|---|
| Arizona | 59.3 | New Mexico | 57.7 |
| California | 76.4 | Oregon | 79.6 |
| Colorado | 61.9 | Utah | 72.5 |
| Idaho | 67.2 | Washington | 92.5 |
| Montana | 71.9 | Wyoming | 62.4 |
| Nevada | 74.6 | | |

**Dipping.**—Before going to the summer range all sheep and lambs should be dipped in order to prevent the scattering of infectious skin diseases. Dipping is under the control of the U. S. Bureau of Animal Industry and is done when the employees of that Bureau consider it necessary.

**Transfer to Summer Range.**—When lambing and shearing are finished it is generally time to move to the summer range. This is more tedious and difficult than the transfer from summer to winter feeding grounds because the ewes must get enough feed to supply the lambs with milk and the lambs are not strong enough to travel fast. The country traversed may be in private hands, presenting much trouble.

**Management on the summer range** consists chiefly in keeping the sheep and lambs on good feed and in protecting them from predatory animals. It requires faithful and skillful herding to keep ewes and their lambs on good feed in the mountains because they are run on definite allotments and it is hard regularly to locate camp so that feed is always accessible. Then, too, the fact that the mountains are rough makes it hard to protect

FIG. 232.—On an enclosed summer range in the National Forest.

sheep, for there are numerous canyons and draws in which they can become lost and exposed to the attacks of their enemies.

**The outcome of the sheep business** as regards profit and loss depends in large measure upon how the lambs develop on the summer range. In certain regions there is no hope of their becoming fat enough or heavy enough to go direct from the range to the markets as mutton. Owners, in such regions, must dispose of their lambs as feeders and manage on a smaller return per head than those who can grow them to marketable condition and weight.

It is now rather common for lambs to be marketed before the summer season closes. In order to get them to market in good condition it is necessary to drive the ewes along to the point of shipment and to have a feeding ground nearby as lambs must have a supply of feed and milk until loaded on cars. Lambs from the National Forests in Washington reach Chicago in good condition and sell as choice and prime lambs (Fig. 232).

**Problems in Both Winter and Summer Management.**—The Tariff Board gave an excellent discussion of losses, as follows:

"**Losses.**—The question of losses is one which haunts the western sheepmen day and night. When the sheep are on the winter ranges, he dreads the possibility of a deep snow, which will cover up the feed and make moving the sheep difficult, if not impossible. This is particularly true in the northwest, where, in the winter of 1910, for example, many sheepmen found their flocks snow-bound miles away from feed of any kind.

"**Losses From Snow Storms.**—In many cases the owners were forced to buy hay at unusually high prices, have it baled and shipped to the nearest railroad point, then moved out in wagons or packed on horses and mules to where the sheep were, the snow being so deep and the road so difficult that wagons could not always be used.

"Others hired teams, and with snowplows a trail was broken through the snow for many miles across the range, over which the starving sheep were carefully driven, some of them so weak that it was necessary to pick them up along the trail and haul them on sleds to where the hay was placed.

"**In the southwest,** during the same winter, the snow would have been more than welcome, for there they faced a drought which caused heavy losses. The sheep had been moved to the desert ranges, as usual, with expectation of lambing there. Neither rain nor snow fell, and at the critical time, just as lambing was at hand, the owners found they must either move the sheep or lose everything. The sheep were worked to the railroad shipping points by means of hay hauled into the desert, and in some cases water was hauled out in tank wagons and given the sheep in troughs from the wagon. In this way the animals were moved to ranges where water and feed were to be had and their owners were saved from a total loss, although the expenses and losses were heavy enough to offset any profit on the year's business.

"During the winter of 1899, owing to deep snows, one New Mexico sheep owner lost, of his entire flock of 40,000 sheep, a total of 18,000 old sheep, while in the spring of 1909 another New Mexico owner lost over 12,000 spring lambs—his entire crop.

"**Lack of Shelter.**—A study of the situation and conditions frequently shows losses to be due to a lack of shelter on the range. A 'norther' sweeps down across the country, and one flock finds shelter under a low range of hills, or a few scattering cedars, while the other, lacking these essentials, drifts into some ravine or dry wash, under the sheltering banks of which they find apparent security from the storm. But the drifting snow falls into the wash, and the sheep are rapidly covered by it, smothering to death before they can be moved. Hundreds of sheep are lost every winter in this manner.

"**Poisonous Plants.**—Losses from poisonous plants are also very frequent. On a good range with plenty of feed few sheep are lost from such causes, but when the range is over-grazed or the sheep have been driven many miles over sheep trails almost as bare of feed as a floor, they will eat greedily plants which they otherwise would not touch.

"Every sheepman in the Rocky Mountain region counts upon a certain percentage of losses each year from poisonous plants which infest the ranges, and against which there seems to be but little protection.

"**Predatory Animals.**—There are also regular losses from predatory animals, which are taken into account by all sheepmen. Thousands of dollars are annually paid out by the State governments as well as the sheepmen in bounties for their destruction. These bounties, often doubled by the sheep owners, are turned over by them to the herders to encourage them in the work of extermination, and they are also freely furnished with ammunition and rifles, as well as traps and poison.

"**Strays.**—Losses by 'cuts' or small bunches of animals which get cut off from the main band and are not discovered by the herders are quite frequent. Sometimes the 'stray gathers' find and return part of these cuts, but more often they are picked off one by one by the coyotes, wild cats, and other predatory animals which continually hang along the flanks of every sheep herd the year round.

"**Coyotes.**—The coyote is the one great scourge of the western sheepman. Unlike other wild animals, the coyote takes kindly to civilization and rather flourishes under it. Every year thousands upon thousands are killed, and yet there seems to be but little reduction in their numbers. To these predatory animals the western sheepman pays a heavy annual toll and one which cuts deeply into his expected profits.

"**Losses of Young Lambs.**—In addition to the losses among the old sheep, there is a regular loss among the lambs between the time of 'marking up,' which takes place when they are about two or three weeks old, and the time of selling.

"This loss is due to a great variety of causes. Two bands are sometimes accidentally mixed on the range. In the worry and 'milling' attending the separation many lambs lose their mothers, and if too young soon die, or if they live are stunted.

"A good many lambs die from docking or from castrating.

"Taking the various causes into consideration, it is a conservative estimate to place the loss among the lambs between marking-up time and selling time at 10 per cent. That is, if 1000 lambs are 'marked up' in May the owner will do well if, counting every lamb in the bunch, whether a 'top' or a 'cut-back,' he has 900 to sell in November.''

**The Range Problem.**—Another problem which confronts the western sheepman is the matter of range. He may have an abundance of winter range or *vice versa*, but comparatively few are comfortably fixed with respect to both. There are so many in control of the range that he has no long time assurance of what will be at his disposal. Harvested feeds help a great deal in tiding over a shortage of winter range, but there is no such comforting supplement for a short supply of summer feed.

**Selling Price.**—Still another problem for the western sheepman lies in the fact that the products he sells are subject to wide fluctuation in price. Perhaps no other one thing would more nearly place him at his ease than a fair degree of stability in the wool and mutton markets. A season of soaring prices unbalances his poise and he over-reaches himself by investing deeper than he should, while a season of low prices forces him to cash in so that he has little wool and mutton when prices are high.

**Factors Influencing Profits.**—Recent studies of the costs of producing sheep in different sections of the range country have shown that range conditions, the percentage of the total investment in sheep, the lamb crop, death losses, weight of lambs, weight of fleeces, and labor charges each had a pronounced effect upon the returns secured by the operator. Although some of these considerations have been discussed in the foregoing pages, their importance permits further statement.

Range conditions are not wholly under the control of the stockmen, as it is impossible for them to control the forage growth beyond a limited degree. The avoidance of over-grazing and the provision of supplementary feeds on short winter ranges appear to be the features most likely to advance the possibilities of success as they are closely associated with the reduction of death losses and the promotion of good growth of lambs and wool.

The range operator who has had a large proportion of his investment in sheep has been more fortunate in securing satisfactory returns than he whose major percentage of his total investment was in lands. Reports given in Utah Bulletin 204 show that ranches running between 2,000 and 3,000 breeding ewes received a larger percentage return than those with a greater or less number. In studies reported in Bulletin 156 of the Wyoming Station the most favorable returns among ranches in the Red Desert area of Wyoming were obtained by those running between 4,000 and 9,000 breeding ewes. It is apparent that there are great differences between the various sections of the west and the operator to be assured of success needs to determine carefully the most advantageous size of outfit and method of handling. The investment in sheep should be from 50 to 70 per cent of the total investment of the operator in sheep and lands. When the later are owned at a fair valuation, they make up from 85 to 90 per cent of the investment.

Large lamb crops that are obtained without an undue increase in expense are found to contribute in a very significant way to the profits obtained. The following statement is taken from Wyoming Bulletin 156:

> "Lambs can be produced at $1 less per hundredweight, and wool at 3 cents less per pound when the wool grower is able to market an 80 instead of a 70 per cent lamb crop. For each 3 per cent increase in the lamb crop the operator will make one per cent more on his investment, providing that his costs remain the same in both cases. An operator can afford to spend 65 cents more per head each year on his ewes, if by so doing he can increase his lamb crop 10 per cent."

The weight of the lambs at marketing time and the weight of the fleeces produced by the ewes bear very directly on profits. While the condition of the range has much to do with the weight of the lambs, Joseph[2] points out that the size of the ewe and some other features of her individuality are very closely allied with the income she produces.

**Wool Production of Range Sheep.**—Numerous conditions enter into wool production and while there are many ranches where Rambouillet sheep are not kept, nevertheless the results of efforts of Spencer[3] and others to determine the factors that influence the wool production of sheep of this breed have wide usefulness. Much discussion has centred upon the relative importance of the factors which contributed to the amount of wool that was obtained from a sheep. A brief summary of the find-

[2] Montana Bulletin 242.

[3] U.S.D.A. Tech. Bulletin 85.

ings which in some instances are based on a study of 1850 fleeces follows.

*Age.*—In studying the influence of the age of ewes upon their wool-producing powers, the optimum age was found to be 3 years. There was a gradual increase in both the unscoured and scoured fleece weights up until that age and a gradual decrease thereafter. While age does not have a decided influence upon the general character of the fleece the length of staple becomes less as the age advances.

*Yolk.*—Many breeders of Rambouillet sheep, especially those in the eastern part of the United States, have been firm in their belief that a large amount of grease (yolk) was necessary to obtain heavy fleece weights. This is true when unscoured fleece weights are considered, but when related to the actual amount of clean or scoured wool produced the matter of excess grease (more than the amount necessary to keep the wool in good condition) is decidedly unfavorable. Those fleeces which had the smallest amount of grease per pound of clean wool were the ones which gave the greatest weights of clean wool. The actual weight of wool, minus the materials which are found in it in the grease or unscoured condition, is the only significant way in which to figure the true yield of wool. A heavy production of wool and a heavy production of grease are not associated. As the amount of grease increased there was a tendency for the length of the wool fibers to become slightly shorter. Neither the fineness of the fiber nor the character of the fleece seemed to be affected in a significant way by the amount of yolk present.

*Dirt* is one of the items which bears an important relation to the grease or unscoured weight of the fleece. As an average for 1496 fleeces studied, 44.83 per cent of their grease weight was made up of dirt. Dirt was most important of any of the four constituents (dirt, grease, moisture, and wool) of unscoured fleece weight, exceeding even the clean wool of the fleece which amounted to 36.81 per cent of the unscoured weight. As the amount of grease increased the amount of dirt increased also. Although these fleeces were produced on ranges that are typical of much of the intermountain region, there would be sections where even more dirt would be found in the fleece. Very likely dirt would be less abundant in similar fleeces produced in many areas of the farm states on bluegrass pastures.

*Length of staple* is a problem which confronts many Rambouillet breeders. There is a very definite and important relation between length of staple and the actual clean wool produced. Increased length of staple does not mean that the fineness of the fibers is sacrificed as the data show that the diameter of the fibers was practically unaffected by the length of the fibers. There is some indication that a slight decrease in density occurs as the length of the fibers increases, but this is not one of the really important considerations, since profits in modern wool growing depend much less upon maximum density than upon length of staple, which helps in securing greater weight of clean wool and less grease and dirt in the fleeces. This length also assures a somewhat higher price. The character seems to improve with length.

*Fineness of fiber* shows a very slight tendency to be associated with some of the other factors, but for the most part the influence of fineness upon the other characters did not amount to much. An increase in fineness does not mean an increase in grease content nor a decrease in staple length, although the finer fleeces in this study had a trifle greater density, a little better character, and showed some tendency toward a decreased amount of clean wool.

*Density* is a factor which must not be overlooked, yet it seems that it should not be emphasized so strongly as has sometimes been done if actual clean wool production is sought. This is the sensible basis upon which to build wool growing. When density is noticeably lacking, there is a tendency for these less dense fleeces to yield smaller amounts of clean wool. Maximum density tends to be associated with shorter staple and finer fiber but not with better character.

*Face covering,* folds in the skin, body weight, and mutton type are other characters which have received attention. There is nothing to indicate that there is any worthwhile advantage in extreme face covering. The ewes having the barest faces had greater fleece weight, both in the grease and when scoured, than the woolly faced ewes. Moderate face covering but complete freedom from wool blindness seem to be most consistent with the greatest efficiency of wool production. This, considered with the great practical advantage of freedom from extreme wool growth on the head, is of vast importance to Rambouillet breeders and range sheepmen.

*Folds in the skin* bear some relation to wool production, as the ewes that were entirely free from folds did not produce as much wool as ewes with moderate heavy folds at the neck. Data on this point are not complete but the longest staple and best character were found on the smoother sheep with no decided tendency for fineness to favor the sheep with the folds. Fleeces of greatest density were found on sheep of the latter type.

*Body weights* of sheared yearling Rambouillet ewes are positively related with the characters that contribute to the greatest profits in wool growing. Yearling range ewes that weigh from 80 to 110 pounds are likely to have longer staple, greater fineness, and more density as well as greater weight of unscoured and scoured fleeces than similar ewes of much greater or lower body weights. There is practically no evidence to indicate that good mutton type in Rambouillet ewes is detrimental to efficient and satisfactory wool production by them.

## QUESTIONS

1. What is the size of the bands in which sheep are handled on the range?
2. How much labor is required to handle a band of sheep?
3. What are the duties of the herder?
4. What are the duties of the camp-tender?
5. Discuss the equipment required in handling sheep in summer and in winter on the range.
6. When is the surplus stock shipped to market?
7. When are ewes bred and how long is the breeding season?
8. How are the rams handled during the breeding season?
9. Discuss winter management after the breeding season.
10. How are the ewes handled during the lambing period and until the lambs are docked and castrated?
11. How is shearing conducted on the range?
12. How many sheep can a man shear in a day?
13. Describe the methods of getting the wool to market.
14. How is wool sold in the West?
15. What are the problems that confront the sheep owners on the range? Discuss each.
16. Discuss factory influencing profits.
17. How is wool production affected by breed, age, size, weight and density?
18. Discuss effects of yoke and dirt.
19. What objection to face wool? To folds of skin?

## CHAPTER XLIII

## SIGNIFICANT CHANGES IN RANGE CONDITIONS DURING THE PAST TWENTY-FIVE YEARS

**Changes in Range Areas.**—When sheepmen first went into the West there was very little land which was permanently occupied. Whenever the obtaining of sufficient range was a problem it consisted chiefly in competing with cowmen whose rights could be defined by no other than that shadowy and shaky term "priority" or "previous occupation," yet these rights were defended to the point of open conflict and not infrequently at the expense of human life. But in the end the sheepmen were bound to gain occupation of what was justly their share because it required less capital to get into the sheep business than into the cattle business, and hence more people were attracted to sheep, and they secured their range through the advantage of superior numbers. In time, however, the homesteaders, a more numerous class than the sheepmen, appeared on the scene, too, and they were bound to triumph in occupying land, not only because of superior numbers, but also because they were armed with legal rights.

When homesteaders became numerous the range began to change to the disadvantage of sheepmen. The homesteader was a poor man whose "claim" was his all, and he resented trespass to the point of demanding payment for damages. He located on the lands having water, and either forced sheepmen to find new supplies of water by digging wells and building reservoirs or to hunt new range. Those who thought themselves shrewd enough to hold large sections of free range for all time by gaining ownership of the land on which natural watering holes were located were in the end defeated by homesteaders who settled on all the free lands around the water holes.

After the homesteader began to collect rents and damages, or fenced his land entirely away from sheepmen, those in control of state and railroad lands were in position to demand rentals for their holdings. Then immense National Forests were created which resulted in bringing vast areas under the control of the Federal

Department of Agriculture. State and railroad lands in National Forest areas were given over to the National Forest in lieu of equal areas of government land located elsewhere. This amounted to a double restriction of free land. Moreover, the National Forest service made definite allotments on which only a stated number of sheep were allowed for a specified time at a consideration of so much per head. Often these allotments were situated so that transfer from them to the plains was difficult.

**Added Cost of Ranges.**—Because of the changes outlined above it is impossible to run as many sheep in many sections as formerly and obviously these changes have added to the cost of running sheep in various ways, as follows:

First, charges are made for all lands except public domain, which is becoming more and more restricted.

Second, the alternation of tracts of private lands withdrawn from grazing with tracts of public and private lands rented to sheepmen has raised the cost of maintenance by requiring additional labor and has reduced the possible returns through lowering the feeding capacity of the range. In eastern Colorado, where homesteaders who have enclosed their lands are numerous, only alternate sections are open for grazing. Under such conditions the bands of sheep have to be about half normal size in order to give the sheep in the rear a chance to find feed. That is, the band does not have the same opportunity to remain spread out while feeding as formerly because of having to pass around the sections in the hands of homesteaders. Thus, one sees that more labor per thousand sheep is required in eastern Colorado now than in the days before the coming of homesteaders. Then, it is impossible for sheepmen in that section to get their sheep in as good condition as formerly, even though the area per head remains the same, because they have to travel so much more than they used to. Since, oftentimes, owners of several bands can not secure all of their summer range in one body in the National Forest more labor is required than when the area of mountain range was not definitely fixed. It used to be common for one tender to look after two or three camps in the mountains, but now he is seldom responsible for more than one. Allotment lines are generally irregular, making many corners and pockets, which prevent radiating out from camp as in the good old free-for-all days. On this account summer bands are not as large as they used to be.

Third, the ownership and withdrawal of so much land has made trailing from one range to another both difficult and expensive. The trails are narrow and must be travelled over by many bands of sheep. Feed becomes scarce, the sheep go backward in condition, and lambs are often permanently stunted by the hardships of the trail. In many sections the land between summer and winter range has become occupied to such extent that the sheep have to be transferred by rail.

Fourth, the changes which have come about in control of lands have forced sheepmen to invest heavily in lands. In recent years homesteaders all over the West have sold lands worth not to exceed $3 per acre at from $5 to $15 per acre. There was a time when it was not necessary for the sheepman to own a foot of land, but that day has passed. He who owns land has advantage in controlling lands for which rentals are paid. Besides, sheepmen should own land on which cultivated crops are grown for the purpose of supplementing range and those who bought land a number of years ago are now best prepared to continue in the sheep business. Not only that, but they purchased when prices were extremely low and the advance of land values have been such that their investments were very profitable.

**Changes in Labor.**—During the last fifteen or twenty years there have been significant changes in labor on sheep ranches with respect to the amount required, its efficiency, and its cost in wages and provisions.

Throughout the West more labor per thousand sheep is required now than a number of years ago. Statements have already been made which show that this is true. As compared with the past, sheepmen now operate under what may be termed crowded conditions. There are the homesteaders on the plains, allotments in the mountains, ranch headquarters for producing and storing feed, all of which did not exist in the past and which add to the amount of labor needed. It is harder now to keep different bands from mixing and to prevent trespassing; hence, bands have to be either cut down in size or tended by more men. Then, too, lands are now used as range which were once discarded because they were of such nature that too much labor was needed in handling the sheep.

Sheepmen emphatically assert that the labor procured now is not as good as that which they used to employ. There are more densely populated communities in the West now which attract many of the best laborers, and the wage-seekers who enter sheep camps to-day do not possess the kind of motives that insure efficiency. In the early days the sheep camps were occupied by ambitious young men who needed money to be sure, but who also wanted the experience that would prepare them for engaging in business for themselves. Therefore, they were up and doing and they were efficient. But now, when it is not easy for the ambitious, poor young man to get into the sheep business for himself and since labor is scarce, practically any one who will go to herd sheep is acceptable. Those who do go are usually wanderers who go from place to place without becoming fixed to any occupation and, although they may work well, they herd sheep poorly because they do not stay with the job long enough to learn how.

**The cost of labor** has increased. In the past twenty years the increase in monthly wages has been very great. The report of the Tariff Board, issued in 1911, states that in 1895, or thereabouts, there was no difficulty in hiring herders at $15 per month in New Mexico and that in California their services could be secured for $25 per month. It would take from three to four times these wages to get herders at the present time.

There is also increased cost incurred in securing labor. In the past a goodly supply of reliable help was easily obtained close to the ranches. That is, it was largely a matter of the laborers seeking the job, but the reverse is the situation now. Owners and superintendents have to go to town and spend several days in finding laborers. This may occur several times in the year, and when special labor is needed, such as in the lambing season, the hunt for men is so strenuous that an owner or superintendent spends time in town which would better be spent on the ranch if help were procurable in any other manner.

**Better Provision Required.**—It requires a greater expenditure per month to provide for sheep herders than formerly. This has come about mainly through the adoption of a higher standard of living which is traceable in part to the scarcity of labor. When efficient laborers began to be scarce the more aggressive sheep owners improved the quality and increased the variety of provisions in order to attract more men and particularly the best herders to their camps. In a short time all owners were forced to provide well in order to get laborers at all. Then with the inception of more settled conditions there was perhaps a general rise in the standard of living which was bound to extend to the sheep camps. But in the southwest the assertion is commonly made that special help can be secured because the liberal supply of provisions in camp affords an opportunity for the village loafers to get a good fill. and it is doubtful whether laborers in villages receiving wages comparable with those paid to sheep herders have as much to eat. In fact, it is well known that they do not. Constant reference is made to the relative simple list of provisions which was furnished to the old-time herders and comparing it with the list of to-day, provisions must cost several times as much as they did in the early days.

**Greater Investment Required.**—Still another significant change in range conditions is the much greater investment in improvements and equipment. The large tracts of land which owners have felt obliged to purchase must be fenced at a cost of about $150 per mile. In many places water has been secured at great expense by digging wells or by building reservoirs. Because of the rise in the cost of operation and in the value per head of the sheep, buildings and corrals have been erected which were not deemed necessary at an earlier time. Horses and machinery for working the cultivated lands are now items of considerable cost which at one time did not appear on the inventory.

All of the changes enumerated above have been in the direction of raising the cost of maintaining sheep in the West. But a few changes have been made which either help to reduce the cost of operation or to increase the returns possible from the sheep.

**Beneficial Changes.**—For example, *railway facilities* have been constantly improving. As railways grew more numerous it was easier to get both wool and sheep to point of shipment, and the expense of getting supplies and equipment to the range was considerably lessened. In the earlier days of sheep ranching in the West, mutton could not be of much importance, for facilities for getting it to market were not developed. Little spurs of railway have penetrated regions and better highways have approached the ranges.

The introduction of *cultivated crops* has made earlier lambing possible in a number of places. Better feed and improvement in breeding, help make the lamb crops better.

Sheepmen are becoming more and more tolerant in their views

concerning the control of the National Forests; this indicates that those in charge are earnestly seeking means of allowing sheep owners to get a maximum amount of good from the forests.

**How Changes Affect Cost of Production.**—After considering all of the favorable changes on the range the fact remains that most of the changes have tended to raise the cost of production and to render the sheep business more complex. He who engages in the business must be equipped with both sheep and capital, whereas in the early days the latter could be very largely ignored. Again, there was a time when anyone who could herd sheep might enjoy a fair degree of success as an owner. That day has passed, for now it requires business instinct and organization to make a sheep outfit pay. He who does not take an inventory and size himself up annually is likely to have to find a new business. Those days when sheep herders rambled around in solitude with their flocks furnished accounts of experiences and adventures which are read with intense interest, but such days could not always exist. Cold figures, close calculations, and clever organization rule now and business men hold the reins if profits are made.

**Cost Per Head.**—A Government report, issued in 1890, estimated the cost of running sheep in the west at from 25 to 50

*Expenses in Maintaining Sheep, per year.*

| States | Value per head of buildings and improvements | Labor per head (including shearing) | Maintenance per head | Miscellaneous and selling expense per head (including provisions) | Total expense per head |
|---|---|---|---|---|---|
| Arizona | $0.89 | $0.79 | $0.15 | $1.13 | $2.07 |
| California | .79 | .55 | .81 | .99 | 2.35 |
| Colorado | .44 | .60 | .26 | .90 | 1.76 |
| Idaho | 1.02 | .59 | .96 | 1.30 | 2.95 |
| Montana | 1.42 | .54 | .54 | .97 | 2.05 |
| Nevada | .95 | .76 | .36 | 1.11 | 2.23 |
| New Mexico | .59 | .56 | .18 | .91 | 1.65 |
| Oregon | 1.30 | .56 | .63 | .80 | 1.99 |
| Utah | .71 | .69 | .38 | 1.20 | 2.27 |
| Washington | .87 | .74 | .62 | .77 | 2.13 |
| Wyoming | .75 | .72 | .36 | 1.01 | 2.09 |
| Average | .89 | .63 | .46 | 1.02 | 2.11 |

cents per head. From figures secured on more than 3,000,000 sheep in the West in 1911, the report of the tariff board estimated that the cost of maintenance had risen to $2.11 per head per year. The table taken from that report shows the distribution of expenses.

The following table shows costs of production from the Tariff Commission for range states for the years indicated:

| State | Year | Sheep Investment per Head | Labor per Head (Including Shearing) | Feed, Rentals and Fees | Total Expense per Head with 6% Interest |
|---|---|---|---|---|---|
| Arizona | 1918 | $13.59 | $1.91 | $0.88 | $ 7.94 |
| California | 1920 | 10.49 | 3.66 | 3.15 | 9.99 |
| Colorado | 1920 | 14.87 | 2.91 | 2.09 | 11.83 |
| Idaho | 1920 | 10.34 | 2.75 | 5.04 | 12.47 |
| Montana | 1920 | 11.19 | 3.21 | 1.20 | 7.69 |
| New Mexico | 1918 | 9.83 | 2.23 | 0.68 | 8.42 |
| Texas | 1920 | 10.55 | 1.17 | 1.17 | 4.92 |
| Utah | 1919 | 14.53 | 3.08 | 1.57 | 7.97 |
| Washington | 1920 | 8.57 | 4.42 | 2.64 | 10.79 |
| Wyoming | 1920 | 8.85 | 3.74 | 2.31 | 9.50 |

*In 1925* the average breeding ewe in the Red Desert area of Wyoming represented an investment of $11.71; her total labor charge including shearing was $2.99; feed and grazing added, $0.69; interest depreciation, and other items brought the total costs to $8.34 per year. In Utah breeding ewes averaged $12.60; the labor and shearing charges were $2.61; feed and grazing, $1.06; and the total cost was $6.48 per ewe. Figures on 147,850 ewes in Idaho in 1925 show an average investment of $11.95 per head; labor and shearing, $2.47; feed and grazing, $3.43; and a total annual cost, $10.37. On 24 ranches in the southwest, ewes averaged in value $10.80 per head. On a few ranches the annual carrying charge was approximately $8.55 per head.

## QUESTIONS

1. What were the conditions under which sheepmen occupied the range?
2. How did the homesteader affect range conditions?
3. What did the state and railroads demand for the use of lands?
4. How have the changes affected the cost of growing sheep in the West?
5. How has labor affected the sheep raising?
6. What changes have reduced and increased returns?
7. How have all these significant changes in range affected the business?

# PART VII

## MISCELLANEOUS

Fig. 233.

Fig. 234.

Fig. 233.—Outside lots arranged so that wagons can drive close to barn to clean it.
Fig. 234.—Gates in normal position to form outside lots for sheep. Sheep barn, University of Illinois.

## CHAPTER XLIV

# BUILDINGS AND EQUIPMENT FOR FARM FLOCKS

THE point which has been emphasized more than any other in connection with the construction of buildings for sheep is that this class of animals does not require an expensive type of shelter. While this is true it does not follow that care in planning a sheep barn or shed is unnecessary. In fact, it pays well to erect a type of building which bears ample evidence of planning for the health of the sheep and for the convenience of those responsible for their care.

**Essential Features of Buildings for Sheep.—Location.—** Sheep buildings should be located on dry, well-drained ground where there are no obstructions to sunlight and good air drainage. A southern slope having the possibilities of a bank barn serves as an excellent building site. The ground to be converted into lots about the building should also be dry and well-drained, for dry footing is one of the essentials to the health of sheep (Fig. 233).

If possible, the barn or shed should be located only a short distance from at least a part of the area that is to be used as pasture or forage for the flock. This will permit of the barn being used throughout the year and it is a much more convenient place than the fields for feeding grain to the lambs in late spring and in summer. In order to economize time in caring for the flock the sheep barn should be located near the other farm barns, provided this can be done without sacrificing the other important factors mentioned above. If only a shed is erected it will be necessary for the sake of convenience to locate it near buildings where winter feed is stored.

**Shape of Barn.**—In general the rectangular barn is the most convenient type for housing a breeding flock of sheep. During certain periods it is necessary to divide the main flock into various smaller groups for which it is easier to provide pens in a rectangular barn than in either a square or a round barn. But in case it is unnecessary to arrange for small groups, the square and round types of barns may be quite as desirable as the rectangular type (Fig. 234).

**Warmth.**—Sheep do not require an expensive type of building because they do not need especially warm quarters, which, together

Fig. 235.

Fig. 236.

Fig. 235.—Sheep barn, University of Illinois. On well-drained ground, no obstructions to sunlight and located close to the pasture and forage areas.

Fig. 236.—Sheep barn of B. F. Harris, Banker Farmer, Champaign, Illinois. Capacity 1,000 sheep. Skylights in the roof of the annex to the main barn.

with the fact that they are easy to keep under restraint, makes it unnecessary to use heavy building materials. Except in cases where lambing occurs in cold weather, single walls will provide ample protection, and, as stated in the discussion of lambing in Chapter XXXII, a warm room can be easily arranged for young lambs in one section or corner of the barn.

**Dryness.**—Any sheep barn which does not keep the feet and the coats dry is practically a failure. In addition to placing the barn on a dry, well-drained site, it is advisable to raise the ground inside the foundation three or four inches by filling in with clay. The lots just outside should be graded so that water will drain rapidly away from the barn and whenever possible they should be coated with gravel (Figs. 235 and 236).

**Light.**—A barn which does not admit an abundance of light invites the collection of dirt and filth, both of which are detrimental to the health and thrift of sheep. Especial attention should be given to arranging the barn so that it will admit a maximum of sunlight in winter and early spring for no other natural agency equals sunlight in destroying germ life and it is of especial benefit to both ewes and lambs in the lambing season.

**Ventilation.**—No other class of animals suffers more from confinement in close, poorly ventilated quarters than do sheep, and hence it is impossible to over-emphasize the importance of good ventilation. The barn should admit an abundance of fresh air, but strong drafts should be avoided. This is not easily accomplished in cold weather, especially if there are young lambs that must have warm quarters. But it should be possible to admit a sufficient amount of fresh air by opening doors and windows on the side of the barn opposite the direction from which the wind is coming. In order to avoid drafts in large barns where there is a large amount of unbroken space, it is usually necessary to construct one or two partitions extending from the floor to the ceiling.

One of the best fresh-air types of shelter for sheep is a shed which is open on one side. Foul air never collects in such a building, and there are seldom any injurious drafts. Systems of ventilation having no connection with windows and doors have not been extensively installed in sheep barns, but doubtless they can be used to advantage in cold climates (Figs. 237–239).

**Floors.**—Earth floors are the cheapest and best for sheep. A floor surfaced with clay will soon become so firmly packed by the sheep tramping over it that very little of the liquid manure can escape. The alleys, the foundation, and possibly the feeding floors should be made of concrete, but a wooden floor is quite as satisfactory as concrete for feed rooms.

Breeding ewes require from 12 to 16 square feet of floor space, exclusive of space for racks; feeding sheep and young stock being

Fig. 237.—Shed, open on one side, University of Illinois; foreground showing fences made of movable panels.

Fig. 238.—A closed sheep shed. (From U. S. D. A. Bulletin 810.)

developed for the breeding flock require only from 5 to 8 square feet of floor space.

**The interior arrangement** of a building for sheep should aim **at** providing for the following: A minimum of waste space; the comfort of the animals, and convenience in feeding and watering, and in cleaning the pens. Since sheep are easily restrained, the partitions between pens should be movable and made of comparatively light material and then the penning arrangement of the barn can be changed from time to time to suit the needs of the flock. Often it is of advantage to construct movable racks which may also serve as partitions between pens.

**Feed Racks.**—A feed rack for sheep should hold a sufficient quantity of feed, but it need not be a great, cumbersome thing; it

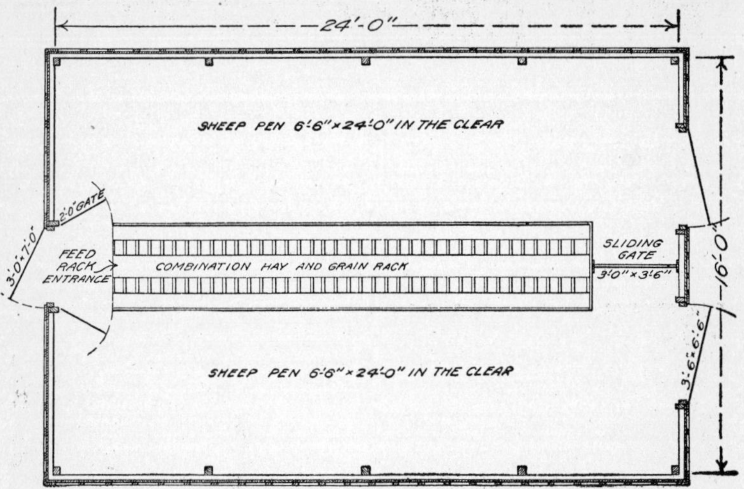


FIG. 239.—Floor plan of shed shown in Fig. 238. (From U. S. D. A. Bulletin 810.)

should be planned so that the animals can get to the feed easily without wasting it or getting it in their wool, and there should be no sharp corners or rough surfaces to pull out the wool or to cause injury to the animals. If possible, racks should be built of surfaced lumber.

In nearly all types of racks for hay or similar roughage, the feed is drawn out between slats. These should be either so close together that it will be impossible for a sheep to thrust its head between them or so far apart that the head will pass between them without danger of becoming fast. Three and one-half to four-inch spaces are sufficient for drawing out feed without inserting the head, while six- to eight-inch spaces will permit of ample freedom for passing the head through (Figs. 240–242).

Where large numbers of sheep are fed, as is the case in large plants where western sheep and lambs are fattened, the grain is

Fig. 240.—Rack with slats four inches apart and with trough for grain below the slats. Suitable for wall rack or partitions.

often fed in troughs separate from the racks in which the hay is placed. In handling a flock of ordinary size, a combination grain and hay rack is usually the most convenient type of receptacle for

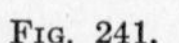

Fig. 241. Fig. 242.

Fig. 241.—Combination grain and hay rack in which slats are upright and four inches apart, suitable for partitions only. This is an uncommon type of rack but very satisfactory for fitting show sheep.

Fig. 242.—Rack 24 inches wide with slats 6 to 8 inches apart to permit the sheep to thrust their heads between them. Suitable for partition only.

feed. Combination racks are of two types; in one the hay is placed in a rack above the trough for the grain (Fig. 240); in the other, the hay and grain are placed on the same bottom (Fig. 239). In using the latter type, the grain is consumed before the hay is fed, and generally the same method is followed with the type in which the rack for the hay is placed above the grain trough. Combination racks are much more suitable than separate racks for preventing waste with hay containing a high percentage of loose leaves. These are very largely lost in racks intended for hay only, but in combination racks they fall on the bottoms intended for the grain and are saved (Fig. 243).

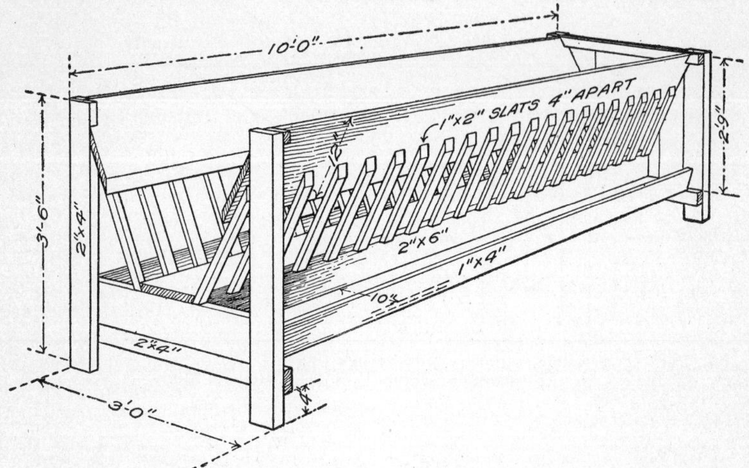


FIG. 243.—A combination hay and grain rack which may be entered by the attendant when feeding grain or hay—for partitions only. (From U. S. D. A. Farmer's Bulletin 810.)

**Troughs** for grain, silage, and roots should be from 8 to 10 inches wide in combination racks and 12 inches or more in separate pieces of construction. The sides should be about 5 inches high and should slope slightly outward. The bottoms should be flat in order to keep the sheep from eating too rapidly and should stand about one foot from the ground. Separate troughs should be constructed so that they can not be easily pushed over, and there should be a railing above them to keep the sheep from standing or lying in them (Figs. 244 and 245).

The amount of rack or trough space required depends upon the size of the animals. Feeding lambs should be allowed about 12 inches each and large breeding ewes as much as 18 inches.

**Lambing pens** are almost indispensable to successful lambing and the movable type is the more convenient to use. Since they are

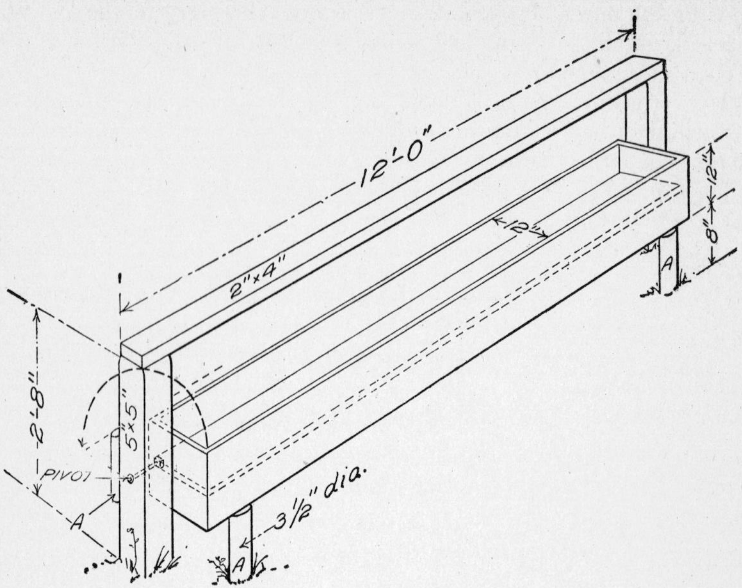


Fig. 244.—A reversible stationary grain trough which is easy to keep clean because it is reversible. (From U. S. D. A. Bulletin 810.)

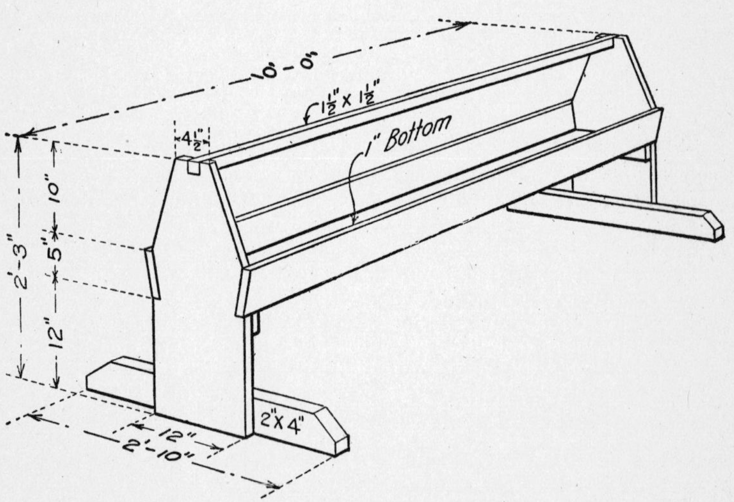


Fig. 245.—A light movable trough for feeding grain, silage and roots. The long dimension pieces resting on the ground make it difficult for the sheep to turn the trough over. (From U. S. D. A. Bulletin 810.)

to be moved from place to place, they are best if made of light boards, preferably white pine seven-eighths inch by three inches, planed on both sides. The pens consist of two four-foot panels or hurdles hinged together. By opening these panels at right angles in a corner of the barn where the free ends may be fastened to walls, a pen four feet square is made which provides sufficient space for the average-sized ewe and her lambs (Fig. 246).

The panels are sometimes arranged by using but one wall, so as to form a triangular pen for a ewe that refuses to own her lamb.

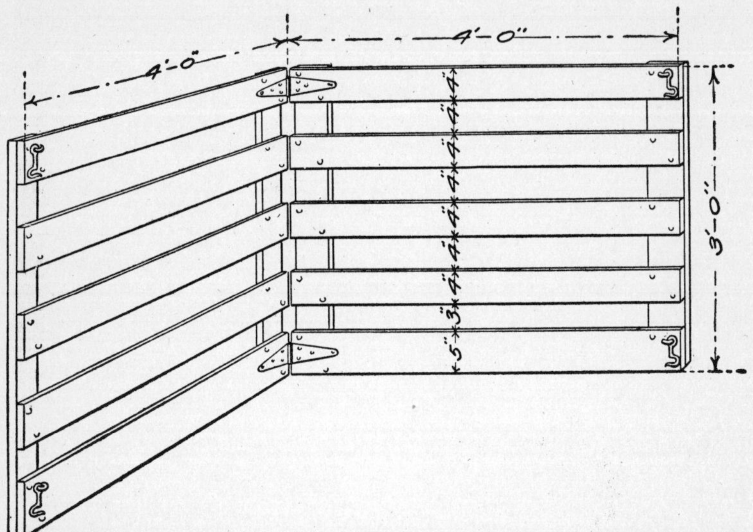


Fig. 246.—Hinged panels for lambing pen. (From U. S. D. A. Bulletin 810.)

If tied up in one corner of the pen she cannot move away from her young far enough to prevent it from nursing. By unfolding the panels so that they stand end to end, they may be made to serve as partitions in the barn. They can also be constructed so that they can be used as lamb creeps (Fig. 167).

**A lamb creep** is a device that admits the lambs to a feeding place but excludes the older sheep. Its construction should be a very simple matter. Provision should be made for adjusting the size of the openings for the lambs and as a rule there should not be more than two or three places for admitting them, so that in the event some of the older sheep are small enough to gain admittance, which is frequently the case after shearing, the creep can be easily closed after the lambs have passed into it. Rather expensive devices,

FIG. 247.

FIG. 248.

FIG. 247.—Small lamb creep made of hinged panels which permit the lambs to eat from same trough as their mother. Useful in teaching lambs to eat.
FIG. 248.—Rack for water pail.

such as rollers for uprights between which the lambs pass in and out of the creep, have been constructed. While such an arrangement is practically above criticism as a "creep" opening, it is really

Fig. 249.—Farm dipping plant. Tank to the left; dripping pen in center, and chute from dripping pen at the right.

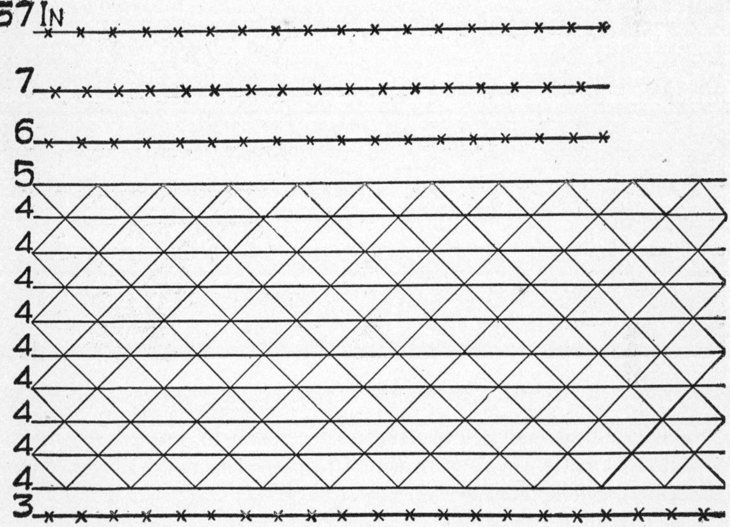


Fig. 250.—A dog-proof fence. (From U. S. D. A. Bulletin 810.)

unnecessary, as the woolly coat of the lamb gives it sufficient protection in passing between stationary uprights having the sharp corners rounded off (Fig. 247).

**Watering Troughs.**—In many cases it is just as well, or perhaps better, to have the water supplied outside of the barn, for it is likely to be somewhat more wholesome, but it should be easily accessible at all times and hence it is often advisable to have it in the barn. The troughs should be located in light, airy places and they should be so constructed that they can be kept clean, which is perhaps easiest done by installing a system of under-drainage, making it possible to drain the water off frequently. Also provision should be made, if possible, to keep the water from freezing in winter.

Fig. 251.—Temporary fence supported by iron posts.

In lambing time, it is usually necessary to water some of the sheep from pails. A rack in which to place the pail to keep it from overturning is shown in Fig. 248.

**Shearing Floor.**—The shearing floor, which should be about ten feet square, can be made of hard pine boards twelve inches wide and surfaced on one side. After the shearing is over, these can be taken up and stored where they will keep in good condition.

**Wool Room.**—While a wool room is a good feature in a sheep barn, it is not absolutely necessary to have it. But if the wool is not sold at once after shearing, it should be stored in a clean place. The feed room or some of the grain bins in the barn may not be in use after shearing time, in which case it will be easy to find a place for the wool. Should storage for a long period be contemplated, however, a separate room for the wool should be provided. It need not be large, as the fleeces can be packed into a comparatively small space.

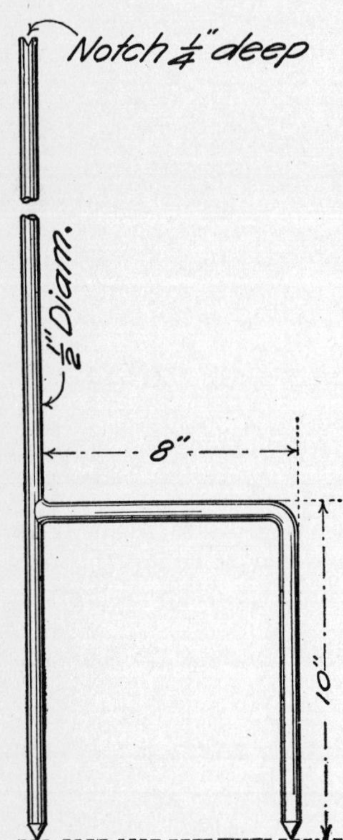


Fig. 252.—The iron post. The bottom wire of the fence is caught in the crotch formed by the junction of the elbow piece with the long rod and the top wire rests in the notch indicated in the diagram.

**Equipment Outside of the Barn.—Silo.**—In case a silo is desired, it should be located outside the barn close to the feeding room; in fact, the chute should be arranged so that the silage will fall from the silo into the feeding room.

**Dipping Plant.**—In connection with every sheep barn there should be an inexpensive dipping plant, located where it will not interfere with everyday handling of the flock. Portable galvanized iron vats can be purchased from supply houses, which are adequate for dipping flocks of ordinary size. When set in place, the top of the vat should be about six inches above the ground. At one end of it there should be a small pen to hold sheep awaiting dipping, and at the other, a draining platform where the sheep are allowed to stand for a few minutes after they are dipped, in order to let the liquid drain out of their wool and run back into the vat. A walk-way can be built as an approach to the vat, and there are various devices for sliding the sheep into it. But, if the sheep are not let down gently into the liquid, a great deal of it is splashed out and lost. In dipping small flocks it pays to lift each sheep and carefully place it in the vat (Fig. 249).

**Fences and Hurdles.**—If possible sheep should be protected by boundary fences that will exclude dogs. (It is doubtful whether any fence is absolutely dog-proof.) The fence shown in Fig. 250, having a barbed wire close to the ground and three barbed wires at the top would be found proof against most dogs. Division fences

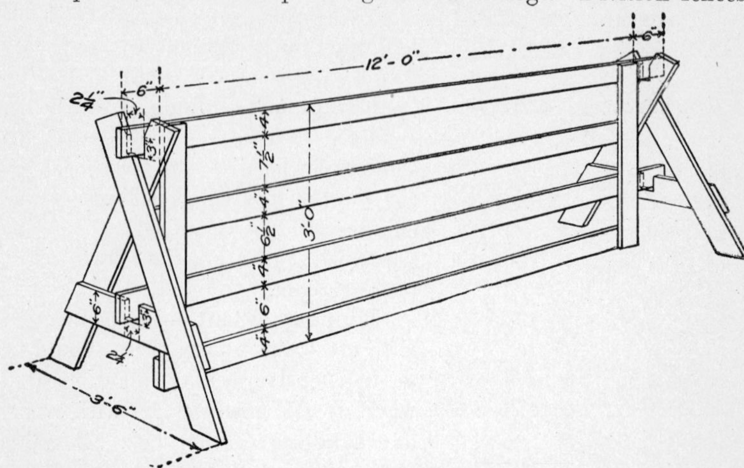


Fig. 253.—A wooden panel, suitable for temporary fencing. (From U. S. D. A. Bulletin 810.)

thirty-six inches high and made of woven wire are adequate for keeping most sheep in place. These fences may be either temporary or permanent in nature, or the temporary fence may be made of wooden panels (Figs. 250–253). The iron post shown in Figs. 251 and 252 was designed by the writer to use with temporary wire fencing.

## QUESTIONS

1. Enumerate the essential features of a sheep barn.
2. Why is it possible to build a good sheep barn at comparatively low cost?
3. What are the essential features of a good sheep rack?
4 Why should the bottoms of troughs be flat?
5. How much floor space do mature ewes require?

## CHAPTER XLV

# PREPARING MUTTON ON THE FARM

**Importance of Mutton and Lamb in the Meat Dietary.**—Mutton and lamb form a very small part of the meat diet of farmers in the United States. The chief reason why they eat so little of these meats is that they believe all mutton and lamb has the so-called disagreeable "woolly flavor." In the majority of cases, this belief is based merely on the "say so" of some one else, but it is so firmly fixed that few attempt to prove or disprove it for themselves. It, no doubt, originated in the early days of sheep husbandry when the wool breeds were popular and mature sheep were the chief source of the mutton supply. The introduction of mutton breeds and the increased demand for mutton and lamb in the larger cities has brought about a great improvement in the quality of the mutton produced, and to-day this "woolly flavor" is almost never noticeable in lambs and yearlings, and seldom in mature sheep (Fig. 254).

Another reason why the farmers have not utilized this source of meat supply is because they think it difficult to properly slaughter and dress a sheep. This, however, is even more fallacious than the belief regarding flavor, for neither the process of slaughter nor of cutting the carcass is any more difficult than killing a hog and cutting and curing the meat, a task which is ordinarily considered quite simple.

**Care Before Slaughter.**—The animal to be slaughtered should be in healthy and as nearly normal condition as possible at the time of slaughter. It should be handled carefully to prevent bruises on the carcass; all undue excitement should be avoided, and if possible, it should be fasted from eighteen to twenty-four hours, but allowed free access to water. Attention to these details facilitates thorough bleeding, insures more rapid cooling of the carcass, lessens the danger of cutting the internal organs, and tends to prevent the disagreeable flavor of the meat caused by the fermentation of feed material in the stomach. The fleece should be dry and reasonably clean, as it is practically impossible to hang up a clean carcass if the fleece is wet or dirty. Shearing is often advisable, since the pelt is easier handled and removed with the wool out of the way, and the wool alone can usually be sold for as much or more than the unsheared pelt.

**Method of Slaughter.—Equipment Required.**—A clean, dry place to work is the first essential. A low bench or box upon which to lay the animal, a sticking knife, and some provision for hanging the carcass is all the equipment required for slaughtering a sheep.

**Method of Sticking.**—The sheep is laid on a low box or bench on its left side with the head extending over the edge. It is held in this position by standing behind the sheep and placing the right

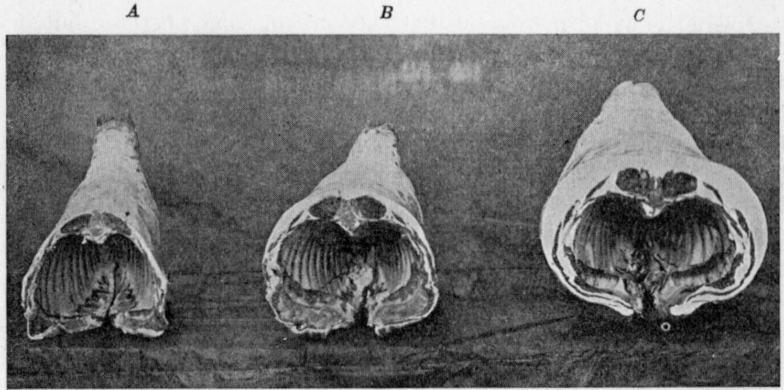


FIG. 254.—*A*, mutton deficient in quantity of fat; *B*, properly finished mutton; *C*, mutton carrying too much fat.

knee in the fore flank. The lower jaw is grasped with the left hand and the knife is stuck into the neck just back of the angle of the jaw slightly below and behind the ear. The knife should go through the neck at one thrust, with the edge of the knife toward the head. If desired, the beginner may then turn the knife and cut out through the neck, thus severing all the blood-vessels. To stun the sheep after sticking, the neck is broken by either placing one hand on the forehead and pulling up on the jaw, or by severing the spinal cord at the atlas joint with the knife (Fig. 255).

**Removing the Pelt.**—The removal of the pelt is begun at the front legs by cutting out a narrow strip down the front of the leg from the neck to the ankle joint, holding the foot, in the meantime, between the knees. The legs, the point of the brisket, and the under side of the neck are then skinned. Following this the flesh of

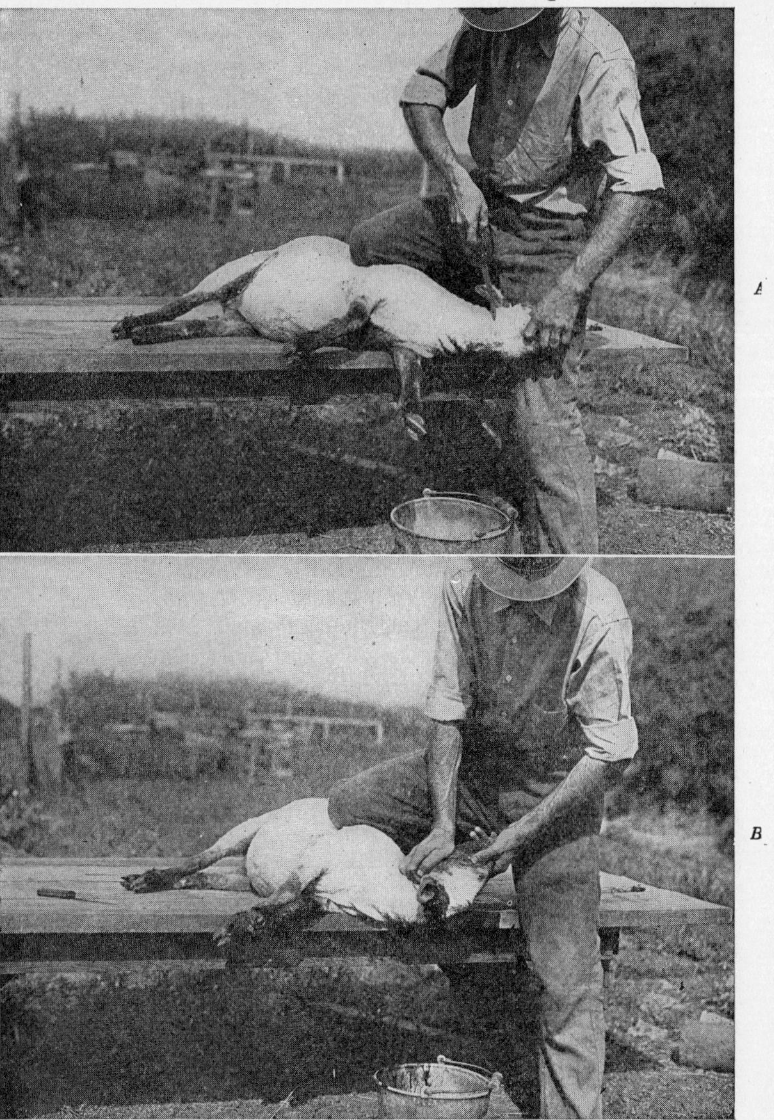


FIG. 255.—Slaughtering. *A*, sticking; *B*, breaking the neck.

the neck is cut through in order to loosen the windpipe and gullet. In lambs and yearlings the feet are removed at the "break joint"[1] by cutting across the raise on the cannon just above the ankle and twisting the foot. In mature sheep, this joint will not break, and the feet are removed at the ankle-joint.

The removal of the pelt at the hind legs is begun by cutting out a strip of skin down the back of the leg from the anus to the lowest point where the feet are removed. The feet should never be removed at the ankle-joint, because the tendons will pull out when the carcass is hung. The hind legs should not be skinned out to as great extent as the front legs; the pelt should be merely loosened along the sides and back of the leg. The leg of mutton is a valuable cut, and by leaving the pelt on as long as possible, it is much easier to keep it clean.

Beginning at the brisket and cod, or udder, the pelt is loosened over the belly by forcing the fist between the skin and flesh. Likewise the pelt over the sides is fisted off, care being taken not to tear the thin muscles at the flanks. This is easiest avoided by fisting first down over the center of the side, and then working each way from this point over the flank muscles.

The tendons in the hind leg are loosened between the hock and the ankle by cutting between them and the bone. The legs are then tied with a cord and the carcass hung at a convenient height. The pelt is further removed by splitting it down the center and fisting it off over the sides, flanks, and legs, and working up over the hind flank and leg, and down over the shoulder. Next the hide is loosened around the tail with the knife and the pelt is pulled down the back to the neck, where it is removed with the head at the atlas joint (Fig. 256).

**Removing the Viscera.**—The first step in removing the viscera is to cut around the rectum and pull it out a short distance to loosen it. The carcass is then opened down the middle line from the cod (or udder) to the breast-bone, care being taken to shield the point of the knife between the fingers to avoid cutting the intestines. The large intestine is then pulled downward carefully to avoid loosening the kidney fat. The operator uses the knife to

---

[1] The "break joint" or "lamb joint" is a temporary cartilage which forms a dentate suture in the head of the shank immediately above the ankle. It will not break in mature sheep because the cartilage is knit or ossified (Illinois Bulletin 147).

detach the paunch and liver from the back, pulls the viscera forward and either cuts the gullet or pulls it out with the stomach. The liver upon being removed from the viscera and the gall-bladder cut away from it should be placed in a pail of cold water. By cutting around the diaphragm the heart and lungs are removed. The inside of the carcass is then carefully wiped out with a damp cloth, care being taken to see that the chest cavity is thoroughly drained. To facilitate rapid cooling, the breast-bone may be split and a short spread stick used to hold the carcass open (Fig. 259,*a*).

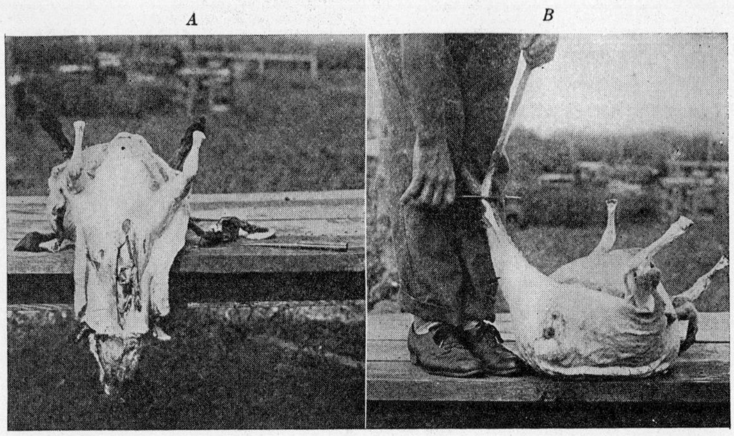


**Fig. 256.—Removing the pelt.** *A*, skinning around forelegs and neck; *B*, skinning around hind legs.

When dressing sheep for market, the forelegs are folded back at the knee and fastened to the shank with a skewer. This gives the carcass a thicker and neater appearance. Likewise, lamb carcasses are given a fatter, more finished appearance by spreading the caul fat over the legs and flank (Fig. 259).

**Care of the Carcass.**—The mutton or lamb carcass should be allowed to hang until it is thoroughly cooled, at approximately 40 degrees F., if possible. After it is cooled throughout it may, in the winter months, be allowed to freeze and can be preserved almost indefinitely if a frozen condition is maintained. Alternate freezing and thawing is detrimental to the quality and flavor of the meat. If carefully protected from flies by some such means as wrapping a

Fig. 257.—Last four stages in removing the pelt. *A*, "fisting" over belly and sides; *B*, cutting through skin on ventral side; *C*, "fisting" over shoulder; *D*, "fisting" over hind legs.

Fig. 258.—Removing viscera.

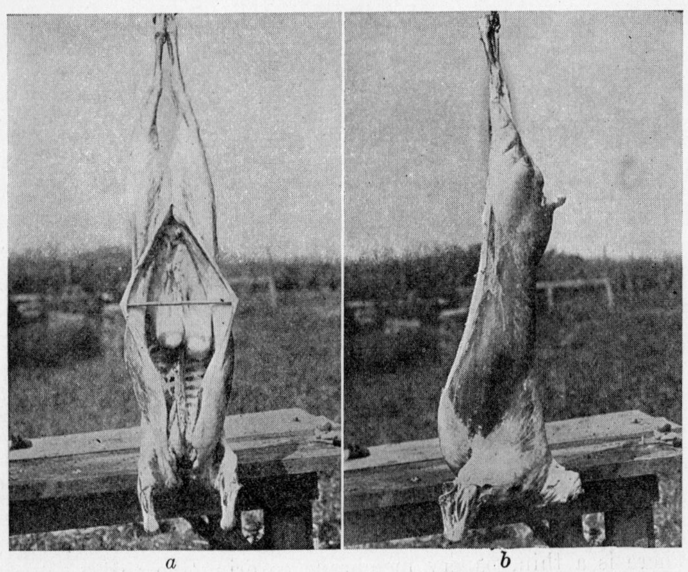

*a* *b*

Fig. 259.—The carcass. *a*, showing spread stick in place; *b*, showing how forelegs are folded.

piece of cheesecloth loosely about it, the carcass may be cooled in the cellar in the spring and summer months.

**Method of Cutting the Carcass.**—The sheep carcass is very easily divided into the various cuts for table use, since each main division yields a cut of suitable size for the average family (Fig. 260).

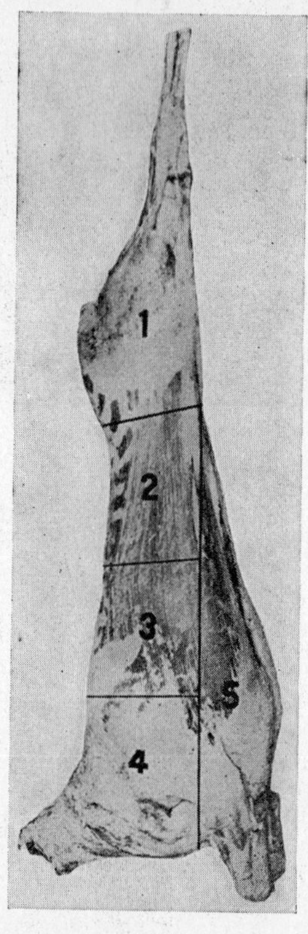


FIG. 260.—Mutton and lamb cuts. Each half carcass is divided into: **1, leg; 2, loin; 3, rib; 4, shoulder; 5, breast.**

The additional equipment required for cutting are a sharp butcher knife, a meat saw, a cleaver, and if possible, a solid bench or block upon which to work.

There is a thin, papery membrane covering the entire carcass known as the "fell," which should always be removed from every

Fig. 261. Fig. 262.

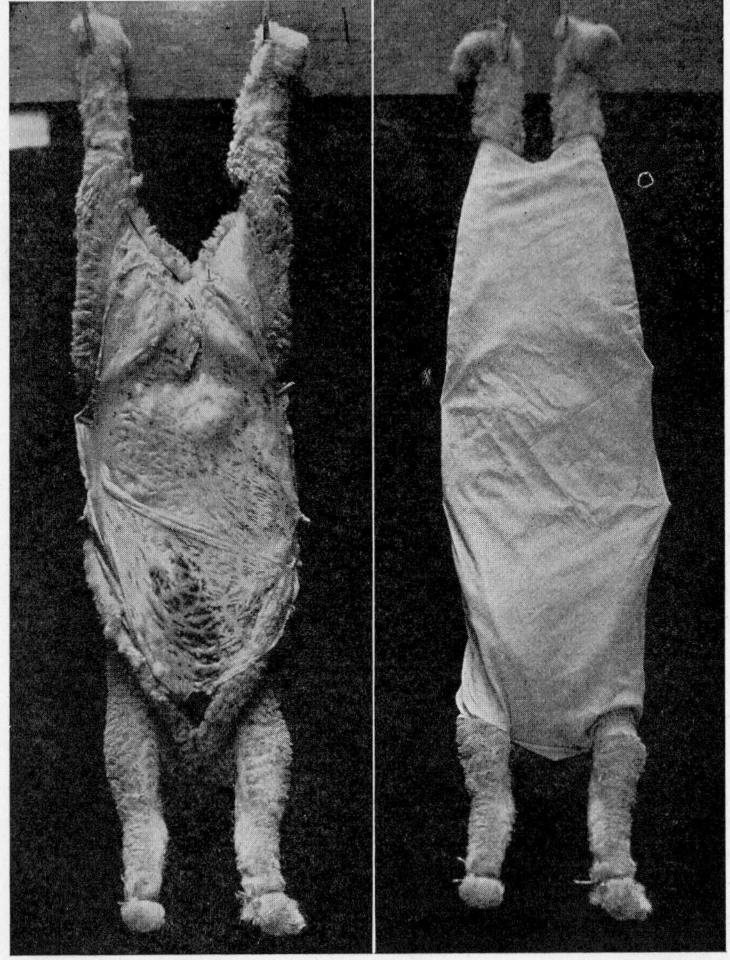

Fig. 261.—Dressed for special market. The pelt is not removed and the caul fat is spread over the opening in the ventral side.

Fig. 262.—Wrapped first with muslin and then with burlap in preparation for shipment to special market.

cut of mutton and lamb before it is cooked. It is very tough and the woolly flavor is often attributed to its presence.

For home use, the carcass should first be divided into halves. With the carcass hanging, the aitch bone is cut through with a knife. The hind legs are spread apart and the carcass sawed down the center of the backbone. Each half of the carcass may then be further divided into the following cuts:

**Breast.**—The breast consists of the flank, plate, and front shank. It is the cheapest cut of the carcass and is used principally for stews. To remove this cut the operator starts at the cod (or udder) and cuts straight forward through a point just above the elbow-joint. The excess fat is then trimmed off and the thin, tough membrane on the inside of the flank is removed, after which the ribs are cracked with a cleaver and the fore shank is sawed through in one or two places.

**Leg.**—The leg of mutton is used chiefly as a roast, but may be used for steaks. Because of the thick lean and small amount of bone, it is the most popular roast cut of the carcass. The point at which it is removed varies with the size of roast desired. Ordinarily it is cut off on a line parallel with the ribs at the point where the spinal cord bends upward. The shank may either be removed at the stifle joint and the strip of shank meat skewered over the joint (American or plain trimmed), or it may be sawed off just above the hock and the meat scraped off the bone for a distance of three-fourths to one inch (French trimmed). The most desirable roast for carving is made by removing all bones and tying the meat in a roll. In all cases the thin flank muscles, the tail bones, and excess fat should be trimmed off.

**Loin.**—The most palatable mutton or lamb chops are cut from the loin because it contains the most tender muscles of the carcass. It extends from the leg to the twelfth or next to the last rib. In preparing this cut the kidney is removed and the chops are cut across the loin about three-fourths of an inch thick. The loin also makes a good roast, although the lean is not as thick as that of the leg or shoulder. To prepare a loin roast, the joints of the backbone are cut through with the cleaver or may be removed and the roast tied in a roll. Boneless rolled chops may be cut from a boned loin, skewers being used to hold them in shape.

**Rib.**—The rib extends from the last to the fourth or fifth rib and is used for chops and roasts. Rib chops are cut one rib wide, and the roasts prepared in the same manner as those of the loin. A crown roast is also made from the rib cuts. The flesh is rolled back from the lower end of the ribs, the spinal process sawed off, and the two cuts tied end to end, bending the ribs backward.

**Shoulder.**—The shoulder is used for either roasts, chops, or stews. The large amount of bone it contains makes it undesirable for roasting unless boned and rolled, when it practically equals the leg in quality. If not boned, its preparation consists of trimming off the neck square, and cutting through the joints of the backbone with the cleaver. Shoulder chops are cut either parallel to the ribs or across the lower part of the shoulder at the point where the shank was removed.

**Slaughtering Lambs for Special Markets.**—Prime young lambs weighing from fifty to sixty pounds that are ready for sale from one to three months before the regular crop of lambs is large enough to market, are often slaughtered on the farm and sold direct to clubs and high-class hotels in the larger cities.

They are marketed with the pelt on and are ordinarily wrapped in two separate covers for shipment, the inner consisting of tough paper or muslin, and the outer of burlap or sacking. This keeps the carcass clean, prevents excessive drying out, and furnishes some protection against bruises.

In dressing the carcass, a strip of skin four or five inches wide is loosened along the underline, and the skin from around the rectum and from the inside of the legs is removed. The feet are cut off at the ankle- and knee-joints, leaving a small flap of skin to fold back over the joint. All the internal organs are removed except the pluck, which consists of the heart, lungs, and liver. In warm weather these, too, should be removed to insure thorough cooling of the carcass. The breast-bone is then split and the carcass is spread open with backsets.[2] The caul fat is placed over the exposed flesh and the carcass allowed to cool thoroughly before shipping (Fig. 261).

A square yard of muslin is sufficient for wrapping one lamb, and should be neatly sewed on so as to cover all the exposed parts of the carcass. The burlap wrapping over the muslin is sometimes omitted and two or three lambs placed in a light crate lined with heavy paper (Fig. 262).

---

[2] Backsets are sharpened sticks 15 to 18 inches long with a shoulder about an inch back from each point. The points are inserted in the loose skin near the breastbone and the turned-back flank on the opposite side of the carcass, crossing them over the back.

## QUESTIONS

1. Is mutton popular with country people?
2. What equipment is necessary to slaughter a sheep?
3. What equipment is necessary to cut up the carcass of a sheep?
4. Which is more palatable mutton, mature sheep, or lamb?
5. How are lambs dressed on the farm prepared for shipment?

# INDEX